MITA

Mobile Internet Technical Architecture

Solutions and Tools

IT Press

Published by
Edita Publishing Inc.
IT Press
P.O.BOX 760
FIN-00043 EDITA
FINLAND

Access the latest information about IT Press books from our World Wide Web site at **www.itpress.biz.**

ISBN 951-826-669-7

Printed by Gummerus Inc., Finland.

Distributor information:

For information about distribution, please visit our Web site at **http://www.itpress.biz/distributors**

This document is an approved part of Nokia Mobile Internet Technical Architecture release.

Nokia Mobile Internet Technical Architecture, aims to provide seamless interoperability between all interaction modes, any network environment and, with any type of access. The ultimate objective of the initiative is to create a user-friendly Mobile Internet experience for everyone.

In developing a clear technical architecture for the Mobile Internet, Nokia aims to limit the complexity of the inherently technical environment; consumers do not want to worry about the underlying technologies.

An open solution benefits all; profitable business scenarios call for interoperability, short development cycles, large volumes and, most of all, global reach. Unless there is a commonly accepted architectural solution, markets will be fragmented as well as requiring separate parameters, and the total volume will be much smaller than in a single global market.

Nokia Mobile Internet Technical Architecture (MITA) is defined by Nokia Mobile Software unit. Any comments concerning this document can be sent to mita.feedback@nokia.com. Please visit the official MITA Web site at: www.nokia.com/mita

Table of Contents

Acknowledgements

The past two years have been an exciting time with the challenges of the Mobile Internet and its defining Technical Architecture. We have seen the summit of the Internet boom and lately faced a more demanding period in the mobile industry. In the interim, the definition of the Nokia Mobile Internet Technical Architecture has matured to a complete release in the form of this book series.

I would like to thank the people involved in this effort:

- All the contributors and teams for their remarkable efforts in creating the content
- The Editors' Board: Jyrki Kivimäki, Juha Lampela, Hanna Passoja-Martikainen, Sari Päivärinta, Krister Rask and Jussi Ruutu for their excellent work in keeping the book process on schedule and in shape
- Sami Inkinen and Mikko Terho for their support and guidance en route to the complete release
- Jani Ilkka, Juha Kaski and the rest of the IT Press team for doing an outstanding job with the publishing process
- Nely Keinänen, Anna Shefl and Michael Jääskeläinen for doing a great job with the language revision and proofreading large amounts of technical material on a very strict schedule
- Eija Kauppinen and her team at Indivisual for numerous high-quality illustrations

And finally:

- My wife, Helena, for her understanding and support, especially in the last few months when the book process has occupied my time

Marko Suoknuuti
Chair of the Editors' Board

The Authors/Contributors:

Ashley Colley
Charlie Schick
Christy Symanski
Esa Eerola
Graham Harris
Hanna Passoja-Martikainen
Heikki Almay
Hilppa Horneman
Jani Hyppönen
Janne Kari
Janne Kilpeläinen
Jarmo Lahtinen
Jenni Rantakari
Joe Coles
Juha Lampela
Jussi Wacklin
Kaarina Sillanpää
Kari Pakarinen
Kimmo Djupsjöbacka
Marika Räisänen
Marko Suoknuuti
Merja Luova
Michael Addison
Nicole Cham
Mikko Terho
Outi Niemi
Peter Wiklund
Risto Helin
Sari Päivärinta
Seppo Aaltonen
Teemu Toroi
Thomas Hasselman
Timo Joutsenvirta
Timo Sivula
Tom Ojala
Tommi Raivisto
Vipul Mehrotra
Virva Latostenmaa

I PROLOGUE

Prologue

The next few years will see the convergence of mobile communications and the Internet resulting in new services, new business models and new business opportunities.

The Internet has become an everyday source of information, entertainment and other services for millions of people around the world. In our vision, the Internet will become mobile and content will go wireless, as voice communication has done. The future is no longer about the Internet but about services on the Mobile Internet. This is a new environment, called the Mobile World, where the evolution paths of mobile communications and the Internet have converged. The Mobile World provides innovative services for consumers, and the development of these services is driven by consumer behavior.

The Mobile World can be perceived as a holistic, evolving environment of the future, but also as an environment on a personal level that enables people to shape their Mobile World through personalized communication services. In the Mobile World, delivering targeted, timely information and services is essential.

The key to commercial success in the Mobile World depends on three main factors:

- Understanding consumer needs, lifestyles and attitudes, and consequently being able to provide a matching combination of service portfolios and products,
- Readiness of the business system to enable service consumption, and
- Being able to match technical architectures to evolving consumer needs and to the evolution of business systems.

Those who deliver product categories and platforms with the right services and technologies will be the victors in the Mobile World.

The winning technical architecture in the Mobile World will enable seamless interoperability between key applications, network environments and the user identity/addressing system, limit the complexity of the technical environment supporting services so that consumers do not need to be concerned with the underlying technologies, support open technologies, standards and relevant initiatives which support and facilitate the deployment of global technologies and services, and stimulate market growth.

The Nokia solution addressing these demands is the Mobile Internet Technical Architecture (MITA). For the players in the field, MITA is the essential framework for creating user-friendly Mobile World experiences. It is an architecture which comprehensively enables networks to be driven by services. MITA addresses relevant technologies and standardization forums for the Mobile Internet, the current solutions and developer environments provided by Nokia, specifies design principles and technology visions for the Mobile Internet, and describes reference implementations.

Long term MITA technical visions and technology evolution scenarios are complemented with a Systems Software Architecture (SWA) that specifies a near term application and service architecture for the Mobile Internet. It has been a contribution of Nokia to open global standardization of mobile services (e.g., Open Mobile Alliance).

The Mobile domain of today is much more than the Short Message Service (SMS) and Wireless Application Protocol (WAP) services which have been readily available for some time now. The aim of the solutions section is to give an overview of both the current and upcoming Nokia solutions with the most important technologies and applications in the mobile domain. Therefore, this section will cover a wide array of different topics, all aiming to illustrate the Nokia approach in the actual product creation and technology choices.

The success of the Mobile Internet requires more than a good set of technologies and standards. It needs services and dedicated applications which provide value for consumers. Success also requires the rapid development of new services and a large community of service and application developers. Hence, application developers have an essential role in the success of the Mobile Internet. A tools section addresses the challenges that developers need to tackle when implementing Mobile Internet services and applications. The section also describes the Nokia solutions for developers.

The Mobile World is evolving as we speak. New consumer needs are arising, and innovation on the Internet is taking place at an accelerating pace. Thus, it is clear that technical architectures also need to be continuously developed. Nokia invites all parties of the Mobile Internet to join and contribute to the development of the Mobile World. For this purpose, we would greatly appreciate input from our readers.

Mikko Terho

Senior Vice President

II INTRODUCTION

- The Mobile World
- Introduction to MITA Specifications

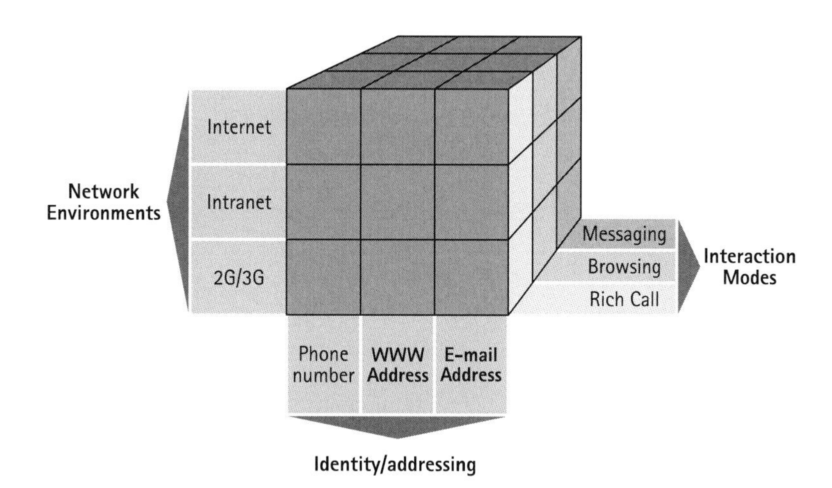

The Mobile World

The next few years will see the convergence of mobile communications and the Internet resulting in various new technologies, new business models and business opportunities.

The Mobile Internet is not simply the Internet of today accessed from a mobile device. We will not spend our time browsing Internet pages for content as we do today, although this will still be possible. Instead, we will use applications to access content, make transactions, do business, link up with friends and family, play games, watch videos, and listen to and download music. More importantly, we will use the Mobile Internet to help control our lives and give us more time to do the things we enjoy.

We are moving towards a Web-based business model where mobility and the Internet are unified. This will not happen overnight and will require new competencies from all parties involved in the industry. Understanding mobility and the unique characteristics of mobile business will be vital in building the networks and services of the future. Success in the Mobile World will be about speed: speed of application and mobile device development for refined consumer segments, speed of new service creation, and speed of cost-optimized network development and roll-out. It will be about the control of services and content residing in your own hands.

From a consumer's perspective, the most tangible element is the mobile device, which provides access to all of these services. To ensure the success of services in the Mobile World, they must be highly user-friendly. Actually, the user should be able to ignore the underlying technologies and purely enjoy the richness of the supplied services, regardless of the access method.

Along with the continually growing importance of mobile devices as life management tools, the Mobile World will become much more than a source for a quick weather information update. The Mobile Internet is not a fixed entity, yet it is starting to formulate its existence with the services and applications to be linked to it. Hence, as the business and technical environments develop, the available architectures will need to match them accordingly.

In the Mobile World, delivering targeted, timely information and services is essential. Consumer behavior drives the development of these applications and services. The key to commercial success lies in understanding consumers, their lifestyles and attitudes, and in creating the product-service combinations which match their wants and needs. Those who deliver winning product categories and platforms with the right technologies will succeed in the Mobile World.

The Nokia solution to cover these demands is the Mobile Internet Technical Architecture (MITA). For the players in the field, MITA is the essential framework for creating user-friendly Mobile World experiences. MITA supports network evolution to the Mobile Internet for both voice and data and is an architecture which comprehensively enables networks to be driven by services. The main target of MITA is to provide seamless interoperation in the consumption of content in all networks and create open and non-fragmented markets with maximum access to all.

Introduction

Nokia is proceeding towards a vision of the Mobile World. In this vision, the majority of all personal communication will be wireless - be it in the form of phone calls, messaging, browsing or images.

The perception of the Internet has been technology focused, i.e., it has been assumed that people wish to access the Internet and huge amounts of data while on the move. Yet, what people will do is something very different. To begin with, in the Mobile World, the Internet will become practically invisible as people are not concerned about "accessing the Internet" but about using services and their favorite applications. A special focus will be on consuming information and producing information to share with others. The consumption will apply to mobile brands, products, information, and advertising.

Consumers want value for money, ease of use, and a diverse choice of personally relevant services. Without an open solution, they are forced into a confusing and fragmented world of proprietary services and terminals. Therefore, the aim will be to limit the complexity of the technical environment so that consumers can enjoy services without worrying about the underlying technologies. As a result, a unified architecture will benefit all users in the Mobile World.

Mobile World Challenge

The Mobile World vision assumes that consumers will use different types of devices for connecting to multiple sets of services via various access networks. These services should be reachable in a unified way regardless of the access technology or mobile device. Naturally, there will always be slight differences between user experiences. However, it is expected that these will be made as transparent as possible.

The above requirements describe technical challenges, which need to be solved before the objectives of the Mobile World can be completely achieved. Interaction Modes, Identity and Network environments are the main elements that the industry needs for constructing an environment for tackling the Mobile World vision. This environment can be described as the Mobile World challenge.

Also, from the MITA perspective, this setting presents those areas that require close consideration in order to achieve a fully functional technical architecture for the Mobile World.

Interaction Modes

Today, consumers have the possibility of making phone calls, exchanging short messages, e-mail or images, and browsing data on the Internet. It is assumed that these communication modes are a baseline for services in the Mobile World. However, the convergence of communication technologies into IP-based solutions enables new services and extensions into baseline communication services.

The Mobile World Challenge addresses this evolution by classifying consumers' communication needs into three types of interaction modes to simplify the definition of basic requirements for applications, terminals, and service provisioning technology.

Messaging

Messaging is non real-time, client-server based communication in which an intermediary server is involved in the communication sequence. The intermediary server stores and/or processes messages before they are delivered to the destination. The intermediary server can be based on store and forward (e.g., Short Message Service and Multimedia Messaging Service), store and retrieve (e.g., e-mail) or even store and push functionality. The intermediary server may also provide queuing services.

Browsing

Browsing is nearly real-time one-way or two-way communication between a source and the destination. It includes one-way audio and video streaming. Differing from Rich Call, Browsing has no delay limitations for communication. In third generation networks, Browsing will be based on an evolution from today's Wireless Application Protocol (WAP) based browsing to graphics and multimedia-enriched browsing.

Rich Call

The Rich Call interaction mode maps to communication using a two-way real-time component. The real-time requirements mean that there are limitations for end-to-end and round-trip delays, and for jitter. Rich Call refers to voice and video calls in their simplest form, and in more complicated cases, concurrent communication (e.g., file transfer is combined with a real-time communication element).

Network Environments

The Internet boom started around the mid 1990s. Since then, an increasing number of corporations have connected their Intranets to the Internet, and a growing number of consumers use Internet services. Similarly, consumers have found attractive mobile services for use in their daily lives.

These three Network environments: mobile networks, the Internet and Intranets are the environments where most of the user interaction will take place in the Mobile World. Moreover, these different environments need to work seamlessly together and enable evolution towards unified service networks.

Identity

Today, each communication mode and its applications have specific addressing mechanisms (e.g., phone calls require numbers, messaging uses e-mail addresses). Luckily, applications have evolved and enable address books for mapping technical addresses to formats which are easier for consumers to manage (e.g., names).

An effective addressing system is vital for handling and simplifying the multitude of e-mail addresses, phone numbers and Web addresses of individuals and organizations. This will be even more true in the future, as the ways of communicating will expand and individuals will be using several different types of devices. The consumer should be faced with as few differences as possible between the addressing methods.

These Mobile World challenges are illustrated in the figure below, which models the interworking scenarios of networks, identities and interaction modes. It is a simple diagnostic framework for highlighting the issues involved in interworking between the layers on the Mobile Internet.

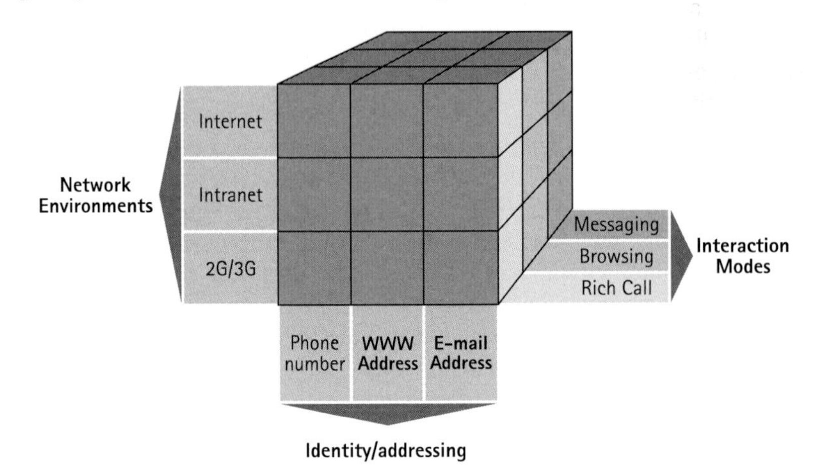

Mobile World Challenge

Mobile Internet Technical Architecture

To make the Mobile World a reality, correct technology choices are required if a technical architecture capable of supporting the myriad of services is to be built. For this reason, Nokia created MITA as a methodology to model the new environment and to understand the inherent technical issues in building the optimal technical architecture. Nokia is using this approach to assist players in the field in making the right technology choices to deliver the optimal consumer experience.

Openness and interoperability are central elements in the MITA approach. Situational analysis is not biased toward any network environment - fixed or mobile - and this maximizes inclusivity; Nokia recognizes the importance of collaboration in this new business environment and MITA gives all the players equally open access to the emerging architecture so that the ultimate goal - a world in which subscribers can utilize the seamless functionality of all Mobile Internet related applications and services - is achieved with the active participation of the whole industry. To achieve this goal, a mobile service market must be created, which offers more business for all companies involved, and provides better and a larger number of services for consumers.

Because all the elements have been taken into consideration, the outcome is highly beneficial to all parties including consumers, carriers, application developers, service providers, infrastructure providers, etc. Only through an open approach from all key players can the industry ensure a seamless user experience and rich service offering on a global scale. At the same time, this approach ensures open competition and rapid growth of the Mobile Internet market.

MITA Objectives

The primary objective is to provide a user-friendly Mobile Internet experience, with browsing, messaging and rich calls working seamlessly in any network environment and with any type of access. Hiding different addressing mechanisms and minimizing the impact of different access technologies from the consumer improves usability. These essential aspects of a user-friendly mobile entity are collected into the following figure presenting the scope of MITA.

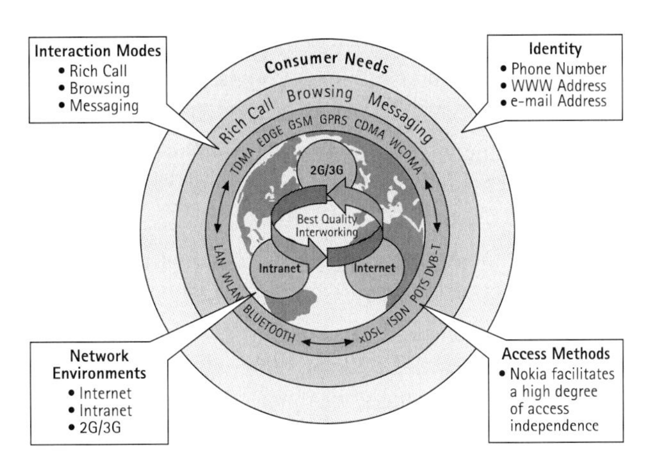

Scope of the Mobile Internet Technical Architecture

In order to lay a solid foundation for the evolution path towards future MITA compliant solutions, the development of current solutions must consider future needs. This backward compatibility will provide valuable building blocks for the Mobile Internet, which will evolve into something much more versatile than it is today. Rapid development is already seen and we can only estimate the future impact of a comprehensive technical architecture for the Mobile Internet.

To ensure far-reaching accessibility, Nokia supports open interfaces bringing new options for the Mobile Internet. Therefore, the Internet itself will not be changed but utilized in more versatile ways, while mobility has a principal role. The value of the Mobile Internet will increase if users are able to access services independent of location and network environment. The Mobile Internet itself will not be a tightly set entity and, hence, the preferred business and technical architectures will need continual revision as the industry and technologies advance.

MITA Work Phases

When the first analysis of the technical architecture was completed, we concluded that following the typical design path (i.e., begin with existing technologies and R&D activities and search for the optimal roadmap towards the Mobile World environment in gradual steps) is not the optimal route to the best technical choices. Because of this, we studied other alternatives, concluding that by following the development cycle in reverse, we could identify new and potentially revolutionary issues on time and take the actions needed to tackle them as a part of normal evolutionary roadmaps.

Based on the above conclusion, MITA work follows three primary phases:

1. **Set targets**
2. **Align with environment**
3. **Influence roadmaps**

The first phase studies current products and technologies, reviews Nokia roadmaps and the products and technologies that are emerging within a 3 year time frame and compares them to problems in the Mobile World and MITA targets. An outcome of this phase is a technical vision which provides direction for the technical architecture and gives it its first model.

In the second phase, the technical architecture model is aligned with the existing R&D roadmaps at Nokia and the activities in standardization bodies. The result is a more detailed technical architecture and an initial implementation view.

In the third phase, the implementation view is finalized and the required R&D activities are addressed for product development.

Every phase has a different relationship with the time frame, as illustrated in the next figure. The first phase addresses MITA on long-term issues, the second phase shifts the focus to mid-term aspects and the third phase completes MITA work with short-term roadmaps, product development plans and reference implementations.

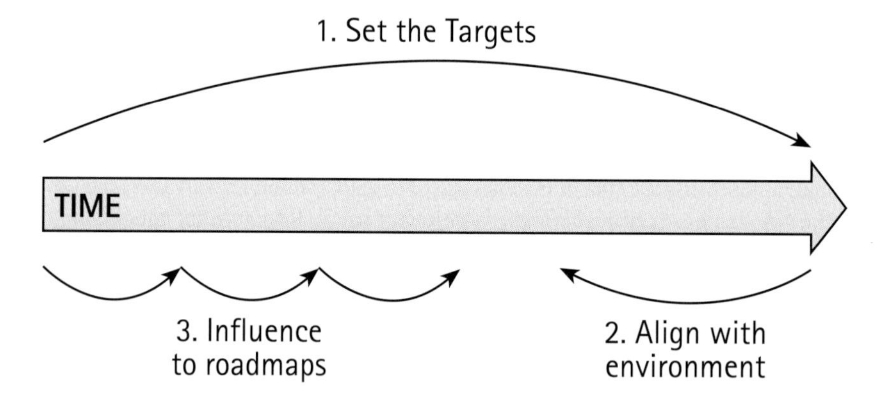

MITA work phases

MITA has already completed the first phase and the key results have been collected in these MITA books. Second phase work has begun with updated work items. The following figure updates the MITA work process for the second phase.

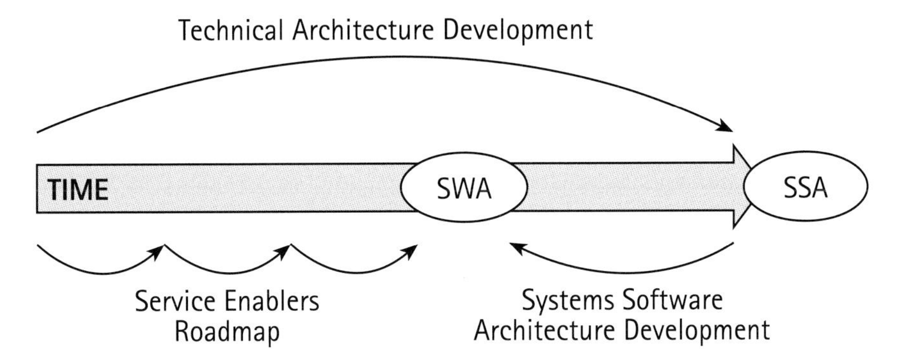

MITA work items in the second phase

The main task in the second phase is to develop a Systems Software Architecture (SWA) for Service Enabler implementations. Another task is to develop a technical architecture into the Subsystem Architecture (SSA), which describes MITA Subsystems and Mobile Internet Interfaces in more detail. The third task is to update technical visions with the latest research results.

MITA Methodology

At the core of the MITA approach is a neutral methodology to help the constituents of the Mobile World understand the critical technical issues in the Mobile Internet. This is achieved through abstract models which describe a conceptual framework for the Mobile Internet environment in progressively more detail and highlight the challenges of interworking between them. MITA tools consist of:

- Architecture modeling principles
- Architecture concept models
- Architecture implementation models
- Architecture specifications
- Reference implementations

Collectively, the MITA tools are used to provide a consistent, unbiased situational analysis and a direction for making technology decisions. And, as the approach is technology neutral, it is flexible and ensures that a consistent approach is applied as new technologies evolve.

Architecture Modeling Principles

The technical architecture modeling is based on principles which should enable the creation of a future-proof end-to-end architecture with high possibilities for the modularity of components in the technical architecture.

The principles for modeling can be listed as follows:

- The architecture divides into independent subsystems while fulfilling business needs
- The architecture is open, modular, and hierarchical, utilizing a layered approach
- The architecture can tolerate varying rates of technological change in individual components. Change in one component should not render the whole architecture useless.

The above principles dictate that layered models are applied to element design, network modeling, and identity structuring. A generic content delivery model is defined for a specification of Interaction Modes and related subsystems. In a similar way, access independent requirements are collected into and specified in a model of an Access Independent Interface.

Architecture Concept Models

For the architecture, there are two approaches worth closer examination. From a business architecture viewpoint, there is the Mobile Internet Business Architecture (MIBA) and MITA can be used as the concept model for a more technical approach.

As a concept model, MIBA defines the interaction between different architecture elements. In the MIBA model, the terminal segment provides the consumer with access to services, the network segment provides terminals with connectivity to service networks, and the server segment provides content and services for consumers.

Within each segment (i.e., content, connection and consumption) the MITA approach models each interacting entity as an element that can be described as consisting of three abstract layers: Application, Mobile Internet, and Platform.

Describing MITA elements in terms of constituent layers enables us to identify the interfaces required for interworking between entities in each segment. Interworking is based on protocols implemented on the Mobile Internet layer and protocol-enabled content exchange between applications on the Application layer.

By mapping the MITA element to the MIBA concept model, a conceptual end-to-end view of MITA is achieved. The MITA end-to-end view is a high-level reference model for more detailed technical architecture design. All architecture elements in MITA can be derived from the same baseline MITA element.

Architecture Implementation Models

The MITA Subsystem Architecture introduces an implementation view of the technical architecture. It is another viewpoint into the technical architecture, encapsulating a group of functionalities into independent, well-isolated subsystems.

In general, a primary requirement is that an implementation of any subsystem can be replaced with another implementation, requiring no or only a minimum amount of modifications to other subsystems or applications utilizing the services of the replaced subsystem. In a similar way, the implementation technology of a subsystem may be completely changed without influencing other related subsystems. The modular MITA implementation model enables a flexible evolution of product implementations according to MITA specifications.

Architecture Specifications

Technical architecture work is divided into MITA specifications, to create technical work items of manageable scope and to enable comparison with other models on the specification level. The MITA specifications are divided into three groups:

- Architecture specifications
- Key system specifications
- Architecture frameworks

The architecture specifications are specifications that have a more permanent nature, whereas the key system specifications represent issues where understanding end-to-end system aspects prior to technology selections is important. The third set of specifications includes frameworks for complicated issues (e.g., security or Mobile Internet Interfaces).

Reference Implementations

Technical architecture development has multiple parallel tracks: reviews of existing products and solutions, analyses of the current actions in standardization, reviews and studies of the latest research results, conceptual modeling actions, and the production of technical visions and specifications. However, these tracks as such do not make any practical implementations or references.

A combination of the Mobile Domain and the Web Domain is by no means without challenges. The resulting environment will contain many relatively complicated components. Without thorough prototyping, an adequate result could be hard to obtain. The experiences and competences obtained from prototyping can be fed quickly back to other parts of architecture development, for example, to protocol developers, which saves development time and requires less work to reach the targets.

However, it is not simply a question of prototyping individual components, e.g., protocols. An equally essential part of prototyping is the integration of various parts to the overall system. While the careful definition of interfaces between various layers can make integration easier, real, hands-on experience is one of the keys to success. This is because reference implementations provide a bridge between the technology visions and the real world, a world that is sometimes full of technical limitations and complicated dependencies. What works in theory may not work well in practice, as additional components affect the overall performance of the system. For example, two technologies can, in a tightly integrated environment, interact in a manner that was not foreseen by the developers of the individual technologies. Essentially, these side effects are the price of increased complexity in future communication systems.

Thus, any far-reaching process, such as MITA work, must be able to face the facts and be able to make the correct conclusions at the right time. Implementations are the right tool for this. They serve as a reality check and as insurance against unexpected problems.

For these reasons, MITA work includes a strong effort to produce so-called MITA Reference Implementations. These do not form a complete MITA system, but are a summary of key technologies needed to build the Mobile World. Note that MITA reference implementations are a continuous development process that adopts new technologies when they are ready to be prototyped.

Compliance with MITA Principles

As described in the previous sections, the evolution towards the Mobile World brings new requirements and various challenges. For product and solution developers, MITA is a framework for building product and solution architectures, as illustrated in the following figure.

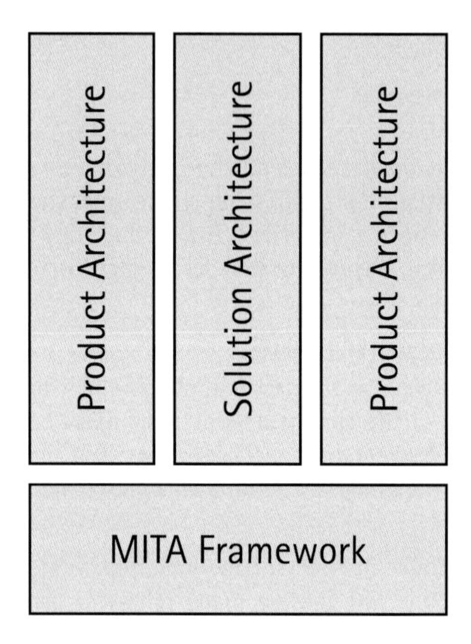

MITA Framework and product architectures

When applying the MITA Framework and methodology to product and solution implementations, three key criteria must be adhered to for compliance with MITA:

- Providing multiple access capable solutions
- Securing the highest quality interworking between networks
- Securing the best interworking between multiple addresses and identities

The above criteria are a very high-level set of principles guiding developers up an evolution path to the Mobile World.

Providing Multiple Access Capable Solutions

Services should not be tied to access methods. If this were the case, new access methods would render the architecture useless. Therefore, a high degree of access independence is a key driver for the technical architecture. Multiple Access Capable solutions are required in order to achieve the global reachability of individuals as well as global access to content.

Securing the Highest Quality Interworking Between Networks

There will also be separate Network environments of mobile networks, the Internet and Intranets. The interworking of these is yet another factor to ensure seamless end-to-end services. These Network environments will be where most user interaction will take place in the Mobile World. To ensure smooth communication between these environments for the consumers, fluent interworking on the technical level is required.

Securing the Best Interworking Between Multiple Addresses and Identities

The reality of multiple access services will require handling multiple identities and addresses that have, historically, been closely tied to networks or applications. A MITA compliant solution recognizes this issue and proposes the best possible way to overcome the challenge.

The dissection of applications should be done in such a way that network requirements are identified, and decoupled from application specific requirements. Requirements for similar applications are grouped under the three Interaction Modes (i.e., Rich Call, Browsing and Messaging). It is important to consider the differences between Network environments, and how to enable applications to seamlessly work between any of the environments, i.e., to ensure service interoperability.

Applications and the Technical Architecture

Nokia classifies applications into four main categories: content, communication, productivity, and business solutions. Example services for each classification category are shown in the following table.

Category	Services
Content	News, Banking, Finance, Local Services, Buy and Sell, Travel, Music, TV, Lifestyle, Fun, Games, Astrology, Dating
Communication	Messaging, e-mail, Fax, Rich call
Productivity	Organizers, Personal Assistants, Tools
Business	Intranet and Extranet access, Information management, Enterprise Communication, Virtual private networks, Telematics

For instance, a game can be downloaded to a terminal from the net and played independently. Here the Interaction Mode is Browsing and the Network environment is the Internet. If the game is played interactively between several people who send messages while playing and, for example, solving game related tasks, then the Interaction Mode is Messaging and the Network environment is the Mobile network, possibly also interaction with the Internet. Finally, if the game is played in an on-line interactive environment, the situation is a Rich Call Interaction Mode in the Mobile network. These game situations highlight the fact that applications must be able to interact freely in all different Interaction Modes and over all Network environments.

In applying the MITA approach to application development, it becomes clear that applications which have been implemented directly on the Platform layer functions while having integrated Mobile Internet layer functions are unacceptable. MITA compatible applications follow the modular implementation model keeping functions between the MITA layers separated.

Mobile Internet Business Architecture

To be able to create a winning solution for the Mobile Internet Business Architecture, Nokia has identified the drivers behind it as well as both the short and long term ramifications which we need to focus on.

Clearly, we cannot overlook the maintenance of profitability, so we prefer solutions which facilitate increases in business revenue. In order to do this, we need to identify the key constituents in the value chain, along with their potential. Hence, consumers, developers and content providers all have to be linked to service providers who in turn link them into the synergy of Consumption, Connection and Content, as illustrated in the following figure.

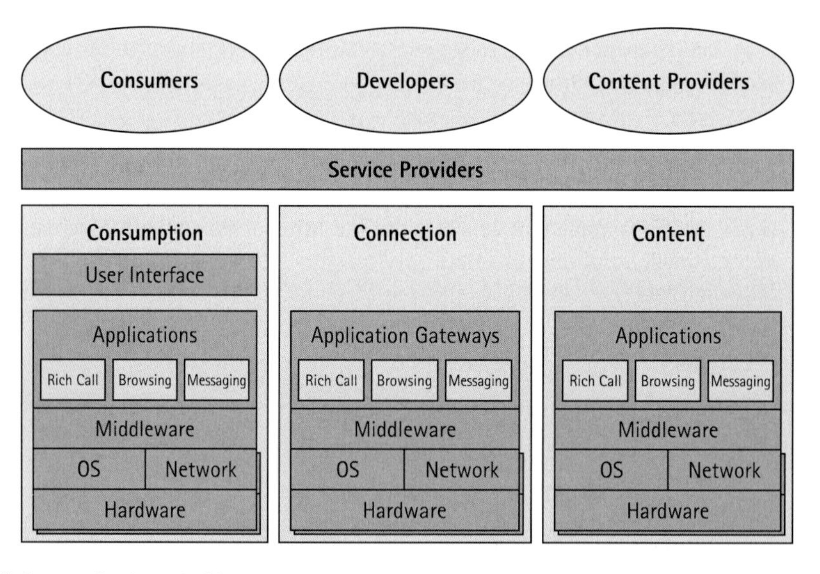

The Mobile Internet Business Architecture

The model contains the key constituencies on the top row, while a simplified architecture with three segments, Consumption, Connection and Content, is presented on the bottom. The key constituencies in the MIBA are consumers, developers, content providers and service providers. The consumer constituency covers both consumers and corporate users, while the service provider constituency covers all types of service providers, i.e., mobile service providers, Internet service providers, application service providers, or in some cases, companies acting as service providers for their own corporate users.

The consumption segment refers to consumers who will be accessing the content provided by a variety of content providers on the content segment. The connection segment (e.g., mobile network) provides a connection between these two segments, and the service providers will manage the connectivity network.

Once all these segments have reached seamless interoperability, all the constituencies will also reach their objectives. Consumers are looking for cost effective and sophisticated services within trusted and reliable coverage areas. Developers will be seeking big volumes and continuity. For content providers, the key issues will be cost efficiency and reachability on a massive scale. Furthermore, service providers are in the business to maintain and maximize their user base and to collect subscription and transaction fees to generate profits.

Middleware Benefits

Middleware solutions provide services for consumers by bringing together software solutions from application vendors and carriers. When the middleware architecture is based on MITA methodology, the following benefits are gained:

1. Support for different network access types from wide area mobile networks to alternate methods. This allows carriers and service providers to build intelligence into their services today and enable their evolution to future technologies.
2. The interfaces are based on open industry standards. Carriers can easily integrate the middleware to their current systems regardless of their network configuration. They can also easily manage their application portfolio. Service providers can provide content using the same standard interface and ensure that applications can utilize their content.
3. Application developers can develop their application to utilize the intelligence of middleware enhancing the features with interoperation capability. This will enhance the consumers experience and make users more willing to use services while on the move, through the Mobile Internet.

Other benefits of middleware for consumers include:

- **Single login** - user logs in once and all services become available
- **Terminal identification through the Mobile Internet layer** - Users will always receive content optimized for their terminal.
- **Preferences** - the user can choose areas of interest and only relevant options will shown (e.g., favorite restaurants, music).
- **Navigation support** - the user can use easy navigation

MITA Deliverables – End-to-End Solutions

It would be impossible to create winning solutions unless extensive end-to-end views guide the design of the technical architecture. These end-to-end views aim to cover all aspects of "Voice goes mobile," "Content goes mobile" and even "Servers become smart" so that overall functionality will be guaranteed.

The architecture elements requiring an end-to-end view are the interaction modes, network interconnectivity, key system elements and access methods. As we are in the middle of the development path towards the Mobile World, coexistent multiple views are already a reality and some new views will be added for completeness.

As the next wave of growth in the Mobile World is expected to come from mobile services, Nokia is actively working with open global standardization of mobile services. The mobile service industry has established a new forum to drive these mobile service standards, it is called Open Mobile Alliance (OMA).

Working within various standardization bodies, the mobile industry will cooperate to create non-fragmented, interoperable mobile services across markets, carries and mobile devices by identifying, endorsing and implementing open standards.

In order for Nokia to ensure the future compliance of these end-to-end views, we already have numerous solutions that fill the MITA model comprehensively and form the foundation for future applications and services. The following table lists many of these solutions and quite clearly illustrates the overall view that has carefully been taken into consideration when aiming to provide optimized creation and delivery of services.

Segment	Services
Consumption	Entertainment phones, Imaging phones, Voice/Messaging phones, Mediaphones, Communicators, Home Multimedia Terminals
Connect	Virtual Private Network solutions, Security appliances, Broadband gateways, Wireless broadband systems, Fixed broadband, xDSL, Wireless LAN, Mobile connection and control servers, Multi-technology radio access networks, Mobility gateways
Content	Mobile commerce, Content applications, Messaging and Community applications, Application developer community, Mobile entertainment services, Mobile Internet services middleware, Connectivity servers , Charging and billing solutions, Advanced call relatedservices, Location services middleware

Conclusions

Nokia is developing a comprehensive technical architecture for the Mobile Internet. The Mobile Internet Technical Architecture aims to provide seamless interoperability between all interaction modes, any network environment and with any type of access. The ultimate objective of MITA is to create a user-friendly Mobile Internet experience for everyone. It will be done:

- by identifying the relevant interaction modes,
- by defining the key technologies required to support them, and
- by driving industry participation to develop a common Mobile Internet platform.

In developing a comprehensive technical architecture for the Mobile Internet, Nokia aims to limit the complexity of the inherently technical environment, as users do not want to worry about the underlying technologies. Nokia sees three key elements as fundamental to the Mobile Internet Technical Architecture: Identity, Interaction Modes and Network environments. Bringing these together and managing the challenges they pose is at the core of MITA and will ensure high-quality and seamless interoperability in end-to-end services.

An open solution benefits all; profitable business scenarios call for interoperability, short development cycles, large volumes and, most of all, global reach. Unless there is a commonly accepted architectural solution, markets will become fragmented as well as require separate parameters, and the total volume will be much smaller than in a single global market.

Introduction to MITA Specifications

Technical architecture work is divided into MITA specifications, to achieve technical teams of manageable scope and enable comparison to other models on a specification level. MITA specifications are divided into three groups:

- Architecture specifications
- Key system specifications
- Architecture frameworks

The Architecture specifications are more permanent in nature, whereas the Key system specifications represent issues where understanding end-to-end system aspects prior to technology selection is important. The third set of specifications includes Architecture frameworks for broader system level issues.

Architecture Specifications

The architecture specifications are more permanent baseline specifications of MITA, covering the structure of the MITA element as illustrated in the next figure.

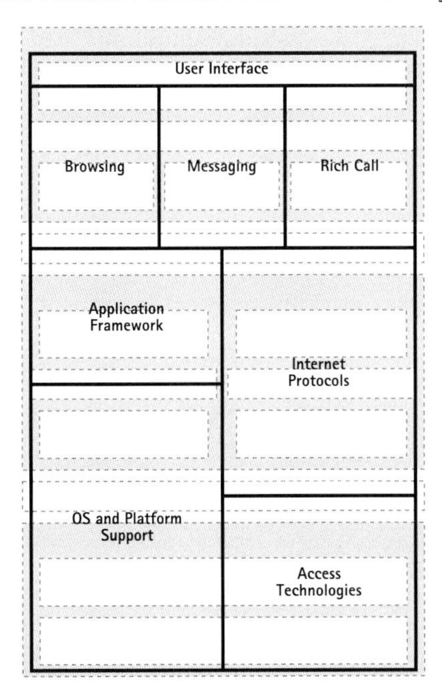

Architecture specifications and the MITA element

UI and Application Framework in MITA

The User Interface (UI) and Application Framework deal with issues related to the user interface and applications. A UI that is simple and easy to understand and use is seen as critical for the successful delivery of Mobile Internet services to the consumer. The importance of applications and their smooth and consistent interaction with the user interface is increasing, as application functionality increases. This becomes crucial when the size of mobile devices limits the display size and the number of user control mechanisms.

In the MITA era, various applications can be active simultaneously, thus providing the consumer with the possibilities to use multiple services at any time. This makes the use of services more convenient and flexible, but also imposes new challenges to introduce these solutions in a user-friendly way. Convenience and flexibility can be further improved by supporting application functionality, which allows seamless communication between applications to exchange any information needed to benefit the consumer.

As applications become downloadable and installable, security becomes increasingly important. Mobile Internet era devices will contain more and more personal and trusted information and functionality and the consumer must have confidence in the behavior of new applications to be downloaded; otherwise, consumer acceptance of new services may be reduced.

It is expected that a combination of revolutionary and evolutionary thinking is needed in order to create UI guidelines for the MITA era. We believe that these targets are best met by focusing the effort on a carefully selected (limited) set of UI styles and mapping the application functionality to the physical UI in an understandable and consistent way, thus minimizing the consumer learning curve and expediting the adoption of new applications and services.

Rich Call in MITA

Rich call is one of the three Interaction modes in MITA. Rich call covers applications which have as their cornerstone a real-time two-way communication component enriched with presence information, text, graphics, images and sounds before, during and after a call. Applications in this category are characterized by having demanding requirements for the underlying transport mechanisms and their integrity due to the real-time nature of the service. Typical applications in the Rich Call category are voice call and conference, video call and conference and real-time interactive games.

Rich call requires consistent behavior over various access networks and Network environments. The access network may impose some constraints over the Interaction mode, but it is desirable that the specific applications can scale their behavior to take this into account. The Network environments and their interworking are also required to be able to interconnect Rich call users residing in various types of networks.

Browsing in MITA

The Browsing Interaction mode covers applications which are interactive by nature, characterized by an interaction between a consumer and services in fixed or mobile servers and, in many cases, nearly real-time:

- o Online browsing (e.g., Markup style browsing interaction, interaction through executable programs and peer-to-peer browsing)
- o Off-line browsing (e.g., Push of content to device, using the same markup languages and executables, but the interaction is limited to local servers and services)

Processed content may be displayable or metadata:

- o Displayable content includes various formats (e.g., text, graphics, animation, sound).
- o Metadata is not directly displayed, but can be used to expand the user experience by giving it a larger scope.

Browsing represents an interactive content consumption and manipulation experience. Initially, the consumer consumes content in an interactive manner, but the experience will soon expand into manipulation of the content (true interactive applications).

The browsing environment, and the browser in particular, will play a significant role as a platform, as the host of a browsing paradigm. The browser is enabled with Extensible Markup Language (XML), and can thus offer XML services to other applications. The concepts of embedded links and metadata in markup documents translate very well into any XML content or content that can be translated into an XML representation, be it contacts, calendar or generic data.

One of the key roles of the browser, as the most important component of browsing, is to serve as a platform for enhanced functionality to be used by other applications. This functionality may include multiple technologies, such as animation services, audio services, and video services. In order to flexibly offer this kind of functionality, dynamic installations and the configuration of software (for example plug-ins) become important.

Messaging in MITA

The Messaging Interaction mode covers applications which provide two-way, asynchronous delivery of content. For example, Short Message Service (SMS), Multimedia Messaging Service (MMS) and e-mail involve a separation between the submittal of content and the delivery to the recipient.

Emerging technologies (e.g., Session Initiation Protocol (SIP) and XML) and applications (e.g., news, chat and Internet Relay Chat (IRC)) address challenges to traditional messaging technologies (e.g., SMS and e-mail) causing new interworking requirements. In a similar way, interworking between MITA applications (e.g., click-to-call and click-to-chat) and the management and processing of the static and dynamic message content and attachments in various conditions address requirements for messaging subsystems.

Internet Protocols in MITA

The underlying fundamentals for the success of IP networking include architectural and technical simplicity, openness, and scalability. The open end-to-end architecture has enabled the efficient development of new services and applications, and fast deployment of them on the Internet. The IP protocols are being extended to globally support user, terminal, and service mobility, which will enable new useful services and applications for all Internet users. As an outcome of the extension, some existing Internet protocols may need modification to meet the new requirements.

The Internet protocols specification introduces the MITA Internet protocols architecture; it explains the functions and roles of the protocol stack layers, and places the protocol layers in the layered MITA network model. This section also introduces the major Internet protocols implementing the protocol functionalities.

Operating Systems and Platform Support in MITA

As an entity, MITA is not about Operating Systems (OS); it is, however, about how operating systems and applications can co-operate with each other to provide a rich consumer experience in a consistent manner. MITA sets certain requirements on the underlying operating systems and support functionality provided by the operating system to the upper layers, such as, SDK libraries, application protocols, and network protocols.

In many cases, the underlying operating system libraries set the base for architectural paradigms. For example, the Linux operating system and Linux libraries and APIs are good examples of the procedural programming style. On the other hand, the Symbian operating system and Symbian OS libraries provide pure object-oriented interfaces. It should be noted that programming languages (e.g., C, C++ and Java) and programming paradigms are separate issues. However, in most cases, procedural programming environments have been extended with high functionality object-oriented designs.

MITA does not define a preferred operating system. Operating system selection is a business decision, not an architectural issue. However, the operating system should always be compatible with MITA requirements. These requirements are set by the upper layers and are collected into this specification for easy access. On one hand, this also means that MITA is independent of operating systems and programming paradigms. On the other hand, it means that the implementation of MITA in different platforms may vary according to platform capabilities.

Another part of the OS and platform support specification are issues related to baseline development environments, and the principles presented for operating systems also apply to them. This specification collects the generic requirements.

Multiple Access in MITA

A typical mobile device consumer is primarily interested in applications and services, while the actual access technology should be as transparent as possible and should not require any technical understanding, when using an application or subscribing to a service. Still, this transparency should not limit potential applications, as all of them might not work in an acceptable way over all access technologies. These technologies have different technical characteristics (e.g., available bandwidth, connection setup time, network delay and symmetric/asymmetric performance), which impact the consumer experience, i.e., the technologies differ in multiple attributes (e.g., data rates, QoS, handover capabilities, latencies).

The Access Technologies Specification defines the elements needed to allow access from a mobile device to an IP network. Due to the differing functionality of the various access technologies, the platform layer varies between different forms of access. The Access Independent Interface is supposed to shield the Mobile Internet Layer from the underlying technology, but access specific functionality is required within the network protocols in order to facilitate some access-specific functionality.

Key System Specifications

The Key systems are end-to-end and cross-organizational building blocks of the Mobile Internet Technical Architecture.

Naming, Numbering and Addressing in MITA

Naming, Numbering and Addressing (NNA) concentrates on the names and addresses of individual people or devices and how names and addresses appear on the user interface. The consumer favored nickname information is translated into globally unique names and finally to routable addresses. The translations between globally unique names and the related directory infrastructure belong to the Naming, Numbering, and Addressing specification. The implications and requirements of the NNA environment (e.g., anonymous addressing and regulator aspects) are also studied in the specification.

Naming, Numbering, and Addressing provides one unified translation infrastructure for Rich call, Messaging and Browsing services. Interaction with presence services enables networked and dynamic resolution of naming layer addresses. On the mobile device, Naming, Numbering, and Addressing functionalities are located in the address book subsystem. However, it should be noted that the NNA services are not limited to the address resolution requirements of the rich call service, for any application may utilize these services.

Presence in MITA

Presence deals with the issues of providing dynamic information about the status and availability of consumers and mobile devices. Presence is a key system for a number of specifications. The messaging specification utilizes presence services to enable instant messaging between consumers.

It should be noted that one consumer could have multiple application level identities. How to manage these and how to dynamically associate them to the current Connectivity layer identities are issues which link the presence specification to the reachability specification.

Reachability in MITA

The reachability of devices and people deals with the issues related to the question of how a device or a person is reached through the Web and Mobile domains. A communication network is not a single network with seamless IP connectivity. A communication network consists of networks, such as IPv4 Internet, IPv4 intranets, IPv6 Internet, carrier IPv6 based mobile networks and Public Switched Telephone Network (PSTN). There are also different types of gateways (e.g., Network Address Translation (NAT), firewall or Session Initiation Protocol (SIP) entities) between networks. Seamless person-to-person and device-to-device connectivity over these fragmented networks is the scope of the Reachability Specification.

Access Independent Connectivity in MITA

The Access Independent Connectivity (AIC) specification deals with seamless access to personal services in all Network environments independently of their location and connectivity/access providers. The primary focus of the AIC specification is to provide continuous connectivity for interconnected MITA end-points. The Access Independent Connectivity specification provides access independent mobility management for the Connectivity layer.

Typically, mobility management is involved in connections between a device and a network. This statement is also valid for the AIC Specification. In MITA, mobility management has been divided between the AIC specification and the Access Technologies specification. The Reachability, Service Discovery, and Presence Specifications also deal with mobility issues.

Service Discovery in MITA

Service discovery consists of three types of discovery methods:

- Service discovery on ad-hoc networks
- Service discovery on the Internet
- A special type of service discovery is provided by the presence and virtual community navigation layer

The Service Discovery specification covers the Connectivity and Application layer service discovery technologies. The access layer-related service discovery technologies are covered in the Access Technologies specification.

The Service Discovery specification addresses requirements for the Access Independent Interface. When the AIC Subsystem identifies a need to change into a new access network domain, after proper authentication, the service discovery service for the Connectivity layer should be activated. In a similar way, the service discovery service provides control and event triggering interfaces for the Application layer subsystems and applications.

Location in MITA

The Location specification defines software and protocol interfaces for location services. In practice, this refers to interfaces receiving location information for applications and to applications that utilize location-based information. A goal in MITA is a mobile location services architecture and interfaces, which are able to deliver location information to applications regardless of the positioning technology and of the division of functionality between devices, networks and servers. The same architecture must be flexible for several business models. In other words, a simple business model should not dictate it.

Location information is also an important element in many other MITA specifications. For example, location can be used to automatically update a user's presence and reachability information, and it can also be utilized in service discovery for local services.

The mobile location services architecture in MITA actually consists of several different architectures, where the positioning infrastructures are different but location interfaces to applications and middleware, in between, should be the same.

Device Management and Data Synchronization in MITA

Device management, including both bootstrap and continuous device management, is very important. A good and correct configuration is a prerequisite for any application to actually be functional. Furthermore, it is to be expected that the complexity of mobile devices will increase with the addition of new and more powerful applications. At the same time, these increasingly complex devices will move into mass-market environments and it is not reasonable to assume that all the consumers will be willing to configure their applications manually. Thus, the need for device management will only increase.

It is highly likely that there will be multiple device management providers. Typically, each provider has access to a subset of the parameter space. For example, there might be different management entities for the device's look-and-feel, for the browsing environment and for the messaging environment. The managing entities, for the above three, could be the device manufacturer, service provider, and the company of the consumer, respectively.

Device management offers services to applications (e.g., provides them with configuration data). Similarly, device management also has its own user interface, for example, to allow the user to control and interact with the management process.

In MITA, data synchronization will cover at least the following issues:

- Distributed applications and databases
- Linkage between presence and contacts/calendar
- Personal Information Management (PIM) related issues (e.g., contacts, calendar, and to-do lists)
- Controlled content download and management, using smart messages or a device management mechanism

Content Formats in MITA

A content format refers to a convention of packaging content. Agreements must be made on content formats in order to build the necessary interoperability between various machines, devices and applications. Given the limitations of the processing environment in mobile devices, we have to select a certain reasonably small set of content formats to be promoted and supported in Mobile Internet offerings. Content formats are to be agreed on in the areas of audio, still images and vector graphics, video and general-purpose documents.

Content Adaptation in MITA

Content adaptation refers to the manipulation of content to make it suitable for specific machines, devices and applications. Although agreement on common content formats is the desirable solution, market segmentation, devices of different generations or categories with varying capabilities (e.g., processing power, display resolution, memory and bandwidth), and the unavoidable introduction of new formats are all true obstacles for interoperability. Content adaptation strives to fill the interoperability gaps as devices and content formats evolve. Examples of content adaptation include: image format conversion and the resolution reduction of images and video. Content adaptation can also modify content modality to suit the consumer's environment. For instance, text-to-speech technologies can be useful for retrieving text messages while driving a car.

Operation Support Systems in MITA

The Operation Support Systems (OSS) specification deals with the Mobile Internet management and support architecture. The functionality of the OSS architecture is divided into management layers:

- Network management
- Service management
- Subscription management
- Subscriber accounting and identity management

By combining the management layers with the possible business players, two frameworks could be constructed:

- Management framework
- Policy framework

Privacy in MITA

Privacy is not an add-on feature. All aspects of a system have to be designed to fulfill the inherent need for privacy. Privacy in MITA covers all relevant principles, solutions and technologies related to consumer privacy on the Mobile Internet.

Nokia is concerned about the emerging privacy threats. As the awareness of the Mobile Internet and privacy issues increases among the consumers, the pressure to maintain and build trust rises among all players. Companies need to address the privacy concerns seriously. Trust, once lost, is very hard to regain. Privacy, once lost, cannot be repaired.

Architecture Frameworks

Part of the MITA work deals with issues which are complicated to solve without having common and unified models. These issues are structured under common frameworks, before a more detailed technical architecture is built. Current such frameworks include directories, security, Mobile Internet Interfaces and Quality of Service (QoS).

Directories in MITA

Directories are network repositories for information about people, places and things. There are numerous instances of directories in the Mobile domain. For example, in GSM technologies the Home Location Register (HLR) is a directory of information about subscribers. Directories consist of three basic components:

- Schema
- Access method
- Directory store

Information in a directory, whether it represents data about a person or a device, is structured in a particular way. The characteristic defining the selection of information that is stored about people, places and things is called a schema. There is also a need to represent directory information when it is transferred around the Mobile domain. Exchange formats provide a standard exchange scheme for such purposes. Significant MITA schemes include those that represent the mobile person object and the mobile device object. Other auxiliary schemes define managed mobile services for these basic objects.

Information in a directory is accessed using a directory access protocol. Directory access protocols provide methods for creating, modifying, searching and deleting entries. The administrators of a directory service can also utilize restricted administrator access methods to create new directory object types. There are a number of directory access methods that are needed for Mobile domain directories.

Information in a directory is maintained and managed similarly to information within a database. In fact, a directory is a specialized database application. Within the Mobile domain, there are numerous directory stores, each being used to capture information about a particular feature of the mobile person object or the mobile device.

Additional components in the MITA directory specification include the use of directory synchronization to keep the numerous mobile directory stores updated with each other. Directories contain critical mobile assets including security information about consumers.

Security in MITA

Security is about safety and trust. Safety is considerably easier to manage than trust, and without safety, it is hard to create trust between unseen entities. It is important to understand that security addresses requirements on all entities of the Mobile Internet Technical Architecture. Security is required when calling someone or making an electronic monetary transaction with browser security functionality or features protecting consumer information from being revealed or being altered during transmission. Similar security requirements also apply to server-to-server transactions.

MITA security objectives are:

- **Integrity**
- **Confidentiality**
- **Availability**
- **Authentication**
- **Authorization**

Integrity deals with the prevention of erroneous modification of information. Authorized users are probably the biggest cause of errors, omissions and the alteration of data. Storing incorrect data within the system can be as bad as losing data. Malicious attackers can also modify, delete or corrupt information that is vital to the correct operation of business functions.

Confidentiality deals with the prevention of unauthorized disclosure of third party information. This can happen as a result of poor security measures or information leaks by personnel. An example of poor security measures would be to allow anonymous access to sensitive information.

Availability deals with the prevention of unauthorized withholding of information or resources. This does not apply just to personnel withholding information. Information should be as freely available as possible to authorized users.

Authentication deals with the process of verifying that users are who they claim to be when logging onto a system. Generally, the use of user names and passwords accomplishes this. More sophisticated is the use of smart cards and biometric authentication. The process of authentication does not grant the user access rights to resources - this is achieved through the authorization process.

Authorization deals with the process of allowing only authorized users access to sensitive information, protected services or resources and controlled actions. An authorization process uses the appropriate security authority to determine whether a user should have access to resources.

Mobile Internet Interfaces in MITA

Mobile Internet Interfaces are fundamental elements of the Mobile Internet Technical Architecture. Elsewhere in this book, both the layered model of a MITA element and the fundamentals of the MITA subsystem architecture were presented. These models identified many interfaces. Some of them are software interfaces within a MITA element and others are protocol interfaces between interconnected MITA elements.

Mobile Internet Interfaces are a group of open interfaces provided by Nokia for both software developers and system integrators, so that they can implement MITA compliant applications and systems. It should be noted that Mobile Internet Interfaces live longer than product generations and have similar features over product and server categories. Open software interfaces in the Mobile Internet Technical Architecture are called Mobile Internet Software Interfaces (MSI) and open protocol interfaces are called Mobile Internet Protocol Interfaces (MPI).

MSIs are divided into Application Programming Interfaces and System Software Interfaces (SSI). In a similar way, MPIs are divided into two parts: Protocol Data Units (PDU), including protocol payload definitions, and content formats, describing presentation formats for the content.

In the Mobile Internet Technical Architecture, all MITA elements have Mobile Internet Interfaces. In terminals, most of the open interfaces are software interfaces for application developers, whereas in servers, the open interfaces are both software and protocol interfaces enabling fast and rich service implementation by system integrators and developers. In network elements, Mobile Internet Interfaces are mainly protocol interfaces enabling different MITA end-to-end views.

Quality of Service in MITA

The Quality of Service (QoS) is an important topic that requires a common and unified model. QoS in MITA is approached by defining the basic objectives for a QoS system on four levels:

- Support the mission of the service provider or carrier
- Serve the principal needs of consumers
- Meet the quantity and quality requirements of applications
- Transmit as many packets as possible

The fundamental assumption is that when defining the actions of a network, a hierarchical structure is formed where the first objective is the most important and the last objective is the least important. For instance, when the needs of different customers are conflicting, we have to look at the upper level in the hierarchy (i.e., the mission of service provider) instead of a lower level (i.e., the applications requirements) in order to solve the conflict. From this perspective, QoS is more about the mission of the service provider, that is, typically business, than the fulfillment of the special requirements of applications. In order to meet the objectives set for QoS, the carrier has to proceed in phases that include defining the fundamental mission, designing the service model, building an appropriate network, and using suitable QoS mechanisms.

The Mobile Internet will consist of several different networking technologies, network environments and services. In some parts of the Mobile Internet, the Quality of Service mechanisms and principles may be based on an approach that is not suitable for other parts of the network. For example, radio technologies often support a natural flow or connection-oriented QoS while the legacy Internet has been designed for packet-based approaches. This implies that the only reasonable way to provide real end-to-end QoS must be based on a common measure, and fulfilling the business goals of carriers is exactly this measure.

III SOLUTIONS

PART 3.1

Introduction

- Service Development Evolution
- Systems Software Architecture
- Service Enablers
- Club Nokia

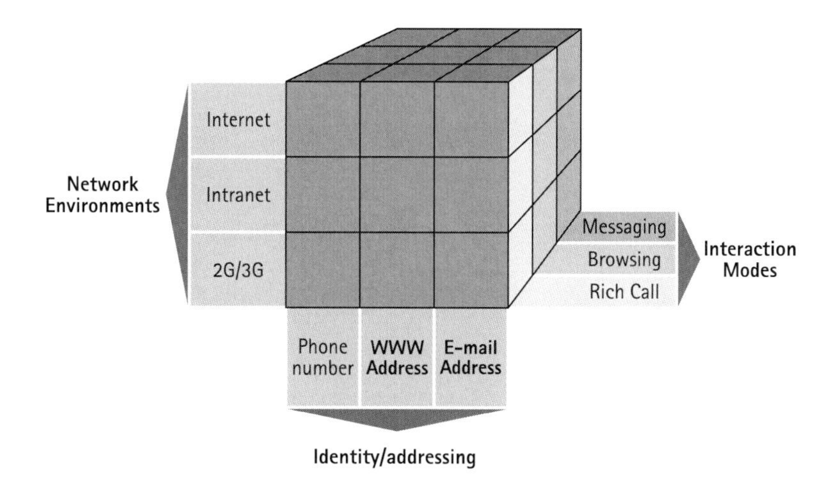

Service Development Evolution

The development of mobile services will evolve in many ways, ranging from consumer behavior, needs, and desires to creating a sustainable business ecosystem within the respective mobile service value domains, and finally technology itself, providing new service capabilities.

When one looks at how technology will enable mobile services to evolve, there is a tendency to simplify the requirements for the delivery of mobile services, the most simplistic view being that all that is needed to deliver tomorrow's new services is a device with a color screen and content being available on the Internet. Device functionality is evolving significantly, in addition to gradual improvements in presentation and interface capabilities; the device is increasingly becoming a software platform. A more sophisticated operating system and, equally important, new client applications are enabling the new service delivery methods to become a reality for the consumer.

To deliver the mobile services, the requirements of a client/server content focussed architecture need to be fully recognized. This is seen today with Short Message Service (SMS) content and Wireless Application Protocol (WAP) based services, but this realization will become increasingly important as the client functionality evolves to support new messaging; content purchase, protection and delivery; and content discovery.

The following diagram depicts the evolution and mapping of the client/server functionality, also illustrating the need for and importance of applications and content in delivering the service.

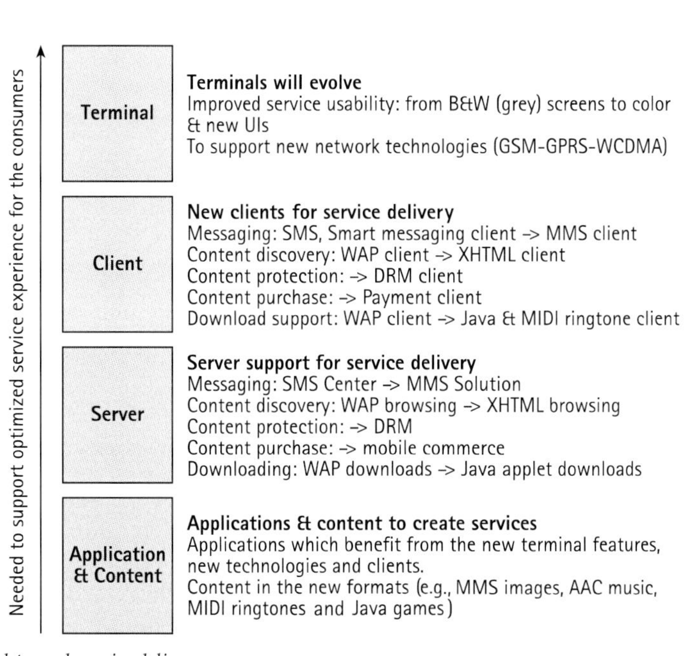

Basics for end-to-end service delivery

Systems Software Architecture

The mobile industry has experienced a period of exceptional growth during the past ten years. The next wave of growth is expected to come from mobile services.

New service enablers based on open global standards, (e.g., the Multimedia Messaging Service (MMS), Java™ and the Extensible HyperText Markup Language (XHTML)) will enable compelling new services for consumers and new sources of growth for the mobile industry.

To ensure successful take-up of mobile services, it is important to minimize the fragmentation of service platforms and to ensure seamless interoperability.

Lack of interoperability between service platforms of different vendors would lessen the attractiveness of many mobile services in the eyes of consumers. Fragmentation of service platforms would also force content developers to perform costly and time-consuming porting for each platform and hence limit the amount of attractive content available. In a similar way, economies of scale and the pace of equipment vendors' innovation would be hurt by service platform fragmentation. For carriers, this kind of fragmented scenario would likely mean slower service deployment, higher costs and longer time to revenues.

The driver for a Systems Software Architecture (SWA) stems from the need for open global standards and non-fragmented service platforms. The objective is to enable consumers to use interoperable mobile services, despite differences in markets, carriers and mobile devices.

A multiple vendors implementation of a uniform service architecture will result in:

- Compelling new mobile services for consumers
- Interoperability across infrastructures, devices and services
- Less market fragmentation
- Healthy competition between suppliers, carriers and developers
- Lower cost of introducing new services
- Fast global service deployment
- Less confusion in user experience with different service providers

The objective of this section is to introduce an overall end-to-end framework to describe the key technology components and interfaces needed to deploy an open architecture, in a way that ensures compelling services for consumers as well as successful business opportunities for all industry players.

Enabling a Successful Business Architecture

In order to expand the total service market, the objective of the systems software architecture is to enable a flexible and open business architecture that makes a wide variety of business models for all stakeholders possible. This will maximize innovation and the creation of compelling services for consumers.

The key stakeholders in the mobile service delivery chain include:

- Carriers
- Service providers
- Corporations
- Content providers
- Developers
- Terminal manufacturers
- Telecom and IT infrastructure providers

Design Principles of the Systems Software Architecture

A systems software architecture rests on the following key design principles:

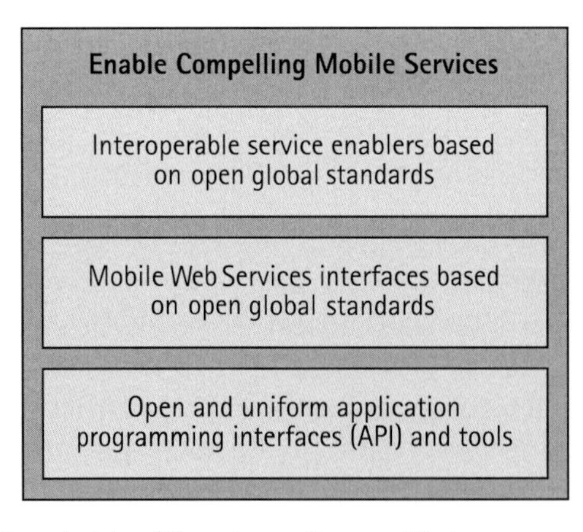

Enable Compelling Mobile Services
Interoperable service enablers based on open global standards
Mobile Web Services interfaces based on open global standards
Open and uniform application programming interfaces (API) and tools
Business Drivers
Successful business for all industry players
Non-fragmented Mobile Services mass market
Bridge gap between Web and Mobile domains
New market for mobile enriched services
Enabling a mass market for application developers and content providers

Key design principles of the systems software architecture

By promoting interoperable service enablers based on open global standards, the systems software architecture creates a foundation for mass-market services. The industry players, who implement interoperable service enablers end-to-end in mobile devices, servers, networks, and developer tools will offer many new compelling services for consumers. The end-to-end view is critical for success because if one link is missing, mobile services will not take off.

Mobile Web Services Interfaces based on open global standards enable a new way for carriers to open the Mobile domain assets (e.g., billing, identification/authentication, location, and presence) and provide the added value of mobility to applications and service providers in the Web domain. By building on technologies that are widely accepted in the Web domain, Mobile Web Services Interfaces will help to bridge the differences between the Mobile and Web domains. This will enable an easy method for service providers to gain access to the advantage offered by the mobile network and portal and to enrich their services to consumers by adding unique mobile value to them. For carriers, this enables new revenue sources from third-party service providers beyond revenues from providing only transport and access. Mobile Web Services Interfaces will attract new innovation potential for services from the Web domain to the Mobile domain in a way that will spur on the total market.

The ability to attract third-party developers and content providers is crucial for creating a successful mobile services market. Currently, developers and content providers face a fragmented market where content and applications must be separately ported to service platforms of different carriers and vendors. This in turn limits the availability of attractive content for mobile services. Therefore, uniform open standard based Application Programming Interfaces (API) and service execution environments for developers, which cover both mobile devices and the service provisioning infrastructure, are a central part of the systems software architecture.

Also, by utilizing developer environments, developer languages, and APIs that already are familiar to Web developers (e.g., Java™, Web Services, XHTML technologies), the systems software architecture will lower the barrier of entry for Web developers. With content creators already well-positioned for making applications for the mobile environment, the mobile industry can benefit from the existing Web developer ecosystem.

Overview of the Systems Software Architecture

This section briefly presents the key elements and interfaces of the systems software architecture. The key components and interfaces built on the mobile network include:

- Terminal
- Service Provisioning Infrastructure (SPI)
- Application Programming Interfaces (API)
- Applications and Content
- Mobile Web Services Interfaces
- Mobile Service Brokers
- Network Servers

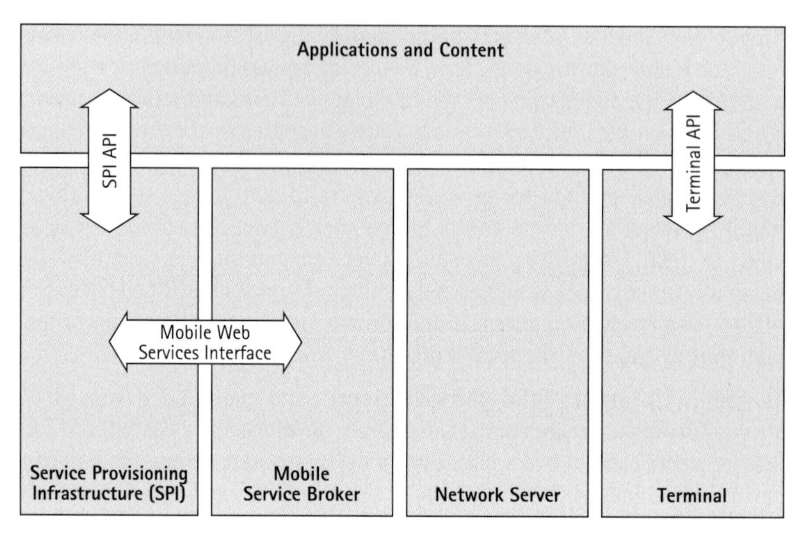

Simplified overview of the key technology components and interfaces of the systems software architecture

Terminal

The terminal software is an essential part of the implementation of service enablers. It consists of two parts: the applications for the consumer and the terminal middleware.

Typical examples of applications for the consumer include address books, calendars, messaging, browsers, music players and games. Applications may be either native or interpreted, and they may be factory-installed or installed on demand over the air. These options provide consumers with access to a large base of valuable applications, as well as developers with a large customer base.

The terminal middleware provides applications for consumers with a comprehensive execution environment, including necessary facilities (e.g., virtual machines, device drivers, networking, rich call capability and messaging). A solid and rich application environment speeds up the application development process by allowing developers to skip the basic plumbing work and focus on the value added, the application itself. The business potential for developers is further increased by applications being portable across all compatible terminals.

Providing developers with easy access to enabling services (e.g., location or presence information) is one key feature of terminal middleware.

Service Provisioning Infrastructure

The Service Provisioning Infrastructure (SPI) includes the software for hosting applications and content outside the carrier's network. The SPI covers typical middleware products (e.g., application servers, virtual machines, Web servers, databases, and run-time libraries). The SPI may also cover the necessary tools and adapters for integration with various back-end systems.

The SPI typically provides applications with a comprehensive application execution environment including all the basic services that allow the developers to focus on the essentials. For example, both Java 2™ Standard Edition (J2SE™) and Java 2 Enterprise Edition (J2EE™) provide developers with a virtual machine. So they can write an application once and run it on practically any hardware platform. J2EE further allows developers to focus on the business logic while all the basic facilities (e.g., scalability and messaging) are provided off-the-shelf for all applications.

Providing developers with easy access to enabling services (e.g., sending MMS messages or acquiring location information) is one important feature of the SPI.

Application Programming Interfaces

Based on the systems software architecture, the end-to-end application environment includes both the terminal and server application environments.

On the terminal, the application environment includes the APIs, called Terminal APIs. Use of technologies such as Java 2 Micro Edition (J2ME™) even makes it possible for a developer to write an application that automatically adapts to different types of mobile devices, with their various screen sizes, colors and other properties.

On the server side, the application environment includes the APIs called SPI API. Portability across multi-vendor SPIs, as well as across different hardware platforms, is a crucial benefit, as on the terminal side.

In addition to the regular application services, APIs provide applications with an easy means to benefit from service enablers and make applications more compelling and user-friendly. These applications will leverage the potential and inherent characteristics of the Mobile domain.

Applications and Content

Applications and content cover software programs and digital material run or consumed on either the terminal or the SPI. On the terminal this includes, e.g., downloadable Java games, XHTML content and music files. On the server side, it typically includes Java beans or applications.

The goal is that applications and content written according to standards will be portable across different software and hardware platforms to a large extent.

Terminal manufacturers and infrastructure providers will offer a large range of Software Development Kits (SDKs) for developers, ranging from API libraries to emulators for terminals and Web services. Having access to these tools will enable the developers to concentrate on the development of the applications rather than on developing their own utilities and make the testing easier and much more efficient.

The Java APIs will enable the developer to use tools that are well-known and support several SPI environments.

Mobile Web Services Interfaces

Web Services are gaining wide acceptance in the Web domain. They are built on existing and emerging technologies (e.g., Extensible Markup Language (XML), the Simple Object Access Protocol (SOAP), Web Services Description Language (WSDL), Universal Description, Discovery and Integration (UDDI), and the HyperText Transfer Protocol (HTTP)). One of the primary targets of Web Services technologies is to enable the automation of business-to-business services.

Mobile Web Services will enable an easy method for service providers to gain access to a carrier network and portal assets and enrich its services to consumers. For carriers, this enables new revenue sources from third-party service providers, which stretch beyond transport and access.

In short, the new mobile network enriched services enabled by open global Mobile Web Services Interfaces will:

- Enable carriers to open their platforms in a new way that bridges the gap between the Mobile and Web domains
- Enable service providers to access a carrier's added value
- Enable customers to get enriched mobile services in a way that creates new business for carriers and service providers

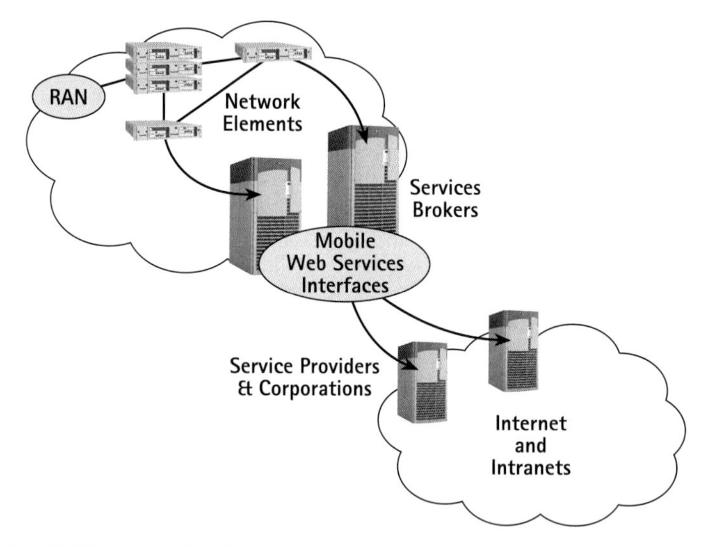

The concept of mobile Web services interfaces

Mobile Service Brokers

The mobile service broker is a technology concept of how to implement functionality for Mobile Web Services Interfaces.

Mobile service brokers include the software in the carrier network that is specialized for providing valuable and meaningful mobile services to any service provider. Brokers may provide useful services (e.g., acquiring a customer's location information for parties within or outside the carrier network). Brokers can also hide the implementation details of different types of network technologies or terminals from developers.

For carriers, mobile service brokers provide an opportunity for increasing revenue beyond transport and access income.

For service providers, the opportunity to use mobile services makes it possible to produce far more attractive services. Also, the possibility to benefit from a carrier's existing authentication and billing mechanisms opens totally new business models and opportunities.

For developers, brokers provide mobile services in a logical, easy-to-use and familiar form that enables rapid adoption of mobile services and seamless interoperability between different carriers.

Brokers on the carrier's premises can open their services to any service provider through Mobile Web Service Interfaces.

Network Servers

Network servers cover the software on the carrier's premises that is for providing mobile services to mobile subscribers. Examples of network servers are Wireless Application Protocol (WAP) gateways and Multimedia Messaging Service Centers (MMSC).

Network servers can communicate with applications directly, as in the case of a WAP gateway. Functions implemented by one or more network servers can be opened to applications through mobile service brokers.

A Usage Scenario to Illustrate the Systems Software Architecture

To illustrate how the systems software architecture works, the following imaginary case of end-to-end usage involving a Java game download is presented.

A graphical Java game is developed by a third-party developer for Service Provider (SP) by using the uniform open Java APIs and developer tools provided by the systems software architecture. The service provider in turn utilizes the Mobile Web Services Interfaces made available by a carrier in order to get access the carrier's billing, delivery and Customer Relationship Management (CRM) capabilities. These are needed in order to allow consumers to download the game in a convenient way. Carriers and game developers can then share the revenues from this transaction in a secure and flexible way by utilizing the clearing mechanisms provided.

Next, each step of this scenario will be presented in greater detail, in three phases:

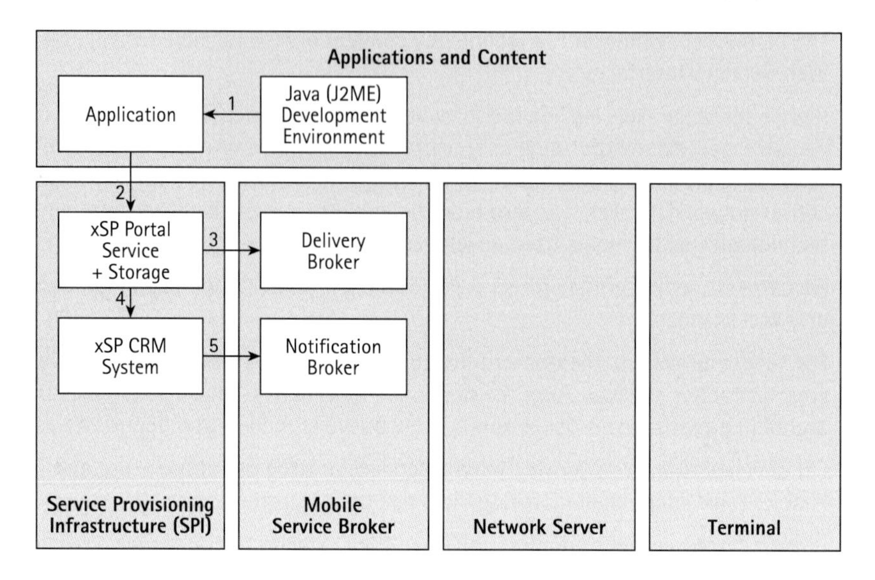

Steps 1-5 of the usage scenario

1. A developer builds and tests the different versions of the game application with the automated code generators, archive builders and visual terminal emulators provided by the Integrated Development Environment (IDE).
2. The game is uploaded to the xSP's portal server's application storage area, together with a game profile file.
3. The portal service registers the game application with the delivery broker in order to enable carrier-based charging and Digital Rights Management (DRM). The registration is done through the Web Service Interface indicated by the delivery broker. The delivery broker then caches the game versions and applies the DRM coding to them.
4. On successful registration, the game profile is sent to the service provider's CRM system.
5. After identifying the optimal customer base, the CRM system contacts the carrier's notification broker to inform the consumer about the released game.

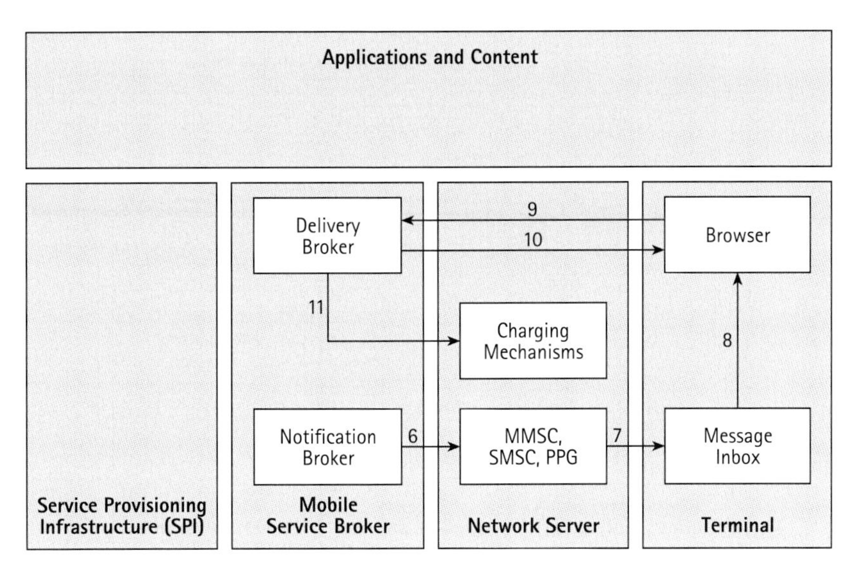

Steps 6-11 of the usage scenario

6. After receiving the service request from the service provider's CRM system, the notification broker relays the message by using the preferred delivery mechanism.

7, 8. The message arrives in the Inbox. The consumer decides to download the game.

9. The browser initiates communication with the delivery broker. At this point, the browser also indicates the mobile device type.

10. After consulting the terminal profile database, the delivery broker delivers the correct version of the game to the consumer.

11. After a successful downloading event, the carrier charges the consumer's account.

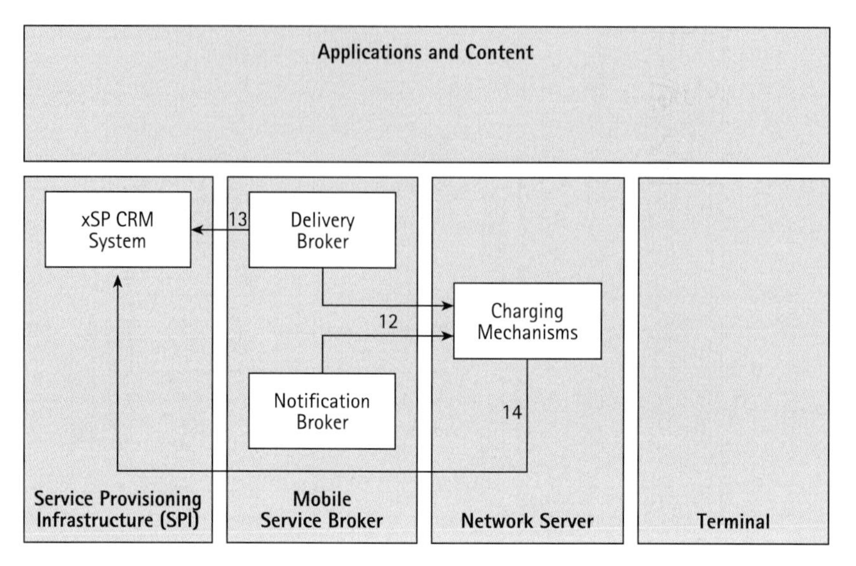

Steps 12-14 of the usage scenario

12. After successful delivery and notification operations, the corresponding brokers charge the service provider's account.
13. The delivery broker informs the service provider's CRM system about the delivery operation. The service provider is later able to distribute the profit to the game developer on the basis of the number of downloads.
14. Clearing mechanisms guarantee that the service provider gets its share of the payment from the consumer.

Deployment of the Systems Software Architecture

The systems software architecture provides an overall end-to-end framework for how compelling mobile services can be offered to mobile consumers through cooperation by different industry stakeholders.

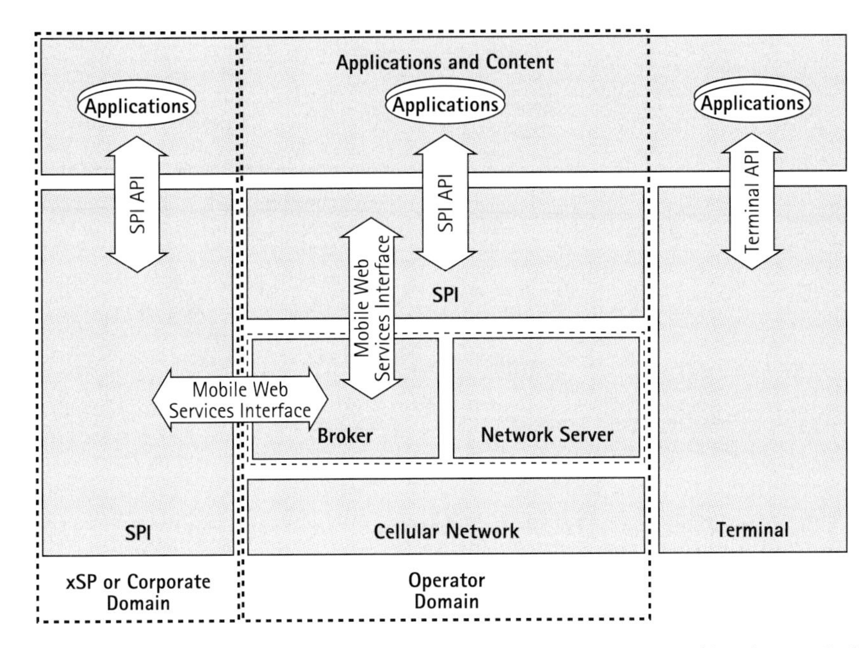

This more detailed picture shows how the systems software architecture components and interfaces can be deployed by the carrier, independent service providers, and corporations.

This illustrates the flexibility of the architecture - the same services can be offered by different parties if desired by the players involved. The technical architecture does not limit the business model configurations.

Benefits of the Systems Software Architecture

The success of open global standards such as the Global System for Mobile Communications (GSM) provides a good example of how open standards and interoperability together fuel market and industry growth. One goal of global open standards is the repetition of this kind of success in the General Packet Radio Service (GPRS) and the third generation mobile services market that expands beyond second generation services.

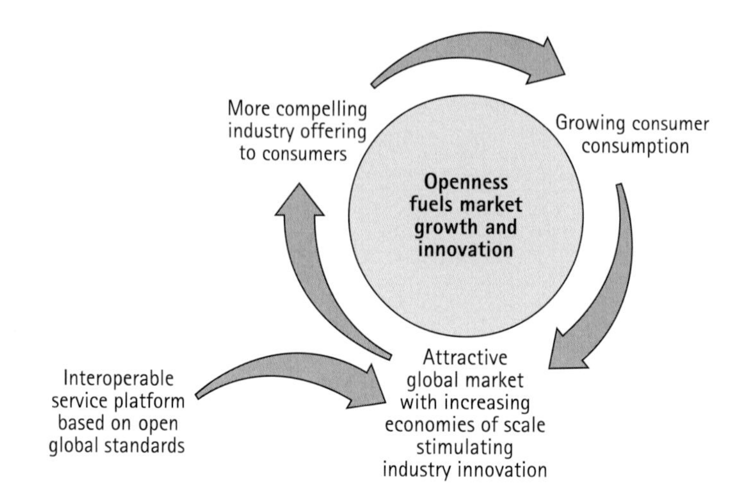

The systems software architecture is intended to start a self-reinforcing cycle expanding the total mobile services market for all industry players.

In order to expand the total service market, the objective of the systems software architecture is to enable a flexible business architecture that makes a wide variety of business models feasible for all stakeholders. This will maximize innovation and the creation of compelling services for mobile consumers.

The list below highlights the benefits of the systems software architecture for different stakeholders.

Consumer benefits:

- The critical service enablers will enable new, compelling services for consumers.
- The open and uniform developer APIs will enable an unparalleled selection of content and applications from a global ecosystem of developers and content providers from both the Mobile and Web domains.
- Consumers will enjoy the benefits of interoperability when they are able to send messages and access content regardless of which vendor's terminals or servers are used. This will avoid the problems that plagued WAP when services did not work across different vendor solutions.

Carrier benefits:

- The systems software architecture will enable a wide selection of compelling new services that will increase carrier revenues.
- The open global standards approach of the systems software architecture will enable a global ecosystem of multiple interoperable vendors, content providers and developers to compete in a healthy open market. This would speed up service deployment by keeping costs down and fueling industry innovation.

- The proposed Web services interfaces will enable carriers to open their platforms to and provide mobile value-added benefits to external service providers in a new way that would expand the total market addressable for all players and enable carriers to extract new revenues in addition to transport and access revenue.
- By building Mobile Web Services Interfaces to technologies that are widely accepted in the Web domain, carriers will get access to a wide variety of the service provisioning infrastructure's offerings and developer communities in the Web domain.
- The open standards approach eliminates the risk of monopolistic lock-in and value migration to a proprietary architecture controlled by a single player.

Developer and content provider benefits:

- The open and uniform developer APIs and environments will take steps to realize the "write once, port everywhere" concept and create an attractive global market with economies of scale for developers and content providers.
- The familiar application development environments, content formats and developer tools between the Web and Mobile domains. This lowers the costs and barriers associated with Web developers' entry to the Mobile domain.
- Digital rights management solutions will ensure content providers sustainable business models, which protect copyrighted content.

Service provider and corporate benefits:

- The systems software architecture will enable service providers to get access to carriers' networks and the unique mobile value which is added via Mobile Web Service Interfaces.
- The open and uniform interfaces proposed by the architecture will take steps to realize the "write once, port everywhere" concept and create an attractive global market with economies of scale for service providers.

IT vendor/service provisioning infrastructure benefits:

- The systems software architecture will open a new global service provisioning infrastructure mass market for IT players in the Mobile domain.
- IT players can leverage their existing server side offerings to target the mobile market with few extra costs, as the systems architecture is built on standard Web service technologies and Java development environments.
- The open standards approach eliminates the risk of monopolistic lock-in and value migration to a proprietary architecture controlled by a single player.

Benefits for the terminal manufacturer:

- The service enablers of the systems software architecture enable new, compelling terminal features and provides means to drive new growth and replacement sales by enabling attractive GPRS and third generation services.
- Open global standards for service enablers in client software create a global mass market with economies of scale and faster deployment of new terminals.
- The open standards approach eliminates the risk of monopolistic lock-in and value migration to a proprietary architecture controlled by a single player.

Service Enablers

Service enablers are the basic technology building blocks for creating mobile services. The implementation of service enablers could take place at many places in the end-to-end chain, in the form of, e.g., mobile device software, server software and development tools. Many new service enablers are needed for the production of new, compelling mobile services and for vitalizing the next growth wave for the mobile industry. The key criteria for service enablers are that they:

- Enable new and better services for consumers
- Provide developers with facilities that speed up the development of new services
- Make new business possible for industry stakeholders
- Are based on open global standards that ensure interoperability

To ensure successful take-up of mobile services, it is important to minimize the fragmentation of service enablers and to ensure seamless interoperability between different vendors. For these reasons, Nokia is strongly committed to open global standards. Therefore, Nokia works in cooperation with other industry leaders in the Open Mobile Alliance (OMA) to promote open global standards and the interoperability of service enablers.

This section introduces what new service enablers, based on open global standards, are needed to create a service platform for the future. The following service enablers will be briefly presented:

- Multimedia Messaging
- Java™ technology
- Browsing
- Device management
- Device profiles
- Delivery
- Identification / Authentication
- Payment
- Mobile Digital Rights Management
- Group Management
- Location
- Presence
- User Profile Management
- Instant Messaging
- Streaming
- Data Synchronization

Introduction

Based on the Short Message Service (SMS) experience three important areas need to be considered, with equal attention: technologies based on open global standards, the business system and the portfolio of services and content.

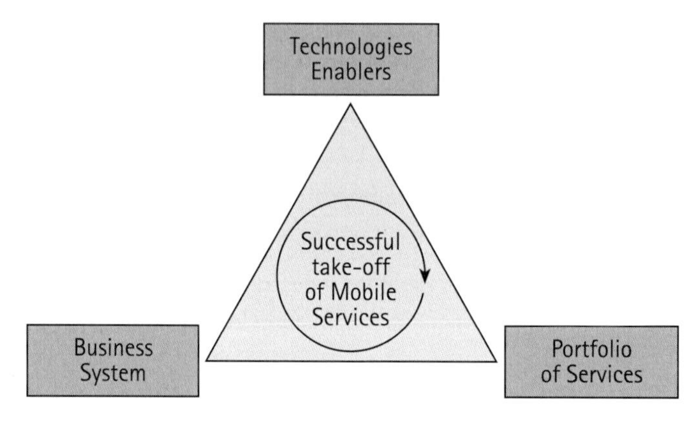

Three cornerstones for the success of mobile services

Portfolio of services and content: Maintaining a portfolio of compelling services and content is a critical requirement in driving a successful mobile services market. The focal point should be the consumer, as the key to service consumption is consumer acceptance.

Business system: The second requirement for success in mobile services is a balanced business system, one based on a healthy profit-making logic for all players within the mobile service ecosystem. A healthy business system maintains a high level of motivation among the members of the business system, to contribute to the success of mobile services.

Technology enablers based on open global standards: The third critical element is service enablers for building new compelling services based on open global standards.

By following and being consistent with open global standards, content providers, application developers, vendors/manufacturers, carriers and IT vendors will be able to provide consumers with a wide selection of different but interoperable devices and services. This will alleviate customer confusion and also ensure that economies of scale are created in a way that will stimulate industry growth.

Lack of interoperability between service enablers of different vendors would lessen the attractiveness of many mobile services in the eyes of consumers. Fragmentation of service enablers would also force content developers toward the money and time consuming porting of applications and services for each platform and hence limit the availability of attractive content. In a similar way, economies of scale of equipment vendors would be hurt by service platform fragmentation. For carriers, this kind of fragmented scenario would likely mean slower service deployment, higher costs and longer time to revenues.

The mobile communications industry has always been based on open standards. Perhaps the best example of this is the Global System for Mobile Communications (GSM), the most successful mobile standard in the world. SMS is an example of openness and interoperability in mobile communications, which has fueled innovation and brought consumers affordable services and products.

Based on the learnings of GSM and SMS, it is clear that interoperable service enablers based on open global standards are important in building up the size of the market and providing economies of scale for all players. This in turn attracts innovative content and application development and results in more appealing services for customers. The resulting boost in usage means that service enablers based on open global standards effectively create a virtuous circle generating business for all parties in the system.

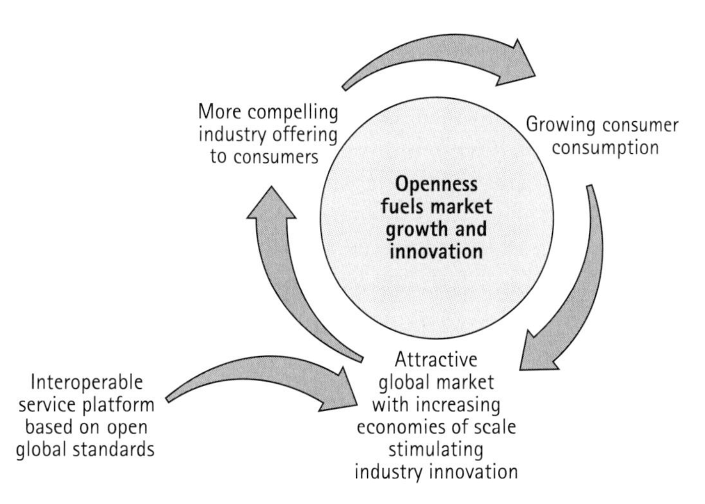

Open global standards expand the total market in a self-reinforcing virtuous cycle.

Opportunities for Successful Differentiation

Complying with open global standards for the underlying service enablers still gives many opportunities for industry players to differentiate their offering to consumers.

Through adjustment of parameters on the service layer, the consumer experience of services can be radically differentiated even though the underlying service enablers are based on open global standards. Examples of such service layer differentiation parameters:

- Content and service portfolio
- Look and feel (e.g., graphics, colors, and layout)
- Usability of services (e.g., menu structure and navigation logic)
- Branding
- Implementation speed
- Pricing schemes

Compared to the 2G era, in which differentiation was limited to voice and simple text messaging, new rich service enablers dramatically increase the differentiation opportunities for all 2.5-3G players despite standardization of the underlying service enablers.

For example, the Extensible HyperText Markup Language (XHTML) Mobile Profile and Cascading Style Sheets (CSS) offer new differentiation features when it comes to differentiating the look and feel and usability of services. With Cascading Style Sheets, carriers and service providers can create a consistent look and feel that is best suited to specific devices. The layout of text can be controlled, as can the font type, font size, margins, borders, bullet types, tables, icons and even color. With this new degree of control, carriers and service providers can truly give their services an individual identity and a strong corporate stamp. By improving the organization and presentation of content, CSS use improves the consumer experience. This is a leap forward comparable to the time when computers moved from command line text input to the graphical user interface. XHTML and CSS bring this same graphical user interface experience to mobile devices. The services look better and are easier to use.

Java enables new sources of differentiation for all players in the value chain. Java makes consumers able for the first time to choose and add new highly graphical applications to the device after the device has been purchased. Carriers will be able to compete on the strength of unique Java content and services. Content can be developed to specifically address the needs of the customers. Also, new services can be created to offer unique services and value to the consumer. Even service delivery can be used as a differentiator, which increases revenue and customer loyalty.

Compared to the text based SMS, the versatility of Multimedia Messaging Service (MMS) content (e.g., images, graphics, sound and text) enables many more differentiation opportunities for all parties.

Also, the versatility of legacy Internet services provides an example of how differentiation of services can take place on the service layer, irrespective of the fact that underlying technologies are standardized. For example, there is a variety of services available on the Internet offering different consumer experiences even though the HyperText Markup Language (HTML) is used as a universal markup language.

Multimedia Messaging Service

MMS is standardized globally and delivers a location-independent messaging experience combined with ease of use. It is a simple and logical extension of SMS. It builds on the well-established SMS model by adding new functions and new content types in steps understandable to the consumer. This step-by-step evolution will encourage the adoption of MMS, leading to rapid take-up and high penetration.

MMS can be used in various situations, business or leisure, and meets the needs of many target groups. The possibility of taking a picture and immediately sending it via MMS allows the consumer to be in full creative control of the content and share it easily. This can be extended for business use, where sending an annotated photograph instantly back to the office might be of immense use. The versatility of MMS content enables photographs, video clips, maps, graphs, layouts, plans and animations to be sent.

The key element in the MMS network architecture is the Multimedia Messaging Service Center (MMSC).

The MMS standard also defines messaging between Internet applications and mobile devices as well as support for flexible addressing of multimedia messages to both familiar phone numbers and e-mail. MMS messages can be created with either Internet applications or devices equipped with an integrated or connected camera. Images can also be downloaded using various Internet applications, through which MMS messages can be created, stored and forwarded.

Technology Platform

Since MMS supports a wide variety of content formats, it can also be seen as a technology that enables many services beyond person-to-person messaging. Hence, MMS technology can be used as middleware for countless services for the Mobile domain. MMS can also be used as an optional delivery mechanism for content protected by Digital Rights Management (DRM) (e.g., ringing tones, animated screensavers and downloadable game packs). DRM mechanisms can also be implemented which allow content to be forwarded to others.

Consumers can also subscribe to MMS based services in the same way they do to Wireless Application Protocol (WAP) and SMS services today. Both push and pull MMS content will be available. These services will include headline news, daily cartoon strips, or the latest sports news, accompanied by a short audio clip covering a high point in the game. The messages can be pure information or may be combined with an element of advertising. MMS adds true multimedia content to these messages.

Billing

Subscriber confidence is vital when defining the pricing structure of MMS. If consumers are unsure of the cost, it is likely that they will not send messages at all. If this reaction is widespread amongst consumers, ultimately it will result in very low MMS revenue.

Therefore, the carrier should ensure that consumers find the costs of MMS predictable and thus feel they can use the service without fear. Nokia recommends that the carriers deploy an MMS charging model similar to the transaction-based billing used with SMS, i.e., basing charges on the number of transmitted messages. However, the great variation in message sizes means that this may require further adjustment in order to reflect the cost of delivering the message.

To prevent the recipient switching off the MMS application to avoid unwanted costs, MMS reception should be free of charge. Again the familiar SMS billing model, where the sender pays all costs associated with a message, will lower the entry barrier for consumers who wish to use the new MMS service. The exception would be some application-originating, mobile-terminating services where the recipient has ordered the content or subscribed to value-added MMS services. In this case, the recipient would pay for the message.

Nokia suggests not introducing a subscription fee or monthly charge immediately, as these may add to the entry barriers for MMS consumers. However, such a model may be of use for certain services as consumer acceptance grows. For example, access to value-added services (e.g., Web mail accounts) could be provided as a subscription-based service.

End-to-End Deployment Architecture

The MMSC performs the store-and-forward operations of an MMS network. It is a highly reliable, scalable, and high capacity platform that supports person-to-person multimedia messaging. In addition to device-to-device messaging, the MMSC supports device-to-application, application-to-device, and application-to-application messaging. It also has an external application interface for third-party application development.

To provide a comprehensive multimedia messaging solution, the MMSC is complemented by application gateways. A Multimedia Device Gateway provides long-term message storage, provides multiple access methods, and supports legacy phones. Legacy phone support is essential to increase the number of subscribers who are able to send and receive multimedia messages, thus helping MMS attain critical mass.

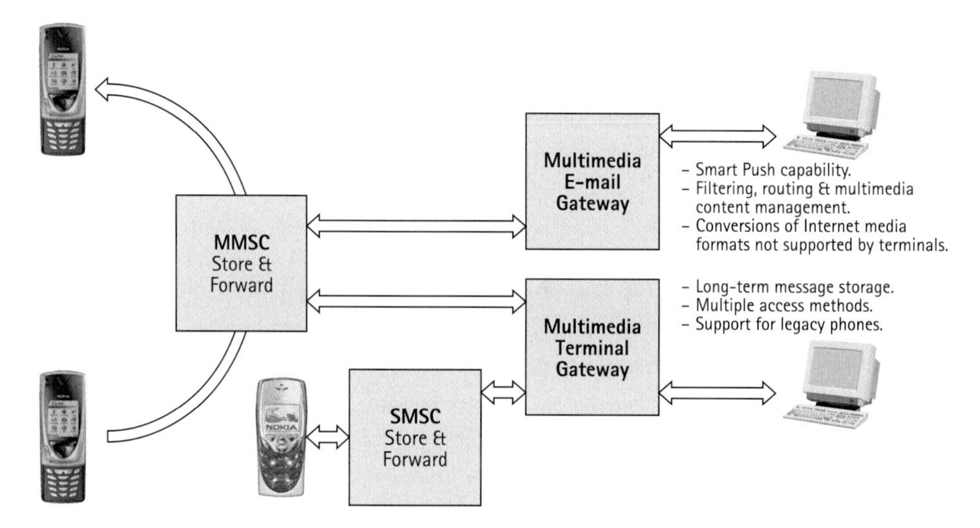

Multimedia messaging implementation

A multimedia e-mail gateway provides consumers with Smart Push capability for e-mail messages by performing filtering, routing and multimedia content management. By offering Smart Push, this gateway changes the nature of e-mail messaging from "store-and-retrieve" to "store-and-forward."

Consumers should be able to filter and route e-mail messages to different destinations on the basis of predetermined criteria. E-mail messages routed to the device that contains multimedia content should be converted from the many image, audio and application media formats supported on the Internet to the media formats supported by the device.

Multimedia content needs to be adapted to fit the display capabilities of the device. The ability to have important e-mail messages pushed to the device and to enjoy multimedia content from the Internet will greatly increase the usage of MMS and will highlight the necessity for Multimedia E-mail Gateway functionality in a complete MMS solution.

Java Technology

The commercial mobile device has so far been a closed platform without the possibility of adding new functionality after the device has been purchased. The introduction of Java has changed this situation and has opened up the mobile platform. Java will enable consumers to add compelling new features and applications to the device anywhere, at any time.

Java technology includes both a programming language and a software platform. In order for Java to be successfully introduced into a global market, it needs to be globally standardized and optimized for the limitations of different devices. The core idea of the technology is that a standardized Java platform hides the complexity of the device from the applications. The applications see the standardized interfaces of the Java platform, and they do not have to deal with the special characteristics of different devices. A standardized Java platform will allow content and service developers to focus on delivering quality services to a larger market. This in turn will bring more attractive services to consumers and increase the total Java market in the Mobile World.

For these reasons, Nokia supports the global Java 2 Micro Edition (J2ME™) standard platform specially designed for mobile devices by joint industry standardization work in the Java Community Process (JCP).

Mobile Information Device Profile

The Mobile Information Device Profile (MIDP™) is a set of Java Application Programming Interfaces (APIs) which, together with the Connected Limited Device Configuration (CLDC) library, provides a complete Java application runtime environment specially designed for mobile devices. The MIDP specification addresses issues such as the user interface, persistent storage, networking and application model.

MIDP Java addresses basic application functionality (e.g., application execution, keypad input, access to the display, network connection and security). This is an extremely powerful tool for creating a wide variety of both standalone and network connected applications.

A stronger and more powerful implementation of MIDP Java is currently under specification in the JCP. This new version, called MIDP 2.0, will replace the current MIDP version in a 2003 timeframe. MIDP 2.0 will address a lot of issues (e.g., the interfaces to sound, graphics and security features), which will make it possible to create even more compelling applications. Also, extensions to the MIDP platform are currently under standardization. These extensions will address issues related to more capable devices with Bluetooth and multimedia capabilities.

Browsing

The essence of mobile browsing lies in its close alignment with widely accepted Internet standards. The WAP Forum and the World Wide Web Consortium (W3C) have successfully defined mobile Internet standards over the past several years. The WAP Forum has now adopted the XHTML Basic standard from the W3C as the basis for WAP 2.0. The transition to the XHTML Mobile Profile will strengthen the position of the mobile browser within the Internet mainstream and allow for a far greater range of presentation and formatting than was previously possible.

The essential elements for browsing content are a page description language, a content formatting language and a scripting language. These elements allow consumers to enjoy a wider array of services, more intuitive user interfaces, and a generally more useful experience. At the same time, carriers will be able to exercise more control over the look and feel of the services they provide through their mobile portals.

Browsing Evolution

The next step in the browsing evolution is a transition from the mobile specific world of the Wireless Markup Language (WML) 1.x to the unified Internet world of XHTML and CSS. The XHTML Mobile Profile and WAP CSS are the foundation of WAP 2.0. To ensure backward compatibility during the evolution phase and to enhance the growth of mobile services, it is important to enable navigation of both WML 1.x and XHTML content. WML is supported, for backward compatibility, while new developments will be based on XHTML. CSS accompany XHTML, to provide a superior standard mechanism for content formatting and rendering.

XHTML provides a clean structure for Web pages by starting with familiar HTML and adding modularity, adhering strictly to language rules dictated by the Extensible Markup Language (XML). The XHTML Mobile Profile is a mobile adaptation of XHTML and includes everything in XHTML 1.0 except those capabilities (e.g., frames) that are unsuitable for small screens.

XHTML is the keystone in W3C to create standards that provide richer Web content on an ever increasing range of platforms. Using XHTML, content providers can more easily produce content for a broad set of platforms, with better assurance of how the content is rendered. CSS are a well-defined specification for layout control, so there is no longer any ambiguity about how a particular document will look. This is of particular concern to carriers and content providers that manage devices from a number of vendors.

Cascading Style Sheets

Central to XHTML is its support for Cascading Style Sheets, which describe how documents are presented on the screen. Using CSS, document creators can control the presentation of documents without sacrificing device independence or adding new markup language tags.

WAP CSS is the mobile adaptation of CSS 2.0 and leaves out just a few properties that are not needed in the mobile devices. It adds a few new properties that improve mobile usability (e.g., assigning shortcut keys to links and controlling the input text format in order to simplify typing on device keypads).

CSS separates the logical content of the document or application from its layout or presentation. This allows developers to easily create browser-specific versions of the same XHTML content simply by creating the appropriate style sheet. For example, when a consumer requests a Web page, the content server identifies the requesting device and returns the content with a link to the appropriate style sheet. The style sheet is downloaded once and cached by the browser for use with subsequent pages, which speeds the rendering of the pages on a site.

The power of CSS lies in the precise control it offers document creators and the ease with which they can optimize content for presentation on different devices. Every aspect of the document appearance (e.g., positioning, fonts, text attributes, borders, margin alignment, and flow) can be defined in the style sheet. A change to any aspect of the document needs to be made only once.

Graphical User Interface

The WML 1.2.1 standard per the June 2000 conformance release does not mandate a standard for GUI form elements. The XHTML Mobile Profile specifies form elements such as:

- Text and password input
- Text area (for long text input)
- Pull-down menus (select/option)
- Radio buttons
- Checkboxes
- Submit & reset buttons
- Hidden form fields for sending *state* information with form data

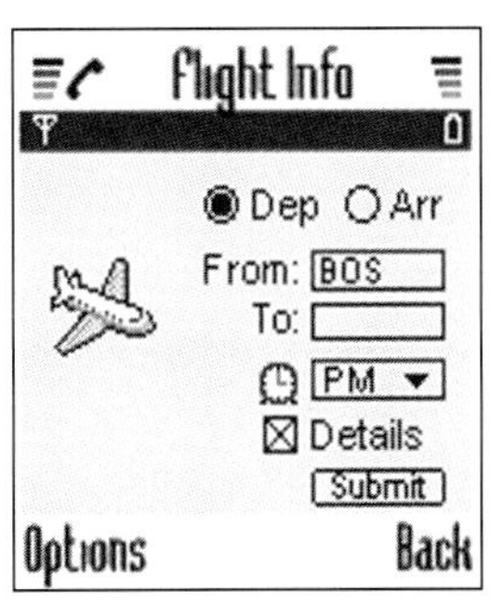

The XHTML Mobile Profile supports GUI elements such as radio buttons, text input, pull-down menus, checkboxes and submit buttons.

The XHTML Mobile Profile specification uses CSS to enable fine control of all these element appearances. This model provides superior results to WAP 1.x and will be supported by all mobile XHTML browsers.

Device Management

A key inhibitor in the uptake of new services has been that consumers are unable to correctly configure their devices to actually start using the service. The outcome has been a slower take-up of new services and features, considerable consumer care costs for carriers and service providers, and poor consumer experience of new services. In short, this dilemma has translated into considerable losses in revenues, increased customer care costs, lost opportunities, and overall poor consumer experience.

Device management is the generic term used for the technology that allows third parties to remotely provision and configure mobile devices on behalf of subscribers. This includes remote provisioning of new services, configuration and management of device parameters and settings, and remote device diagnostics and troubleshooting. Key usage scenarios for the technology include:

- Device management in new device or service purchase
- Helpdesk problem identification and resolution
- Device backup/restore
- High-volume configuration
- Advertising

Device management is a critical enabler for making it easier for consumers to adopt mobile services and for carriers to cost-effectively manage the devices in their customer base. By alleviating the consumers' dilemma, carriers and service providers are able to dynamically differentiate their service offering and customize the services for different categories of consumers. Incorporation of device management technology will translate directly and indirectly to the bottom line, via revenue growth, cost reductions, and reduced churning due to enhanced service levels.

There are two main elements in device management: bootstrapping and continuous provisioning. The WAP Forum 2.0 provisioning specification for bootstrapping and SyncML Device Management for continuous provisioning fulfill the criteria for openness and offer sufficient flexibility and extensibility to become industry standards.

Bootstrapping

The WAP Forum 2.0 provisioning specification provides for the initial provisioning of key parameters to the devices. WAP Forum bootstrapping enables carriers to initially provision key parameters and to enable continuous provisioning by establishing a trusted relationship between the managed device and the SyncML Device Management server. By provisioning key parameters during bootstrapping, carriers can enable full functionality of key applications for the consumers at the point of sale. By using the WAP Forum mechanism and security features, bootstrapping is made secure and safe.

Continuous Provisioning

Continuous provisioning functionality for repetitive provisioning and device management is defined in the SyncML Device Management specification. Continuous provisioning enables:

- Over-the-Air device configuration
- Inventory
- Diagnostics

SyncML Device Management is a session-based management technology. During November 2001, the SyncML Initiative released the alpha specifications for SyncML Device Management to its members.

Device Profile

The wealth of emerging mobile data applications and the continuing variety of form factors in mobile devices make it impossible to abstract entirely the differences in capabilities among mobile devices. In contrast to the Web, mobile devices exhibit striking differences in their display characteristics, their support for handling content types, their input and output modes, the bearers over which they communicate, and their memory capacity, among other things. As a consequence, these different capabilities must be explicitly considered. For example, if one wants to avoid situations where, devices receive content too large to be stored or in a format they cannot display properly. Alternatively, abstracting out these differences and designing applications based on the lowest common denominator does not result in appealing services.

Device profile management comprises the technologies required to provide information about device capabilities to all elements of an end-to-end service chain so that they can be taken into account during application development, selection, adaptation and content delivery.

Device profile management addresses the following issues:

- Representation of device profiles via a formal, structured notation amenable to automatic processing
- Standard vocabularies upon attributes and their allowable values that serve to define device profiles
- Protocols enabling devices to inform network elements about their profile
- Rules for interpreting and manipulating device profiles

These four aspects are covered by the User Agent Profile (UAProf) specification, which is part of the WAP standard. UAProf has become mandatory in the Mobile Station Application Execution Environment (MeXE) and GSM Association M-services, and it is being taken as the basis for the device capability negotiation framework in Third Generation Partnership Project (3GPP) S2 and S4 as well. UAProf was originally based on the Composite Capability/Preference Profiles (CC/PP) from W3C, but the WAP Forum has elaborated upon this technology to incorporate the specificities of mobile environments, including detailed vocabularies for WAP browsing and MMS applications.

The elements of the end-to-end device profile management chain play the following roles:

- **Device**: sends a Uniform Resource Locator (URL) pointing to the Web site from which its complete profile can be downloaded. The URL is sent at session establishment or with each request. Hardware plug-ins and downloaded software components can also send their specific URL with the device URL.
- **Gateways and proxies**: relay the URL to the next element in the chain. Intelligent proxies and gateways can retrieve the complete profile from the URL and use it to adapt the content returned by application servers to the device.

- **Application servers**: retrieve the profile from the URL and use the information to optimize the application response to the device requests.
- **Device profile servers**: are normal, public Web servers where manufacturers of devices, hardware plug-ins, and downloadable applications publish their product profiles.
- **Authoring tools**: can also retrieve the profiles from the profile servers. They rely upon the information contained therein to guide the design of applications.

Knowledge of a device profile makes it easier for application developers to build applications for mobile devices. Among others, device profiles serve the following purposes:

- Select automatically the most suitable content to send to a device
  - Select the version of a Java application corresponding to the Java version supported on the device
  - Select between WML and XHTML content depending on the content types understood by the device
- Adapt content automatically to the characteristics of the device
  - Scale a picture and adjust its colors to fit in a device display
  - Split a large WML deck into smaller fragments
  - Reduce the size of an image or audio file to accommodate limited device buffers
- Overcome limitations in the content accepted by a device
  - Translate HTML to WML, or Graphics Interchange Format (GIF) to Wireless Bitmap (WBMP)
  - Convert from Unicode characters to Japanese shift characters

Device profile management does not prescribe whether, or specify how applications can be optimized for specific device characteristics. Application providers and carriers are free to determine how to take best advantage of device profiles. Device profiles can be combined with subscriber profiles, thus providing further possibilities to optimize or tailor applications.

The hosting of device profiles and their access then occurs via Web browsing and thus does not require any new infrastructure. Accessing UAProf over protocols (e.g., Hypertext Transfer Protocol (HTTP), Wireless Session Protocol (WSP), or Real-time Stream Transport Protocol (RSTP)) is quite simple. Some care must, however, be taken to ensure that device profile management does not entail overhead during application execution. Thus, only the essential features of UAProf must be retained.

Furthermore, one must be wary of introducing overly rich vocabularies to describe device profiles. Only those characteristics that have relevance for gateways, proxies and servers, must be retained. A device profile should not degenerate into an encyclopedic description of all minor aspects of a device. Similarly, it is essential to avoid duplication of attributes, or loosely defined attributes.

Delivery

Delivery is a family of technologies that delivers digital content (e.g., entertainment and business applications) to mobile devices. Another important application area for delivery is the personalization of devices. Content delivery can be initiated by a consumer or by a network application.

The download mechanisms presented are logical and complement each other: interactive download and non-interactive download.

With interactive download, the discovery process and the actual download are an integrated process. This means that discovery of content to be downloaded and the actual mechanics of downloading are part of a single session. This single session is often referred to as browsing.

In non-interactive download, the discovery and the delivery processes are typically separate. This happens when messaging is used as the main download mechanism. The discovery may happen using text, graphical, or voice browsing, or it may happen by sending unsolicited trigger messages (e.g., SMS) to a service. The actual download of the content uses messaging as the main transport mechanism.

These two mechanisms are also referred to as browsing-driven download and messaging-driven download.

With interactive download, a consumer may discover content (e.g., images or Java games) on a service portal and download it within the same browsing context. The ability to pull content into the browsing context enables seamless content discovery and download. The consumer does not need to switch between applications on the mobile device. Content download over browsing is very convenient for the consumer. For example, clicking on the next image will result in receiving another image within the same browsing context.

However, non-interactive downloads, are equally important. This method serves different uses and business models.

An open, multi-vendor market is created for device vendors, as well as for network server and broker vendors, when the content download mechanism acting between the mobile device and content site is based on open technologies (e.g., HTTP or WSP).

Carriers could deploy download servers that allow selected content providers to leverage the carrier's billing capability in order to cost-effectively sell content by using open technologies and suitable business logic. This could be done by, for example, redirecting the download transaction to be executed via the carrier's download server.

Download Mechanisms

Content Retrieval

HTTP and WSP provide the means to download any content from a server to a client. This happens at each new page request in a browsing session. The only difference between plain browsing and content download is that a content saving operation is performed in the latter case. This is a very efficient and important mechanism.

However, plain HTTP (or WSP) provides no tools to execute transactions with the result that the server is sure that the client has received a content object.

Reliable Download

A reliable download mechanism involves a transaction; there are means to verify the success of transfer of content.

Two closely related, content-specific methods create this reliable download. The first method is the download defined in the MIDP specifications. The other method is an adaptation of the MIDP download, but enhanced to handle generic content types. The two models are conceptually and technically very similar and enable the deployment of identical business models for Java and non-Java content.

Both mechanisms for reliable download integrate well with discovery using browsing as well as with download operations triggered by messaging. The mechanisms can also be used in combination with application specific discovery mechanisms.

Over The Air Provisioning for Java

The Over The Air (OTA) User Initiated Provisioning Recommended Practice for the MIDP 1.0, defines the mechanism to download MIDP objects. The key event of this download process is the downloading of a Java Application Descriptor (JAD) file and the download of the actual application as a Java Application Resource (JAR) file.

The JAD file defines:

- URL to the JAR file
- The size of the JAR object
- The memory requirements of the MIDP object
- The version of the JAR suite of MIDP classes

After downloading the JAD file, the client downloads the JAR file, which includes all the information on how to install the resource. The transaction is completed with an installation notification posted by the client to the server. A device that supports MIDP specifications will also support JAD technology.

Generic Content Download

Reliable download of generic, non-Java objects is handled by an adaptation of the MIDP download process. First, a Media Descriptor file is loaded onto the device. The descriptor file describes the following entities:

- The URL where the content object can be retrieved
- The media type of the content object
- The URL where the installation notification is sent
- The logical name of the content object

When the client has loaded and analyzed the descriptor file, the client proceeds with the download of the actual content object. The transaction is finally completed by sending a notification to a specified URL.

Messaging

Messaging is useful for delivering content to mobile devices. Messaging is most suited to store-and-forward delivery of contents which are suitable for device-to-device and network-to-device push-type delivery mechanisms. For example, the consumer may subscribe to a weather service to receive daily weather maps over MMS.

Messaging download typically relies on two separate contexts. The first context comprises a discovery and purchase phase during which the consumer agrees to receive a content object and perhaps to pay for it.

The second context is a delivery phase during which the servers use a messaging mechanism to deliver the content to the device.

Many business models rely on this separation of phases in time and space. The delivery transaction can even be executed with a client different to the one that performed the discovery and purchase.

End-to-End Deployment Architecture

The key network element in delivery is the download server, which is used to handle the actual download transactions. The role of each element of the browsing based content download solution is described in the next figure.

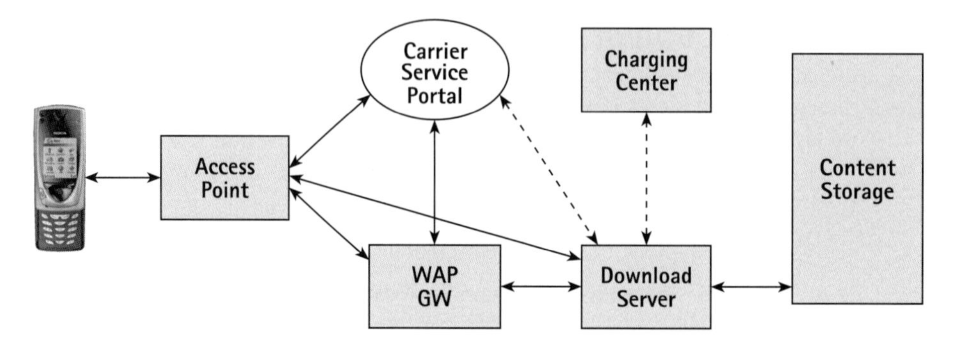

Browsing based content download architecture

- The Access Point is either a Circuit Switched Data (CSD) dial-in service or a General Packet Radio Service (GPRS) access point.
- In WAP connection, a protocol conversion (WAP to HTTP) is performed in the WAP Gateway.
- The Service Portal promotes downloadable content to consumers.
- Content Storage holds the items and information delivered to consumers.
- The Download Server manages the download transactions, receives download requests for content, fetches the content from content storage, delivers the content to the consumer, and handles billing following the completed transaction.
- The Charging Center processes the Call Data Records (CDR) received from the download server. It also provides in-advance credit check capabilities and support for innovative pricing and business models.

Identification/Authentication

Identification and authentication are critical functions for practically all services. A consumer and a client need to be identified and be authenticated before gaining access to services ranging from mobile networks, wireless LANs and corporate intranets to valuable WAP and Web sites on the Internet. It is also equally important that the consumer can trust the service, to ensure that no sensitive information is given to unknown parties.

Although there are a number of protocols and standards for authentication, there is not yet a widely adopted open standard for identification and authentication for a variety of service types. Hence, the Liberty Alliance Project, which is driving open specifications, is important for the mobile industry.

The system for identification and authentication should enable subscribers to:

- Identify themselves with an appropriate level of traceability and security
- Disclose some of their private data to various services in a controlled and confidential manner so that personal services can be provided
- Authorize services and other agents to use brokers.
- Achieve single sign-on

The identification and authentication system should have:

- Client authentication that is secure enough to satisfy the carrier or service provider policies for service access or for the transaction being undertaken.
- Management and Authorization tools to simplify provisioning and configuration of the consumer accounts and devices.
- Development tools to aid smooth deployment of the authentication and identification system and to enable third-party application developers to use the system more easily.

A consumer may have a number of virtual identities (e.g., credit cards, debit cards or loyalty cards). When the consumer accesses a service, he/she may choose to present one or more of these identities. In its simplest form, such an identity contains an account and password specifically for the service. It can be expected that some identities can be used for a growing number of services, analogous to a credit card that is widely accepted.

The next extension is that an identity card contains additional information, a part of the consumer profile. And instead of a simple account name and password, the presented identity could include a signed certificate. While the consumer will be in control of the content and use of the identities, the carrier plays an important role in enabling the use of such identities.

Identification support is expected to grow in phases. The first step includes identification for third-party Web services. Consumers who access such services through a mobile network will enjoy seamless authentication based upon the Subscriber Identity Module (SIM) card in the device. Later, identities can be used for authentication with intranet Virtual Private Network (VPN) access gateways, and for authorizing and charging for network access (e.g., to public Wireless Local Area Networks (WLAN)). Similarly, the same identities can be used to support local services where mobile devices communicate directly over local links.

Carriers in Identification

Carriers are well placed to become the favored identity providers and authenticators. Carriers already have a large existing customer base, which will encourage third-party service providers to choose carriers as their identity provider partners. Furthermore, roaming agreements will enable carriers to collectively be the largest identity provider and authenticator group.

In their role as identity provider, carriers will bring added value by being able to authorize consumers and service providers to access the Web services.

Today, SIM dependent (e.g., Mobile Station Integrated Services Digital Network Number (MSISDN), International Mobile Subscriber Identity (IMSI)) authentication identities can be used for many authentication needs. SIM cards will evolve to support Wireless Identity Module (WIM) functionality, which in turn supports digital signatures and Wireless Transport Layer Security (WTLS) client authentication. The existing secure relationship between the mobile device and the carrier will enable carriers to grant additional certificates for multiple purposes using the Wireless Public Key Infrastructure (WPKI) protocol. Such additional certificates will provide extra revenue from corporate customers who demand cost-effective and secure authentication methods.

With privacy being crucial in mobile services, carriers are likely to be in a good position when offering other broker services, such as user profiles. Acting as an identity provider, carriers will strengthen their customer relationships and provide new services to external service providers and corporations.

Mobile Payment

Mobile commerce is creating a whole new meaning for mobile devices and services. Mobile devices, being personal and always with the consumer, are evolving toward being Personal Trusted Devices (PTDs) that will be used for a wide range of mobile transactions.

In addition to paying for physical goods, a major part of mobile commerce consists of the purchase of different types of digital content that in most cases ends up being utilized in the mobile device. Consumers want to personalize their mobile devices with ringing tones, graphics and picture messages from content providers. Ticket services, downloadable applications (e.g., games and MIDI ring tones, and music and video feeds) will soon follow.

With mobile devices, services become far more accessible and can be tailored to consumer's needs. The mobile device allows spontaneous purchases, as it is ready to use in seconds. With GPRS devices, the consumer is always connected and can instantly access mobile services.

Providing the means and the security for conducting transactions over the mobile network will be an important key function for carriers and service providers.

Security in Mobile Transactions

Security is a key enabler for mobile payments. To make these services trustworthy and inspire trust in them is in the interests of the service provider and the consumer alike. The challenge is to implement the security scheme so that it remains convenient and simple to use.

WAP has determined specific security elements that ensure security and ease of use in mobile commerce. The WIM is one of the WAP security elements that enable security in mobile transactions. The WIM stores and processes information and security keys needed for consumer identification and authentication. Its main function is to enable the digital signatures that are required for authenticated mobile transactions.

A digital signature is the electronic equivalent of signing a receipt. It is the element that can replace the need for visual checks of ID cards, hand-written signatures and paper receipts. Digital signature technology can fulfill the requirements for authentication and non-repudiation, which are key conditions in establishing the merits for legally binding commercial transactions. Technically, WIM can be implemented in several ways (e.g., on a SIM card or on a second separate smart card in a device). The main differences are in business and usage considerations.

Wallet Application

A wallet application enables consumers to make convenient mobile transactions. The application is capable of storing protected personal information (e.g., notes, virtual cards, and debit and loyalty card information), inside the device. It simplifies storage and use of personal information in mobile transactions.

Open technologies (e.g., WAP and the Electronic Commerce Modeling Language (ECML)) support the creation of wallet-type applications in mobile devices.

Payment Mediation Services

Consumers look for convenience as well as security in mobile payment services. Carriers, service providers, financial institutions, or other parties may assume the role of a payment service provider, acting as a trusted party between merchants and consumers. These payment mediators collect, manage and clear payments initiated from mobile devices and other Web-enabled devices using the consumer-preferred payment methods. This model allows convenient and secure payments through seamless and session-based authentication, privacy at the merchant's end, and centralized transaction follow-up.

Standardization forums (e.g., Mobile Electronic Transactions (MeT)) play an important role in defining these open interfaces.

Mobile Digital Rights Management

Carriers will only be able to gain value from their mobile services by protecting downloaded content against misuse. Mobile Digital Rights Management (DRM) provides the infrastructure for usage and transaction control of content delivery service.

Mobile DRM is aimed primarily at over-the-air delivery (e.g., ringing tones, screensavers, games, Java applets and images). However, mobile DRM will evolve to meet the needs of more demanding media types as well (e.g., high-quality music). The mobile DRM architecture will be designed, standardized, and supported in the spirit of openness, relying on the work of existing mobile industry self-governance bodies and Web Domain standardization bodies.

A mobile DRM evolution based on open standards will bring carriers four main benefits:

- Content protection: Addressing immediate content protection requirements
- Increased airtime: First through browsing and subsequently based on MMS superdistribution (peer-to-peer sharing of content)
- Rights clearing revenue: usage rights given to new consumers who have received content from their friends
- Healthy content retailing environment: no single vendor dominance in DRM technologies and a wider set of technology vendors offering DRM infrastructure

Mobile DRM Evolution

DRM technology will create a sustainable environment for the retailing of mobile content with a transaction-based business model.

3GPP Release 6 is the target for mobile DRM standardization. A work item on the topic was opened in November 2001, with completion expected by June 2003.

The proper security level, even for highly demanding media types, can be achieved using various well-known, openly governed security and media technologies (e.g., XML, PKI and digital signatures). Consequently, there is no need for the mobile industry to adopt any proprietary DRM solution for volume use.

During 3GPP standardization, interim solutions will be needed to address immediate requirements as well as to build consumer habits and related infrastructure. The following figure shows the evolutionary phases of DRM, with two major interim phases, download protection and superdistribution.

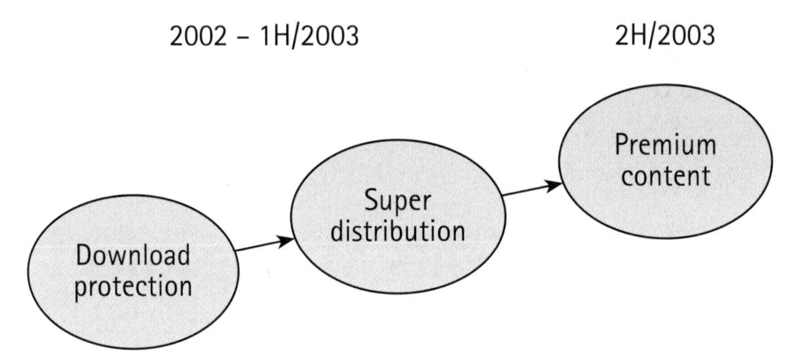

Mobile DRM evolution

The existing structure and roles of the content business will provide the basis for the mobile DRM system. The evolution of copyright protection will begin by allowing the consumer to preview content before paying. The next step is to move from content download control to usage control, allowing protected peer-to-peer content distribution.

In the download protection phase, the content and its associated rights are packaged together. Consequently, a basic level of download protection is achieved. A further added value will be the ability to express a preview capability, which allows a consumer to receive a package that enables the content to be viewed once for free before purchasing.

The superdistribution phase defines the ability to deliver the usage rights and the content independently and at different times. This will enable a consumer to forward content to a friend, who will not be able to access it without purchasing the corresponding rights from a carrier-run service, for example. This feature enables peer-to-peer distribution of quality content from one consumer to another.

The premium content phase adds PKI-based security for protecting usage rights. This will require complicated key management schemes and related investments, hence the need for jointly agreed-upon open standards.

Presence

The emergence of presence technologies and services in mobile communications will be one of the most fundamental changes affecting communication behavior in the coming years. When communication is initiated today, the consumer rarely knows if the other party is available or wishes to communicate. Making a call has been a game of chance. It is no surprise that one growing trend in mobile communication has been the consumers' need to be able to better control their own availability and thus their communication.

The expanded concept of presence enables a new communication paradigm: look before you communicate. Prior to initiating communication, the consumer is able to see if other parties are available to communicate, whether they wish to communicate, or by what means they would prefer to be contacted. The concept of presence has been popularized by Internet instant messaging services where users are able to see if their buddies are online and available for messaging. Within mobile communications the value of presence information will not be limited to messaging. Rather, it will facilitate all communication. This is also the key for the success of presence services in the mobile mass market: there must be utility in presence services within existing mainstream mobile communication and communication behavior.

Being able to manage one's own availability and communicate it to other consumers will lead to more appropriate and effective communication for all parties. Presence services create a delicate background communication layer that lets consumers share information, control services, and create rich virtual representations of them. This gives consumers a powerful tool for personalization, self-expression and fun, as well as for managing their communication.

Presence is a dynamic attribute profile of a consumer (or a place or a thing). It involves information stored in the network on a presence server and can be accessed by other consumers as well as by presence-enabled services. Presence information may consist of anything that is valuable for watchers to know and that consumers are willing to publish. Typical examples of presence information are:

- Consumer availability (is the consumer available/willing to communicate)
- Device status (is the mobile device on/off)
- Communication capabilities (what communication methods are available)
- Preferred communication method (how does the consumer wish to be contacted)
- Location (where or what time zone is the consumer in)

Privacy is often discussed in relation to presence. Obviously, the consumer needs to have the control over what information is published and who is able to access it. The nature of that information sets the requirements for the level of privacy. While there is likely to be some limited information that can be shared freely, the consumer must have clear control over any information that is considered private. For presence services to be of great use, it is necessary for consumers to be able to share different statuses and levels of information with different consumers or groups.

A key aspect of presence services is the immediate nature of the exchange. For presence information to be valuable in managing communication, the consumer must have convenient access to it prior to initiating communication. The always-on characteristics of the GPRS and 1XRTT services perfectly complement presence services. Using a GPRS/1XRTT service, the consumers will remain connected to their service providers at all times and receive immediate updates of a change in the relevant presence information.

The carrier is in a key position to offer presence services, having a strong, established relationship with consumers. Extending that relationship to offer a presence service in addition to existing mobile communication is natural. Some of the critical presence information is mainly available from the mobile network (e.g., location or device status). The carrier is also in a position to offer more added value through presence-enabled services in the network, such as rich call.

The adoption of presence services is driven by the number of consumers with whom one can share presence information. Interoperability between services and manufacturers is vital to guaranteeing market acceptance and rapid service adoption.

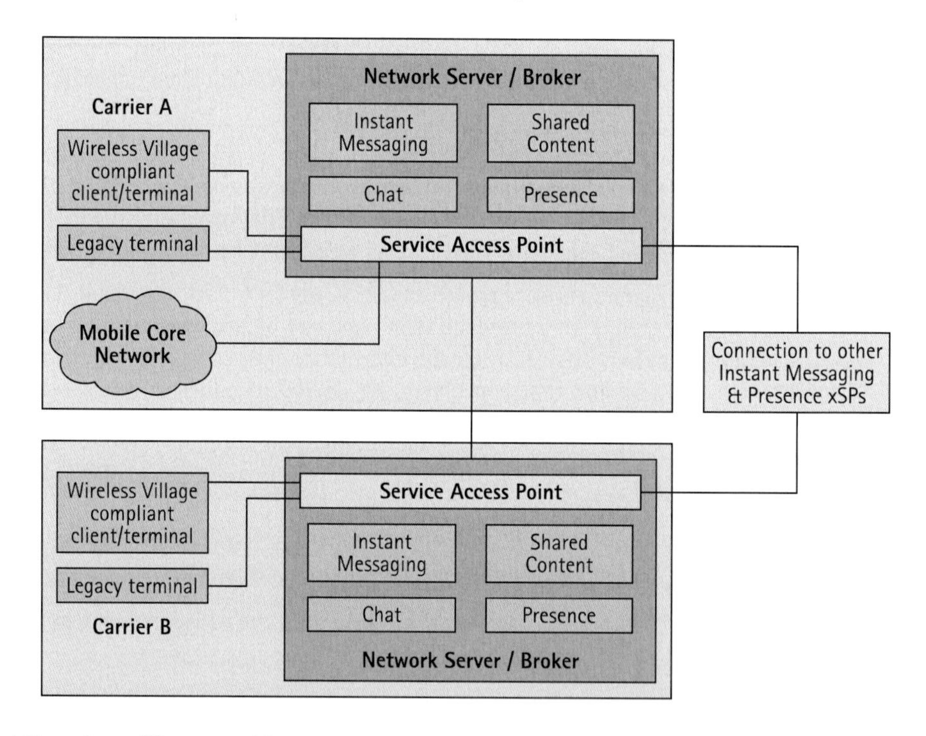

Instant Messaging and Presence architecture

The figure above illustrates the Instant Messaging and Presence (IMPS) architecture and its relation to the mobile network and the Internet. This is a client/server-based system where the server integrates both, the network server and broker functions. The term *clients* refers to mobile devices, other services/applications or fixed PC clients. For interoperability, a Server-to-Server Protocol (SSP) connects the IMPS servers and gateways.

Instant Messaging

Instant Messaging services have been very popular on the Internet. They enable users to exchange short, simple messages that are delivered immediately. Instant messaging is also the first presence-enabled application. Knowing if friends are online has been the key in popularizing instant messaging services.

Instant messaging services are now going mobile. Consumers will benefit from no longer being tied to their desktops. They will be able to engage in instant messaging or chat sessions anywhere and at any time. With mobile devices, instant messaging will facilitate all communication and allow consumers to be connected to their friends from anywhere.

User Profile Management

A user profile is a set of attributes of a consumer. A user profile may be physically distributed. Usually, a party that holds some of the user profile may not disclose it to other parties without the consent of the consumer. The user profile may contain simple attributes like name, language and address. But it often also contains more sensitive data, (e.g., credit card numbers). Often a user profile includes preferences and hobbies or interests.

The user profile is the key component needed to provide personalized services. Personalization is especially important for mobile services (e.g., to avoid cumbersome and unnecessary interaction, to increase value, or to maximize the limited amount of display space). The user profile should then be made available to various services but in a way that respects the consumer privacy. Indeed, a user profile is a valuable asset, and related services will offer the consumer value in exchange for the profile. Many services will maintain consumer relations with the help of a local service specific profile, but there could be a number of services that offer enhanced value by simply using some of the consumer's preferences.

Carriers are in a good position to act as profile brokers. Although some parts of the user profile can be expected to be located in a wallet and phonebook on the device, the carrier has important presence and location information. Moreover, the device is often not in a position to serve the profile data. A carrier can host a network copy of the user profile and combine it with the other subscriber information it has, thus providing a much more complete profile.

Standardization Efforts

Elements of a user profile are a crucial part of the consumer's identity as presented to a service. Not surprisingly, work on uniform exchange of profile information has been commenced within the Liberty Alliance Project.

The Generic User Profile (GUP) effort within 3GPP aims at unifying profile data across all elements within the Mobile domain. This unification will enable carriers to enhance their subscriber management and Customer Relationship Management (CRM) processes and offers a great opportunity to broker the user profile.

Data Synchronization

Data synchronization is a critical technology enabler in the Mobile domain. This is due to the fact that devices are only intermittently connected to the network, due to practical reasons (e.g., network coverage) and due to the expenses of maintaining an always-on connection. Also, as the number of local databases grows and operations on them continue growing, there is a growing need for a convenient tool for sharing the updated information. In short, there is a growing demand for a data synchronization solution for the Mobile World.

Synchronization Markup Language (SyncML) Data Synchronization is the only open technology available today. An open industry forum, the SyncML Initiative, has developed the technology.

For a carrier, SyncML Data Synchronization offers possibilities for differentiating its services from those of other carriers - at first by offering synchronization services with Personal Information Management (PIM) support and later by combining PIM applications with information the consumers are looking for. Later, carriers can expand and build vertical applications using the data synchronization technology, depending on the particular requirements of their customers.

SyncML Technology

SyncML is a specification for a common data synchronization framework, based on XML. The SyncML specification aims to synchronize networked data with that on mobile devices and to ensure interoperability. SyncML describes how common data formats are represented over the network to ensure interoperability.

SyncML Data Synchronization is used between mobile devices that are intermittently connected to the network and network services that are continuously available on the network. SyncML can also be used for peer-to-peer data synchronization. SyncML handles instances where the network services and the mobile devices store the data they are synchronizing in different formats or use different software systems.

Users of SyncML devices will always have up-to-date data (e.g., calendar and contacts). Carriers will be able to offer a common data interface to their customers, regardless of the type of mobile device.

The key benefits of SyncML Data Synchronization are:

- Open technology standard with wide industry acceptance
- Efficiency and interoperability in the Mobile domain
- Robust and expandable
- Access independent

The data synchronization architecture includes a SyncML client agent and a synchronization engine. They support both, OTA and local synchronization. The synchronization works over the WAP protocol stack. Local synchronization is supported over Bluetooth and Infrared Data Association (IrDA) and can be implemented using the Object Exchange (OBEX) protocol.

Streaming

Basic multimedia streaming services must use open standards to enable interoperability between devices and services, as well as to enable content and service creation. The key principles for the technology are: suitability for mobile implementation, working with other standard mobile multimedia services and open standards. Mobile streaming services will be interoperable between different devices and carriers.

Prior to the transition to All-IP networks, radio access technology will evolve to allow streaming over packet switched GPRS and Wideband Code Division Multiple Access (WCDMA) bearers to mobile devices. The take-up of mobile streaming is vital for the market's development.

Standardization

The 3GPP has standardized a Packet Switched Streaming (PSS) service, transparent to the network, for mobile streaming in Release 4. New enriched content types and service optimization tools will be introduced in Release 5.

Real-time packet based multimedia streaming services are to be based on the most suitable packet based bearers. Both UMTS Terrestrial Radio Access Network (UTRAN) and GSM/EDGE Radio Access Network (GERAN) are optimized for mobile streaming, enabling real-time multimedia with Quality of Service (QoS). For example, these services enable high quality video trailers as well as streaming for messaging applications. PSS defines an application framework with control, presentation, and transport plane protocols from Internet Engineering Task Force (IETF) and W3C and a comprehensive yet expandable set of content types (e.g., speech, video, audio, graphics and formatted text). The harmonized media decoder environment with MMS and PSS gives the multimedia content providers a media consumption platform from which content can be consumed via streaming or downloading.

Evolution of Streaming Services

Early applications using High Speed Circuit Switched Data (HSCSD) entail concise content, preview or pre-listening applications and audio content. The challenge for streaming over GPRS is Quality of Service (QoS). Alternative technologies for the technical architecture (e.g., progressive downloading), are also being evaluated. Key factors for cost-effective service provisioning in mobile streaming will be:

- The QoS mechanisms brought by third generation networks in Releases 4 and 5
- A suitable set of media codecs for the limited guaranteed usage rates available in 2.5G and third generation networks
- Low total cost of ownership based on a selection of royalty-free open standards as technical building blocks for services whenever available
- The creation of PSS-compliant content server infrastructures and content creation tools on carrier networks and the Internet
- Application-aware firewall systems
- Flexible charging mechanisms applied in the streaming service infrastructure

PSS can be deployed as a downlink transport mechanism for MMS services, which will enable a new set of MMS-originated services. It will also remove the obstacles of limited memory storage in devices because streamed content does not require downloading and storage prior to playback.

New features standardized for PSS will enable services that include vector graphics animations, subtitles with formatted text (PSS only) and synthetic audio (e.g., MIDI). Tools will be provided to improve service provisioning from servers to clients based on the devices' media capabilities. With 3GPP Release 6, the multimedia services will use standard DRM tools to provide copyrighted content to consumers in a secure fashion.

Location

Location based services are enabling a variety of new applications and complementing many existing applications with a new dimension. Location based services add value to the consumer but also for many other parties. One could categorize these parties as:

- Business users
- Private users
- Private users with advanced needs
- Carriers

Basically, each of these has its own requirements for quality of service. The type of mobile device will also determine the usability of a service.

Commercial users (e.g., transportation companies and taxi companies) can utilize the new services. Fleet management might be a basic level whereas route finding and navigation will require a higher level of quality. Additional investment in high-end mobile devices could be justified to improve the company's operational efficiency.

For the mass of private users, other applications are of more importance (e.g., a friend finder and a business directory). Here, the usage of location based services helps in receiving answers more quickly. The normal private user is more sensitive to mobile device costs.

There are also private users with different needs and who require more accurate location information. Those users certainly use basic services, but in addition they require a quality of service more in line with that of a commercial user. Important applications here can be found in navigation, which requires fast download of a large amount of data. The typical private user could be a person on the move (e.g., a motorcyclist).

Service Availability

Different locations have practical boundaries. If one compares an urban to a rural environment, one can easily see that in an urban environment, basic location methods are quite accurate due to the small cell sizes. The consumer might be located with a predictable accuracy. Here the content seems to be more important. The following example should illustrate this. When a consumer wants to know the location of the closest Automatic Teller Machine (ATM). It does not matter if the response indicates a distance of 150 meters or 250 meters as long as the nearest ATM indicated is from the correct bank. On the other hand, many people live in rural areas in which a mobile device does not always have contact with more than one base station. Here, the situation could be such that the consumer would be happy to find the nearest ATM within a few kilometers and would also be happy to pay the additional fee if the ATM belongs to a competing bank.

Emergency

Emergency requirements set by the authorities also play a role in positioning services. Whereas in the US, the Federal Communication Commission (FCC) has set requirements concerning the accuracy of detecting the location of a consumer, the European approach seems to be more to ride on the commercial users and take advantage of the investments the carriers make. It might be that the same accuracy will be reached in urban areas in both cases, but a rural environment imposes restrictions. It might be a huge investment for a carrier to provide similar accuracy as in urban areas since the carrier would have to build an impractical number of additional base stations in order to fulfill the requirement that a mobile device have contact with at least three base stations at the same time. In such cases, it would be more economical to move the responsibility to the consumer, who could purchase a different device, one which allows accurate positioning within meters.

Privacy

The consumer's privacy shall be given special respect. This encompasses many factors (e.g., trusting the carrier and consumer personalities). When a consumer does not want to be located for a period of time, a sensitive solution is needed. However, a network carrier or service provider must respect each consumer's privacy requirements.

Roaming

Many applications are targeted at the home user (e.g., location-based games). However, typical situations where one would need location-based services are often found outside of the home in other towns or even abroad. This has additional value if the consumer is not able to communicate in the country's language and would like assistance in English, for instance.

Location Enabler

End-to-end mobile positioning service quality covers design of the service, robustness of the system and positioning method quality. The enabler can support different methods for use in different radio access networks. It can be upgraded to meet the accuracy needs of more enhanced systems.

The location enabler provides added value by offering:

- Multiple positioning method environments with flexibility. Furthermore, different positioning methods are available for GSM, GPRS and third generation networks.
- With multiple positioning methods, the enabler supports all mobile devices, multi-vendor networks and all consumers and thus creates more revenue, reduces costs and ensures a future-proof solution.

- Privacy: subscriber policies and anonymity.
- Security: application authentication and secure connection.
- Roaming: application level roaming for the carriers.
- Geographic Information Systems (GIS) capabilities to provide geo-coded and reverse geo-coded information to applications. The application provider does not have to invest in expensive GIS systems.
- Common services meaning that the mobile network does not need to be activated if there is location information already available in the history database. Statistics also provide valuable information for the carrier to utilize in service planning.

Group Management

The group management services enabler is designed to make it intuitive, easy and secure for consumers to manage their contacts and communications as well as share presence information or personal content with their natural communities and groups.

Conclusions

Service enablers are the basic technology building blocks for creating mobile services. The implementation of service enablers potentially takes place in many places in the end-to-end chain (e.g., mobile device and server software or development tools). Many new service enablers are needed to produce compelling new mobile services and enable the next growth wave for the mobile industry.

To ensure successful take-up of mobile services, it is important to minimize the fragmentation of service enablers and to ensure seamless interoperability. Therefore, service enablers should be based on open global standards.

Complying with open global standards for the underlying service enablers still provides many opportunities for mobile industry players to set apart their offering to consumers. Parameters on the service layer can radically differentiate the customer experience of services from that offered by others, even though the underlying service enablers are based on open global standards.

Nokia believes that the following service enablers based on open global standards are needed to create a service platform for mobile devices:

- **MMS** - enables seamless person-to-person and person-to-application exchange of messages with rich multimedia content, including text, images, audio and video.
- **Mobile Java** - enables executing powerful Java applications (e.g., games) in any mobile device. Through the J2ME technology, application user interfaces can adapt to different device capabilities (e.g., screen sizes and colors).
- **Browsing** - enables consumers to access a wide range of content and services using a browser. With technologies (e.g., XHTML and CSS), the content can be rendered in an optimal manner in different types of devices.

- **Device management** - enables remote provisioning and management of service settings in devices.
- **Device profile** - information about device properties (e.g., screen size, number of colors and available memory) enables applications and content to be optimized and personalized for any particular device.
- **Delivery** - enables downloading various contents. The process covers preliminary negotiations (e.g., supported media types, available memory) as well as post-download operations (e.g., delivery confirmation).
- **Identification/Authentication** - enables service providers and applications to identify and/or authenticate consumers for offering personalized and private services in a user-friendly manner.
- **Payment** - enables transactions with monetary value using commonly accepted payment methods.
- **Mobile DRM** - enables business models related to the consumption of digital content through copyright protection for the digital content owner.
- **Group Management** - enablers targeted to make it intuitive, easy and secure for consumers to manage their contacts and communications as well as share presence information with their natural communities and groups.
- **Location** - information about customer location enables making location-sensitive content and applications and taking full advantage of the potential in the Mobile domain.
- **Presence** - information about consumer presence status (e.g., availability and current activity) enables making content and applications context-sensitive, personal and valuable.
- **User Profile Management** - information about user profile and preferences enables the creation of personalized services.
- **Instant Messaging** - popular instant messaging complemented with mobility enables persons and groups to communicate easily and effectively anywhere and at any time.
- **Streaming** - enables real-time transfer of content to the device. Streaming is particularly valuable in transfer and immediate viewing of audio and video clips.
- **Data Synchronization** - Personal information management is among the most important applications for consumers in the Mobile domain. Data synchronization enables bandwidth efficient synchronization of local data in devices and data in networks.

Club Nokia

This chapter discusses Club Nokia as a loyalty and consumer relationship program and also describe the possibilities that Club Nokia opens up for the industry as a channel for digital services and content. It will first discuss the loyalty scheme, Club Nokia membership, and the community, then move on to the development principles for new services and the possibilities this approach opens up for the industry.

Club Nokia in a Nutshell

Club Nokia is an online community and loyalty program designed to help new and existing Nokia device owners to make the most of their Nokia device. The mobile device is no longer just a voice communications device, but a platform, which the consumer can personalize according to his/her preferences. It has become a central part of many people's lives today, containing personal information (e.g., calendar and contacts) as well as providing an entertainment and information channel. Gradually, the device's features extend to the services. Here is where Club Nokia digital services step in as they complement the total offering for Nokia customers.

Club Nokia was founded in 1996 as an online community and consumer loyalty program. Today, it offers exclusive, device-specific services to owners of Nokia mobile devices around the world. The Club Nokia Web and Wireless Application Protocol (WAP) services can be accessed once the Nokia device is registered with Club Nokia. In the Americas, this approach has been phased in, starting with the digital services and adding the other Club Nokia service elements later.

Club Nokia is part of Nokia's total offering for mobile device consumers. Nokia's target position is, by partnering with carriers, to be the preferred branded service provider for Nokia mobile device consumers. Nokia will provide Nokia device-optimized entertainment and personalized content. By demonstrating the added functionality of Nokia devices, it also boosts the image and volumes of those devices, which then will create increased revenue for the carriers.

Club Nokia Consumer Relationship Program

Club Nokia Membership and Community

Joining Club Nokia is free and easy. The only prerequisite for becoming a member is that one must own a Nokia device. Prospective members can join online via the Club Nokia Web or WAP site or by sending in the Club Nokia form that comes with a new device.

Registered Club Nokia members enjoy a wide range of exclusive benefits like instant service and support, sneak previews of new Nokia products, special priority offers, access to the Club Nokia Web site, Mobile Club and much more. Club Nokia offers digital services for its members, starting from ringing tones and carrier logos and extending to the latest technologies supported by the mobile devices (e.g., Java™ MIDlet downloads and polyphonic ringing tones).

All Club Nokia services are localized. When a member logs in for the first time via a generic address, the member is directed to his/her localized site, e.g., www.club.nokia.de. From that point on, the local Club Nokia handles all correspondence. Thus, Club Nokia services vary from country to country and depend on which Nokia product the consumer has. As new products enter the market and the member upgrades to a new device, he/she can then upgrade the service accordingly by changing the primary device to the new model.

Club Nokia Consumer Care

Club Nokia has a community and consumer relationship functionality built in. Club Nokia's Web site offers information about Nokia products: product and accessory information, user guides and tips on how to use the device and related services, and information about new products. In addition, Club Nokia provides news regarding local Nokia events and campaigns, as well as information about mobile communications in general.

The Club Nokia Careline provides technical assistance and information about Club Nokia activities through telephone or via e-mail. Careline numbers are country specific and can be found in the device sales package and user manuals.

When a member's device needs to be repaired, he/she can take it to a Club Nokia Service Point. Members can find their nearest Service Point by looking at the Welcome Pack or consulting the Club Nokia Web site. Club Nokia service is exclusive to Club Nokia Members. A membership card and proof of purchase should be shown when visiting a Service Point.

Nokia Digital Services Overview

Since Nokia digital services offering is based on the enablers that the mobile devices have, it will thus evolve together with them. Today, Nokia digital services offered via Club Nokia cover imaging, music, games and personal information management services. These services manifest themselves to the consumer in different ways. Currently, ringing tones, carrier logos, animated screensavers, picture messaging, game level downloads and high score sending are common and highly visible. The consumer also has the ability to create his/her own ringing tones and graphics.

Some examples of Nokia services

In the future, the services will take full advantage of new open technologies (e.g., Java Mobile Information Device Profile (MIDP), eXtensible HyperText Markup Language (XHTML), Musical Instrument Digital Interface (MIDI), Multimedia Messaging Services (MMS) and Synchronization Markup Language (SyncML). Also, location-based services will open up new possibilities for service creation.

In the content delivery arena, digital rights management will have a key role in enabling secure content delivery to mobile devices. This is a key enabler that will be built into the services offering.

Club Nokia web provides all Club Nokia members with online storage for their personal data.

Development Principles for Nokia Digital Services

Every time Nokia develops a new service, a strong device linkage is built in. This is done in order to enhance the mobile device value proposition to the consumer, so that the device can be smoothly customized to match the consumer's lifestyle and preferences. Services are designed simultaneously with new devices, and they can therefore influence mobile device design.

The aim of Nokia service design is to create a seamless consumer experience and offer convenient payment methods. An example of a seamless consumer experience is embedding service access menus in user interfaces.

As the services are based on using open technologies, this expands the opportunities for developers to create different types of content and applications to cater for different consumer needs and types.

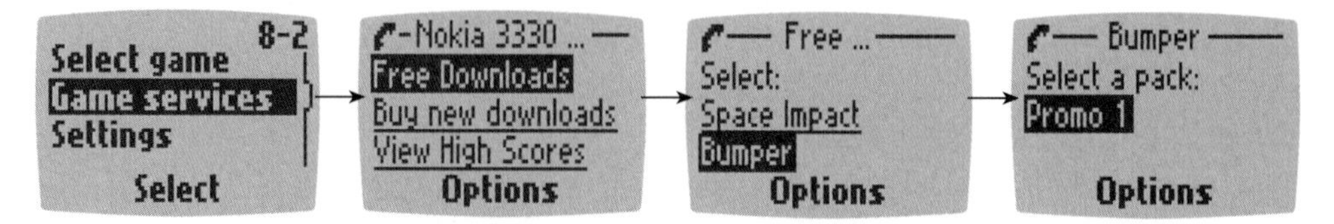

An example of a service embedded in a mobile device menu

Accelerated Mobile Service Offerings

There are multiple applications for each type of consumer, multiple brands owners, and various content license owners. The number of technology enablers and content formats is growing, as well as the number of devices on the market. There is a need for legacy support and optimized services. All this is evolving into new service delivery mechanisms, with new value chains and stakeholders - a new business ecosystem.

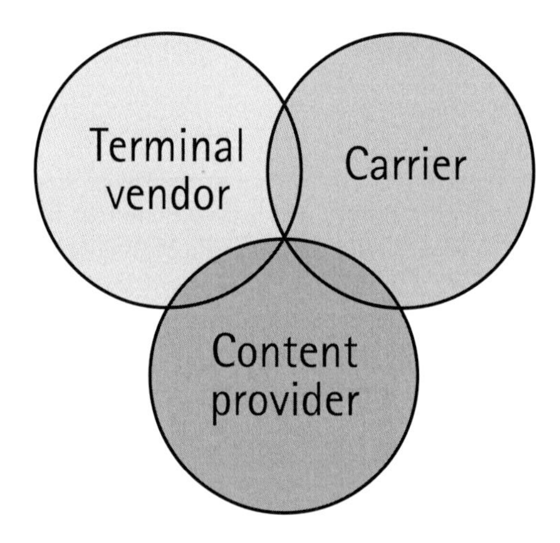

New business models emerge

A digital service is a combination of application, content and timely delivery. The carriers provide access, trust, billing and security for the new services. Even though there are strong interdependencies between different parties, it is clear that carriers will become the primary providers of mobile services.

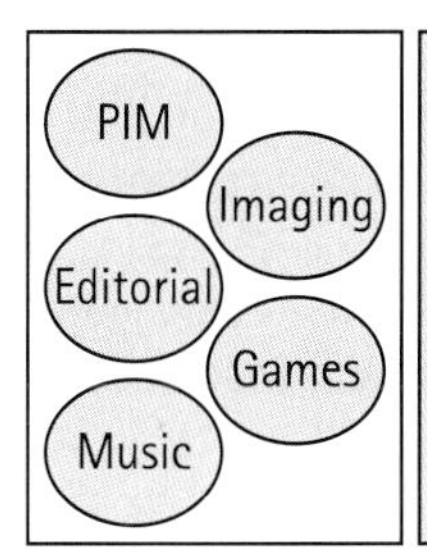

Club Nokia and carriers

Nokia believes that a business model has been created which could be called the 4W drive; it is a win-win-win-win business model:

Win 1: the consumer:

Club Nokia offers convenient and easy-to-use services for the consumer. The services, available from day one, are integrated into the mobile devices.

Win 2: the carriers:

Club Nokia extends the carriers' service offering, which will drive usage up. This will in turn means more traffic for carriers.

Win 3: the content players:

Club Nokia is an easy and trusted way for content players to reach the mobile consumers.

Win 4: Nokia

Increased loyalty for Nokia customers and a new revenue opportunity through digital services.

Club Nokia Digital Services Components

Club Nokia consists of five main logical components:

- Digital content and service platform
- Content sourcing and content management
- Business administration: Accounting, Administration, Authorization, Customer Relationship Management, Billing
- Digital service access and delivery
- Sales and marketing channel management

The digital content and service platform element consists of the actual service software and hardware, as well as serving as a storage point for the content. This platform interfaces with the payment service providers, reporting and administration tools for both the content and financial reporting. The services are accessed and delivered through different delivery media, (e.g., Short Message Service (SMS), WAP, MMS or the Web. The business administration component comprises elements providing Authentication, Authorization and Accounting (AAA) services; billing elements; and consumer relationship management. The content sourcing and content management component ensures the availability of Nokia-specific content. It is designed to maximize the content consumption potential of each and every mobile device model, and every consumer. This is done through acquiring world class content from leading content providers. Nokia takes the editorial responsibility for content selection and frequently-changing content.

Sales and marketing channel management in turn handles the consumer-facing contact points as well as discussion with the sales and marketing channels about the different possibilities for co-branding and joint marketing campaigns.

Club Nokia payment methods are Club Nokia Credits, which is a form of advance payment, or carrier billing, wherein premium priced SMS messages are included in the phone bill. The latter is the preferred payment mechanism, as it is the easiest way for consumers to purchase services.

Club Nokia Credits can be bought in card form or, in some countries, via SMS or Interactive Voice Response (IVR). Club Nokia Credits can be used on the Web or via WAP for purchasing service items. In addition to these payment methods, a consumer can also buy a given amount in Club Nokia Credits through the local Club Nokia Web page with a credit card.

References

http://www.club.nokia.com/

PART 3.2

Terminal Solutions

- o Mobile Devices of the Future
- o Terminal Software

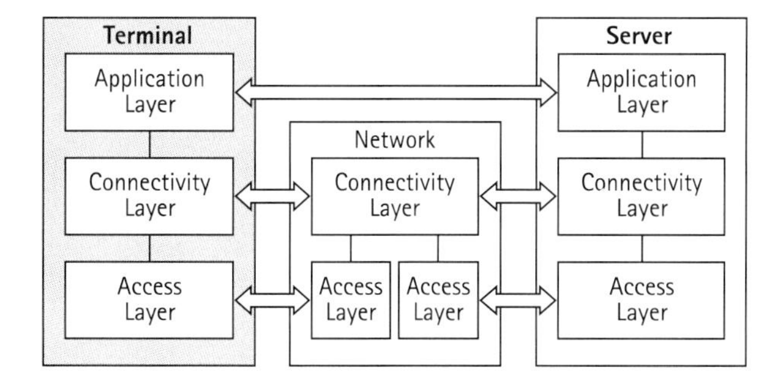

Mobile Devices of the Future

Evolution of Mobile Devices

When one looks at Nokia's mobile device portfolio of today, one sees a wide selection of products which are the benchmarks for personalized mobile communication. However, Nokia's device portfolio has gone through several phases of evolution in parallel with the various stages of development of the mobile device market.

In the early phases of the market, mobile devices were significantly more costly and larger/heavier than they are today. Initially the portfolio consisted of a single product, targeted for business customers, and the key competitive parameters were size and performance (e.g., talk time).

As the market matured and penetration grew among business customers, Nokia's portfolio expanded and price segmentation was introduced. Higher performance products targeted at business customers were complemented with lower-priced, cost-driven products targeted at more price-sensitive private customers. Price, size and performance became the key dimensions in defining the portfolio.

As penetration started to increase among private customers, Nokia introduced lifestyle segmentation as the basis for its portfolio. This created a much wider range of products with strong differentiation in design and styling matched to different consumer segment needs. Price, performance and style became the key dimensions in defining the portfolio.

The mobile industry has developed based on bringing the benefit of mobility to voice communications. So far, Nokia has mainly concentrated on mobile devices optimized for voice functionality - with a few exceptions: the Nokia Communicator, Nokia Card Phone, Nokia 7650 and Nokia 5510.

Matching Technology to Consumer Demand

The future evolution of 2G technology towards third generation and digital convergence provides opportunities to create new value for consumers and industry players by bringing the benefit of mobility to functionalities other than voice.

In order to create the winning products of the future, it is necessary to identify the most attractive new functionalities and create devices which are optimized for the use of those functionalities, while at the same time providing a full set of mobile applications to ensure the usability of the device as the preferred personal companion.

For an example, one can consider two devices optimized for different applications - an imaging phone and a Communicator.

For a device to be optimized for imaging, it must excel in the capturing, handling, sending and storing of images; i.e., the device must have a large, color display and an internal camera and support the Multimedia Messaging Service (MMS). In addition, support is needed for all the regular mobile applications (e.g., voice, Short Message Service (SMS), Personal Information Management (PIM) and games) that the consumers are already used to.

In contrast, the Communicator is optimized for business use and provides the ultimate efficiency for the mobile professional. It is optimized to provide seamless integration into corporate information systems and support a wide range of third-party business applications. A different input method (e.g., a QWERTY keyboard or stylus) and a higher resolution VGA-compatible display are needed to optimize the mobile device for corporate systems and applications.

Path to the Future Devices

The evolution of future mobile device functionality must be coupled with the coordinated development of related services, which then together comprise the total offering for the consumer. The final purchasing decision is made by weighing the prioritized use of the device (e.g., sharing a moment with a friend via imaging or increasing one's professional efficiency) and design against the price of the preferred device and its closest alternatives.

The three main steps for device evolution are the following:

1. **From a mobile device to a functionally and operationally optimized personal device** - consumer delight: functional satisfaction that is supported by the design and styling
2. **From fixed functionality to a platform of continuous excitement and emotional attachment** - consumers can vary and upgrade the applications and synchronize their personal information with other databases
3. **From a specific communication device to a central hub of personal communications, interactive services, and life management** - all functionality can be executed via the device or with accessories

Winning Device Categories

It is clear that the "everything for everybody" approach will not receive industry acceptance, as all stakeholders in the industry need structure and simplicity when deciding on the direction in which to take their choices. As far as mobile devices are concerned, it is important to decide on the new functionalities that will have the broadest appeal for the consumers and industry players, in order to create a healthy business environment for industry growth.

At this stage of the industry's development, there will be five winning device types optimized around specific functionalities, which fill the requirements described above.

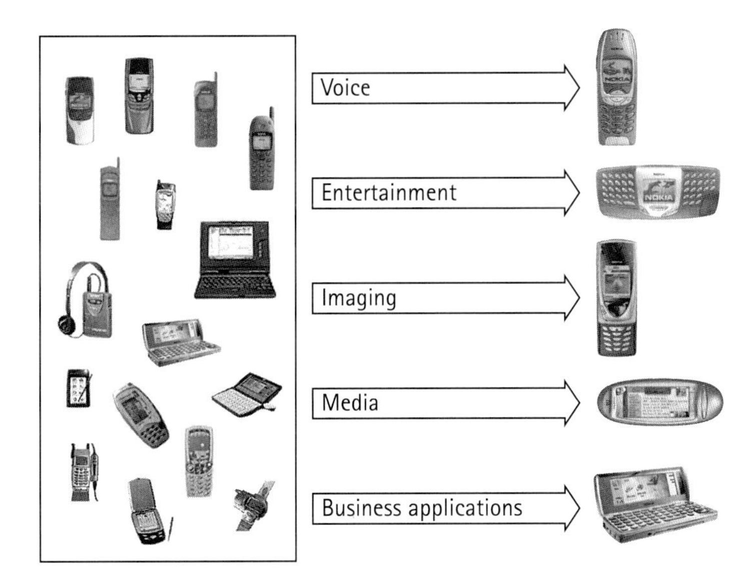

Winning device functionalities

Voice Devices

The Voice/SMS devices have set the benchmark for mobile personal communications by supporting the individual lifestyle of the consumer through multiform design as well as wide personalization options. These devices emphasize voice-centric usage and messaging applications (e.g., SMS), for personal use.

Key features:

- Excellent, personalized voice product
- Good messaging capabilities and efficient data solutions
- Meeting the needs of individual lifestyles through design and personal relevance

Entertainment Devices

Entertainment devices offer new experiences that extend the traditional scope of entertainment in the mobile context. Mobile entertainment devices are primarily devices which combine mobile connectivity with the most desired entertainment applications.

Key features:

- Messaging, music and games
- Ample opportunities for personalization
- New means of social interaction
- Cost-efficiency
- Timeliness

Imaging Devices

This includes devices with a strong emotional attachment, devices for sharing experiences through rich communication. Focusing on person-to-person(s) multimedia communications, with self-created content, the category represents a natural evolution of today's communications paradigm and comes one step closer to virtual presence.

Key features:

- Quality device with excellent messaging and imaging capabilities
- Exciting and easy-to-use interface for instant sharing of emotions and experiences
- Compact, transformable concept and attractive design

Media Consumption Devices

Media consumption devices offer the preferred mobile platform for personalized access to Internet services, with Personal Information Management functionality and easy-to-use, integrated device features. It provides time- and place-independent access to services and seamless integration of both audio and data functionality. These devices expand the device platform and mass appeal by supporting third-party applications and software development. In short, it provides full-scale mobile deployment of the Internet.

Key features:

- Ultimate Mobile Internet companion
- Migration to comprehensive support for existing Web content
- Distribution channel for third-party digital services and content

Communicator Devices

The Communicator is a mobile business device with seamless integration into corporate information systems, as well as with selected mobile services. It includes e-mail, a networking office application suite, and access to corporate applications, with full input and output capabilities. It is the most powerful platform, with an optimum size/ergonomics ratio and facilitates real-time information consumption and decision-making, shortens consumer response times, and improves logistics, with optimum use of time while the consumer is on the move.

Key features:

- Complete business communication: voice, messaging, image communication, fax
- Seamless integration to corporate information systems, telecommunications, and the Internet, with transparent mixing between device- and server-based applications and data
- Powerful tools for viewing, editing and creating business-related data
- Excellent development platform for third-party applications and services, on both device and server platforms

Terminal Software

The mobile industry is going through a transition period. The fast growth of the past few years has practically stalled. To stimulate new growth, the mobile industry now looks forward to new enablers (e.g., digital content, new applications, evolving technologies and new business systems). Furthermore, it is important to create a unified market and counter fragmentation, so that the industry grows as a whole.

While mobile devices and mobile infrastructure will remain in Nokia core business, software is clearly becoming the key enabler of new services and revenue for consumers. The business model for Nokia remains the same – the only difference is that the software platforms and service enablers are considered separately.

Nokia Terminal Software

Nokia has two software products available for licensing to device manufacturers. These products are licensed as source code, giving the device vendor freedom to differentiate and adapt the software to its own device designs.

- The Terminal Software Suite is a selection of key mobile application middleware components (e.g., a Wireless Application Protocol (WAP) Browser and Multimedia Messaging Service (MMS) client), optimized for size- and cost-driven mobile devices. These components are platform independent, which means that the User Interface (UI) and Operating System (OS) are excluded. The Terminal Software Suite allows manufacturers to easily implement one or more technologies on devices with an operating system other than the Symbian OS, and on any user interface.
- The Series 60 Platform is a complete Symbian OS based smartphone software product. The large-sized color screen, easy-to-use interface for single-handed navigation, and suite of applications makes this software ideally for new mobile services (e.g., rich content downloading and MMS). Devices based on this software are interoperable with MMS, WAP, Java™ Mobile Information Device Profile (MIDP), General Packet Radio System (GPRS), Synchronization Markup Language (SyncML), Bluetooth, and many other open standards.

Terminal Software Suite

The Terminal Software Suite is a collection of technology enablers for mass-market phones and is usually built upon a proprietary operating system and a manufacturer-specific user interface. Therefore, Nokia licenses these enablers without any user interface or operating system dependency. This permits the enablers to be ported to a wide range of operating systems and user interfaces. And, because the enablers are offered as source code, the licensee has many differentiation opportunities.

Components

The components currently available are the Mobile Browser and the MMS Core. These components are available individually. They have also been designed to use a common component framework that provides more interactivity and communication between individual components. This component framework becomes more useful as more components are integrated into a single device. Future components will also make use of this component framework for easier integration with existing terminal software components.

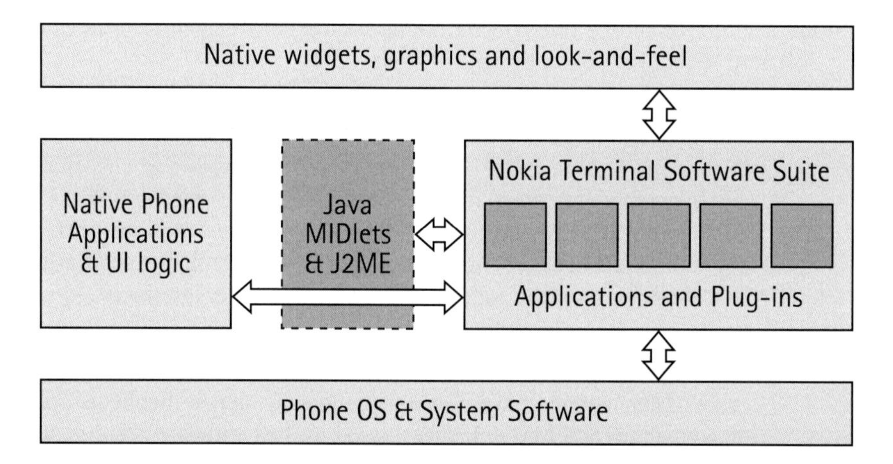

The relation of the Terminal Software Suite to the software environment of the target device

In the future, other enablers will be available as the technologies are standardized in public fora. These components include:

- Digital Rights Management (DRM) Client
- Downloading Client
- Mobile Wallet for mobile commerce
- Device Management and Service Provisioning with SyncML
- Instant Messaging and Presence Directories

MMS Core

The MMS Core software component provides a well-implemented and standards-based core MMS functionality that has already been proven to work with all major Multimedia Messaging Service Centers (MMSCs). It is also optimized for memory-constrained mobile devices.

The MMS Core component enables the sending and receiving of multimedia messages and notification of incoming messages. It contains Application Programming Interfaces (APIs) for integration into the WAP stack and message composer. The user interface is fully customizable by the licensee. A reference UI is included.

Mobile Browser

The mobile browser component is a dual mode WAP 2.0 browser - it supports Wireless Markup Language (WML) 1.3 and the Extensible HyperText Markup Language (XHTML) Mobile Profile. The XHTML parser is adaptable to multiple markup languages and is able to handle less strict markup languages (e.g., HTML). Also, the architecture is extensible. Therefore, a manufacturer can modify the browser to handle other markup languages or formatting tags. Or new content handler components can be integrated into the browser.

Graphical user interface for the XHTML Mobile Profile

A complete rendering engine is part of the browser. The Mobile Browser also uses Cascading Style Sheets (CSS) for optimized layout. It supports Multi-purpose Internet Mail Extensions (MIME) type registration for DRM, downloading of Java files, and use of other content types (via Content Object Descriptor, COD).

The browser supports the Wireless Identity Module (WIM), Wireless Transport Layer Security (WTLS) Class II and III, and Enterprise-to-Enterprise (E2E) navigation security.

The user interface is fully customizable by the licensee. A reference UI is included.

Series 60 Platform

The Series 60 platform extends the Symbian OS with an optimized user interface and a set of key applications, as illustrated in the next figure.

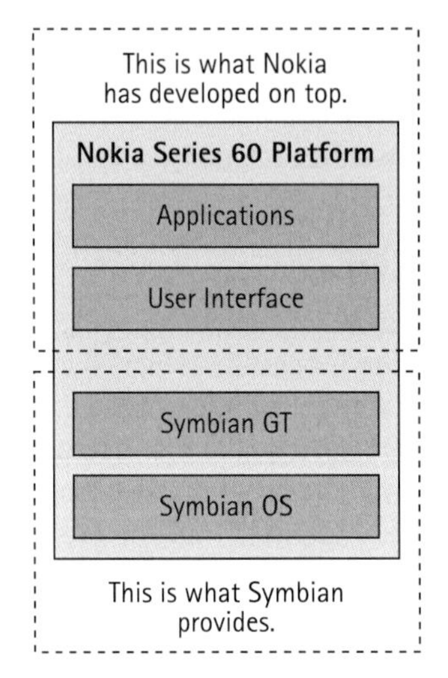

The Series 60 Platform is built upon on the Symbian OS

Series 60 User Interface

The Series 60 Platform user interface was specifically created as an easy-to-use smartphone interface for one-handed use. It is optimized for a large, color screen (176x208), 2 selection keys, "Send" and "End" keys, an application launching and swapping key, and having a five-way navigation system. It has been globally tested for ease of use. The layout is optimized for vertical movement. The menus are logically organized by context and arranged into an application structure allowing for flexible application management. There is a menu key that enables application multitasking.

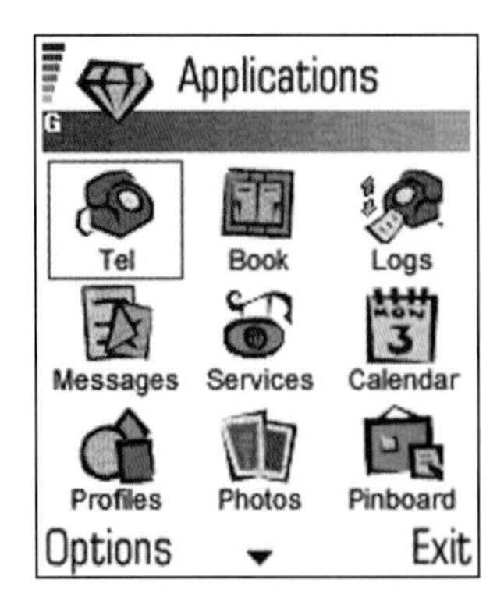

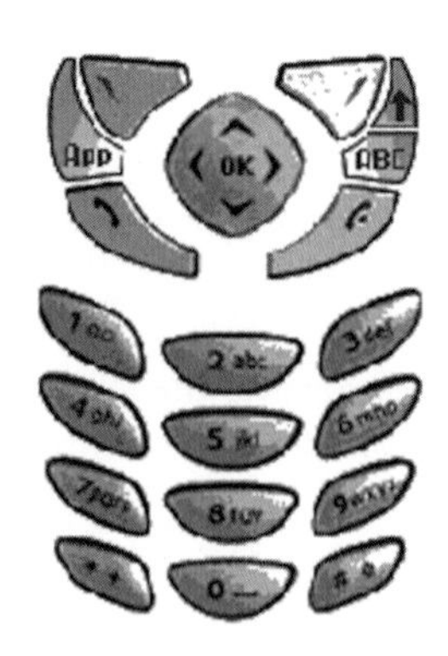

The Series 60 user interface's physical elements include a color screen, navigation keys, and a standard telephone keypad

As with the Terminal Software components, the Series 60 is licensed as source code, permitting the licensee a wide range of differentiation opportunities. For example, the licensee can change all the graphical elements (e.g., icons, and change the menu terminology). Of course, the licensee is also able to create its own special smartphone design, resulting in a smartphone that is visually quite different from Series 60 Platform UI.

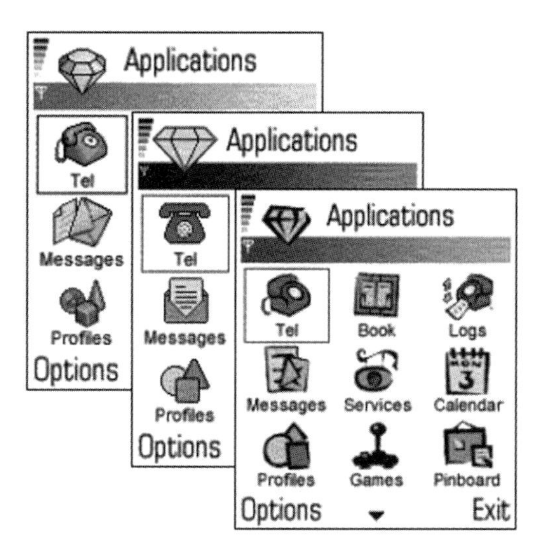

Three different user interface styles derived from simple graphical changes

Series 60 Applications

The Series 60 Platform provides basic telephony and Personal Information Management (PIM) applications. The Series 60 Platform also supports a wide range of applications that can be used as a basis for advanced mobile services.

The telephony applications give consumers the ability to manage their voice calls. The applications provide call logs and message indicators, device profiles, speed dialing and voice dialing. The Series 60 Platform also supports device enabled call services (e.g., voice call barring, three-way calling, sending of Dial Tone Multi-Frequency (DTMF) tones and call transfer).

The PIM applications provide the consumer with a contact manager and phonebook, for storing phone numbers, contact information, and e-mail addresses. There is a calendar application with multiple possible views (e.g., week or month). There is also a to-do application and a notes application for managing to-do lists and text notes. Other useful applications include a clock with alarm, a calculator, a ringing tone composer, a voice recorder, and a favorites list in which to place bookmarks and other shortcuts to information. The Series 60 Platform can synchronize data with a PC-based PIM client via the PC Connectivity Suite. A SyncML client provides over-the-air synchronization of information in the Calendar and Contacts applications with server-based PIM data.

November 2001

Wed, 7 Nov 2001

	Mo	Tu	We	Th	Fr	Sa	Su
44	29	30	31	1	2	3	4
45	5	6	7	8	9	10	11
46	12	13	14	15	16	17	18
47	19	20	21	22	23	24	25
48	26	27	28	29	30	1	2
49	3	4	5	6	7	8	9

Options Back

The calendar's month view

The Messaging application provides a unified interface to all messaging. It allows the consumer to create and manage MMS, SMS and e-mail messages as well as files received via Bluetooth or infrared transmission. It supports concatenation of SMS messages that are longer than a single SMS. Predictive text entry makes it easy to compose text messages.

An example of a multimedia message on the Series 60 Platform

The Photo Album is provided for customer to store and manage images. The Series 60 Platform supports various graphical formats (e.g., Graphics Interchange Format (GIF) and Joint Photographic Experts Group (JPEG)).

The WAP Browser is a native WAP 1.2.1 browser. Because the Series 60 Platform has a large, color screen and supports color graphical formats, the browser can view complex WAP content containing tables and color graphics.

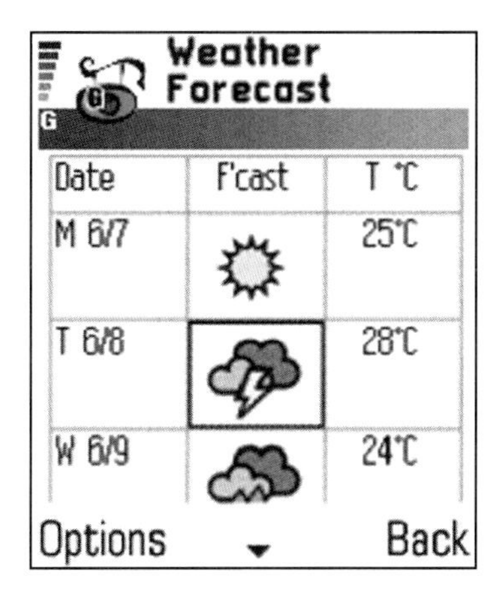

An example of a color WAP table viewed with the Series 60 Platform WAP browser

Installing Applications

The Series 60 Platform provides the ability to download and install native Symbian applications. The Series 60 Platform also includes a J2ME Application Execution Environment for MIDP Java applications. With Symbian and Java applications, consumers can extend and personalize their devices. Applications can be downloaded via e-mail, MMS, the browser, Bluetooth, infrared or a PC connection. The download mechanism for Java applications is compliant with the Java Community Process for Oover The Air (OTA) provisioning of Java 2 Micro Edition (J2ME™) applications.

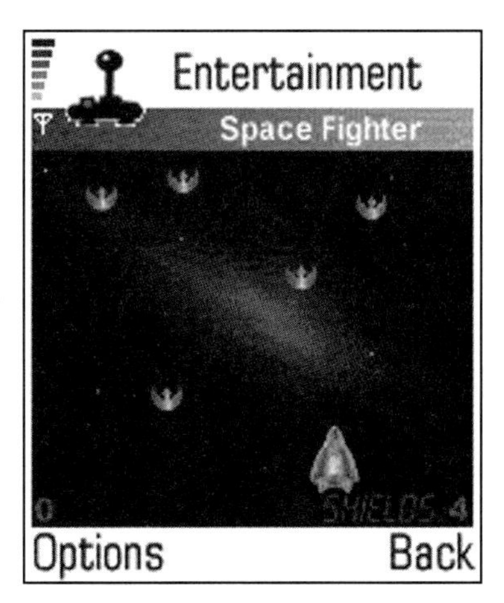

An example of a Java MIDP application on the Series 60 Platform

Community

To expand the smartphone market based on the Series 60 Platform, Nokia has created a governance model that supports an open community, the sharing of innovation, and a wide range of differentiation.

The Series 60 Platform is provided as source code, to provide maximum freedom for licensee differentiation. By receiving source code, the licensees are freed from binary code dependency. Access to source code means licensees have freedom to innovate and find their own direction for their smartphone programs. Also, the licensing model is modular, permitting licensees to remove or replace applications or features to create a Series 60 Platform package that is consistent with their smartphone designs.

The Series 60 Platform community is a voluntary online development environment for licensees. It allows licensees to either keep uniquely developed technologies as a differentiation point or license back these innovations to the community for all Series 60 Platform licensees to make the most of.

While there is freedom for licensees to make the Series 60 Platform their own or to modify the graphical look and hardware sufficiently to create a unique smartphone, it is important that there be compatibility between Series 60 Platform devices. Therefore, there is a minimum level of compatibility to ensure that applications and services designed for one Series 60 Platform smartphone can work with other Series 60 Platform based devices.

Differentiation in a Technologically Equal Environment

It is important to create a terminal software market with interoperable implementations of technologies based on open standards. This is to ensure that carriers and developers can build upon a common technology available across devices from multiple manufacturers.

Yet, spreading a common technology across different devices does not mean that all the devices will be the same. That is why the Terminal Software Suite and the Series 60 Platform are offered as source code. It is the only way to allow the maximum level of differentiation, while still maintaining some framework of compatibility and avoiding fragmentation of the market.

There are many areas where device manufacturers or carriers can differentiate themselves. As in many other industries where there is a commonly available technological platform, differentiation comes through integrated elements (e.g., design, look, quality, applications and services).

For example, with the Terminal Software Suite components, the licensee has complete choice as to what operating system or user interface to integrate the component into. There is no branding by the component (e.g., a splash screen or an external device label). There is no user interface for the component. The licensee can use a device user interface customized according to their own needs, so there is no user interface discontinuity and the consumers do not notice when they use the component application.

With the Series 60 Platform, the licensee can modify the bitmaps for graphics, the sounds, animations, color schemes, or the menu and application terminology. The licensee can also create their own distinctive design, their own applications and their own services. For example, Nokia created the 7650 based on the Series 60 Platform. It has a distinctive hardware design, a camera application, and graphical elements consistent with Nokia branding. Other manufacturers will create different hardware designs, a different look and different applications.

As these software components and modules begin to be adopted in the marketplace, licensees will be freed from the work of creating interoperable implementations of technologies based on open standards. They can focus on what they do best - creating exciting new hardware and compelling services.

Benefits of Software Components and Platforms

Benefits for device manufacturers - Nokia terminal software provides device manufacturers software for application-driven mobile devices. These applications are designed to help manufacturers create devices that support the new mobile services. They are based on open standards.

Licensable software components and platforms bring time and cost savings to research and development, lowering the manufacturing cost per device. Ready-made terminal software components and platforms help manufacturers bring devices onto the market more rapidly. Also, with the source code being provided, the terminal software is adaptable to a manufacturer's target device and category, permitting differentiation within a framework of compatibility. Manufacturers are able to focus on device brand and design rather than technology.

But, more importantly for the manufacturer, when a manufacturer creates devices that are interoperable with devices from other device vendors, the apparent value of the manufacturer's devices to carriers and developers increases.

Benefits to carriers - These software components and platforms provide carriers with a richer selection of applications and services. In some cases, they also present opportunities to carriers for customization and differentiation. Most of all, carriers look forward to interoperability between devices from a wide range of manufacturers, due to the adoption of a common technology implementation (e.g., the Mobile Browser or the Series 60 Platform). Carriers prefer to support services based on open standards rather than separately support services for various devices using technologies that are not interoperable or, worse, that use proprietary technologies. By not having to deal with each device individually, carriers can provide services to a whole range of devices from different manufacturers. They want to focus on their brand and services and not on which devices support which technologies.

Benefits to developers - Developers also gain by the creation of a larger applications market founded upon common interoperable implementations of mobile technologies across devices from different manufacturers. A larger market in which to sell solutions is more attractive to developers than a smaller single-vendor market. Also, developers will have the freedom to create applications for widely available technologies and benefit from the efficiency of a common API lowering development costs. This will enrich the device platforms of all devices that are part of this unified market.

PART 3.3

Network Solutions

- Nokia All-IP Network Vision
- Packet Transport in Mobile Networks
- Nokia Operator Wireless LAN
- Mobile Virtual Private Networks

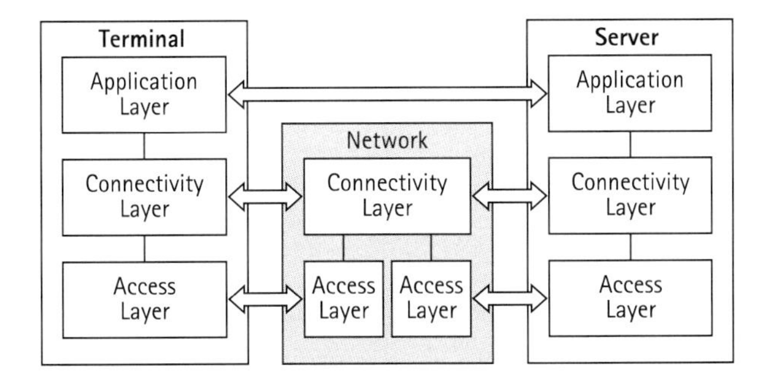

Nokia All-IP Network Vision

The All-IP Architecture is an industry vision of future networks, with different access options seamlessly integrated with an IP network layer.

Rapid upheavals and changes in the communications industry are influencing our means of communications today and in the future. Mobile communications, the Internet and digitization are all changing when, what and how we communicate.

New business paradigms, in which mobility and the Internet are combined, will be necessary if carriers are to succeed in the third generation mobile industry. Carriers who make the right choices will stand to reap a huge market share and many other rewards. Key to this is the choice of technology and the right technology partner.

With third generation technology, the consumer will also benefit. New services, applications and features will become personalized, location-aware and accessible anywhere and at any time via a single device.

The Nokia All-IP Mobility System is a solution to address the mobile connectivity business model. Designed specifically to support the needs of mobile carriers, it provides a scalable and multi-phase approach to re-engineering existing mobile networks for the All-IP mobile network of the future. It unifies the mobile network architecture and provides the best means to create and deliver a cost-effective and efficient combination of services.

Vision for the All-IP Network

Today, there is a blurring of the business boundaries between carriers of different networks (e.g., fixed, mobile and Internet). Similarly, to support the future needs of carriers, the technology must also become integrated.

These technology choices can be integrated into a single industry vision; the All-IP network.

All-IP enables seamless network integration of different access options (e.g., broadband, mobile Internet and existing mobile systems), into a single IP layer.

IP allows all communication services to be carried over a single network infrastructure, enabling the integration of voice, data and multimedia services.

The All-IP networks will offer carriers a number of important benefits, including cost savings, scalability, flexibility, efficient network operations, and - most importantly - new revenue opportunities.

Changing Traffic Patterns

Current estimates show that in advanced mobile communication markets, packet-switched traffic will overtake circuit-switched traffic by 2005. The growth in data bits used in communications will exceed the growth in revenue, driving carriers to optimize their networks to support the dominant traffic type.

To support this growth in data traffic, many carriers are building General Packet Radio Service (GPRS) networks that will more efficiently support data traffic. This is a key step in evolution to the third generation and the All-IP system.

Mobile networks based on the third generation standards will better support packet services and will accelerate the explosion of data traffic.

All-IP communications combines different media and services in a single session, generating additional traffic and revenue. The Nokia All-IP network solution supports both circuit and packet traffic in a single core network.

Nokia All-IP Mobility System

The Nokia All-IP Mobility System is the wireless component of the All-IP network. The system is designed to provide service flexibility, service deployment, evolution, and backward compatibility with current networks.

The Nokia All-IP Mobility System will be fully compliant with Third Generation Partnership Project (3GPP) release 5 standards, with open interfaces and IPv6/v4 support.

Whereas second-generation networks were primarily optimized to support mobile voice services, the All-IP Mobility System is optimized to support multimedia packet services.

With All-IP, network resources are used more efficiently and capacity can be deployed as necessary to meet demand. Standard network elements (e.g., routers) can be used throughout the network, which:

- Simplifies network design,
- Shares capacity more efficiently, and
- Significantly lowers the investment required

The different functions of the All-IP Mobility System are divided into different network layers (i.e., transport, mobility/connection/control, and application) and network subsystems (e.g., Access, Core and Services). These are all seamlessly integrated with open and standardized protocols.

The benefit of this approach is that subsystems or even layers can be evolved separately or coexist with other layers and subsystems without affecting the overall network.

Examples of this include:

- o The high-speed backbone in the Gateway Layer can be upgraded (i.e., Asynchronous Transfer Mode (ATM) to Multi-Protocol Label Switching (MPLS)) with minimum impact on the Services and Control Layers.
- o The radio and core networks can be upgraded without affecting the services and applications.
- o Control elements, gateway elements, or service elements can be upgraded independently of each other based on users, traffic or service types.

IP Multimedia Capabilities

All-IP allows voice, data and multimedia services to be carried over a single network. This yields two main benefits for carriers:

- o new and better ways to develop and offer applications and services, and
- o generating greater revenue and lower costs compared to a single core network using common IP technology.

The All-IP Mobility System is optimized to support multimedia services. The adoption of Session Initiation Protocol (SIP) is a key ingredient in providing this new functionality. 3GPP standardized SIP is a common signaling protocol joining the Web and Mobile domain. It provides integrated multimedia capabilities for IP enabled devices.

For a consumer, this means integrated voice, video, and browsing experience in a single call. With SIP, numerous applications can be implemented which combine traditional telephony with messaging and multimedia.

For instance, instead of a blinking telephone number on the display, the caller can introduce himself at the beginning of the communications session with a personalized logo or business information. The subject of the call can then be immediately displayed to the recipient in text, voice, or picture format, depending on the devices' capabilities.

With IP multimedia, it will also be possible to create richer profiles that include additional features (e.g., sending tailored information to predetermined callers, or to incorporate e-mail/ media-on-demand content) so that the voice call can be converted to a text message and forwarded to a Web mailbox if the recipient is unavailable.

The Nokia All-IP Mobility Core can be used in with any major radio and data network standards, to bring carriers a secure, complete, future-proof, end-to-end network for the third generation mobile multimedia and multi-services environment.

IPv6 and IPv4 Supported

The versatility of the Internet protocol makes it easy for carriers to provide a wealth of customized services, and it is clearly the best way to transport everything from voice to broadband data. However, the Internet protocol presents some challenges itself.

The limited size and structure of the current Internet address space, lack of end-to-end security, and sub-optimal performance are seen as critical weaknesses in Internet Protocol version 4 (IPv4). IPv6 avoids these problems with IPv4 and represents the next generation of the protocol.

The All-IP Mobile System will be IPv6 enabled from day one. IPv6 is seen as a key requirement for implementing real-time IP multimedia services with inbuilt Quality of Service (QoS) indicators. The most important benefit of IPv6 is the huge address base, meaning that all IP devices will have their own globally unique IP addresses.

Security is also a major feature of IPv6, with IP Security (IPSec) providing the ability to encrypt or authenticate all traffic at the IP level; i.e., all applications running over the All-IP Mobility System will be secure.

Mobility is also catered for, with Mobile IPv6 being a standardized part of the protocol. In Mobile IPv6, each mobile element is identified. This means that consumers are always reachable with a single IP address.

IPv4 and IPv6 will coexist at first, with IPv6 gaining ground as its capabilities are realized. To support IPv4, dual protocol stacks, tunneling and translation mechanisms will provide backward compatibility in the All-IP Mobility System.

Radio Access Network

All mobile radio standards (e.g., Global System for Mobile Communications (GSM) / Enhanced Data Rates for Global Evolution (EDGE), Wideband Code Division Multiple Access (WCDMA) and Wireless Local Area Network (WLAN)), have distinct network architectures and transport mechanisms. In the future, IP will be the protocol of choice to fully integrate these standards into one uniform radio access network. Again, IP is the ideal protocol for enabling closer integration of both radio access and core technologies. More importantly end-to-end IP services will become possible from the mobile device to the Internet via the All-IP Mobility System.

All-IP Radio Access will drive down the carrier's production cost per bit, improving carrier profit capability. In the Nokia All-IP Radio Access Network (All-IP RAN), an Internet type of architecture has been adopted in which user and control planes are separated; the control functions are shifted to the edges of the network. With this fundamental architecture change, several advantages are achieved:

- Scalability to allow any mix of services in the future - enabled by separating the control and user planes.
- Dynamic resource sharing between different network elements. The adoption of a distributed architecture enables flexible network expansion and full use of element capacity.
- A single multi-radio network that is easier to operate and uses resources better. Also, investments can be focused on one set of network elements.
- Optimized Quality of Service, ensuring the required service performance with the lowest costs to the carrier

- Increased transport network efficiency by combining the transport of radio access technologies and other technologies offering IP-based services
- Smooth evolution to All-IP, protecting existing and future investments
- Lowest cost per bit, with significant annual capital expenditure savings compared to conventional radio access networks.

Migrating to Nokia All-IP RAN will enable carriers to produce radio access capacity at a clearly lower cost than by using conventional network architectures. The distributed, multi-radio Nokia All-IP RAN architecture provides the same advantages that were achieved using the principles of IP for the Internet. In addition, All-IP RAN greatly adds to the value of existing networks by extending their life.

Multi-Services Environment

All-IP networks provide a more efficient platform for consumer applications. Compared to circuit-switching, All-IP provides more bandwidth, more efficient network usage, more freedom in service creation and more flexible billing.

An All-IP core network enables the implementation of services that are not possible with separate circuit-switched and packet core networks. For example, rich calls are not easily implemented in circuit-switched networks.

Carriers and service providers that can provide reliable access to exciting and useful mobile services will develop brand loyalty and secure their profits. Those that cannot will be more vulnerable to consumer turnover and tightening competition.

Nokia realizes that making the Internet accessible through mobile devices opens a vast new business opportunity. However, since much of the information required for this is freely available, the value provided by the carrier will be based on pinpointing what is relevant.

Nokia sees four service groups having major relevance in the third generation:

- Information and entertainment content,
- Communication,
- Productivity-enhancing services, and
- Business solutions.

When deciding to implement a third generation mobile network, carriers need to consider these services as they build the infrastructure. They need to discover creative ways of packaging these services and using existing services to promote the usage of new ones. Excelling in the following four key areas will provide maximum value for consumers in the world of third generation technology:

- Services that are personalized,
- Services that provide timely information,

- Transactions that are simple to complete, and
- Services that are location-specific.

Coverage, capacity, and pricing are used as key differentiators today but will not offer a sufficient competitive advantage for gaining a profitable market share in the third generation.

The success of third generation carriers will be based more on their ability to provide a suite of personalized services to consumers, and thereby decrease the chance that the consumers will move to another carrier for better services.

The All-IP Mobility System is designed to more economically and flexibly support existing services in GSM, GPRS and Release 99 networks, by creating a multi-service environment.

Furthermore, it provides a solid foundation upon which future services can be created, and one allowing their easy deployment. Discrete applications and disparate services can be integrated into seamless service packages.

Coherent Evolution Strategy

Although the All-IP Mobility System represents a fundamental change in mobile networks and their capabilities, it does not represent a discontinuity in the existing Nokia technology portfolio.

Nokia GSM, GPRS and Release 99 networks can evolve in stages to support the All-IP Mobility System.

There are three key phases:

1. Evolution from Release 99 to the All-IP Mobility System
2. All-IP Mobility System based on Release 4/5
3. All-IP Mobility System beyond Release 4/5.

Evolution from Release 99 to the All-IP Mobility System

The process of moving toward the All-IP Mobility System in the core network has already begun with the GPRS.

GPRS based packet-switched, always-on network services are the first stepping stones. They provide the basis for the mobile packet core network of Release 99.

The Nokia Mobility Core network is complemented by a unique radio access network capable of supporting several radio interface technologies.

Release 99 is focused on seamlessly integrating these different radio access technologies into a single Release 99 core network.

GSM radio access networks will gradually develop into IP-based networks offering end-to-end packet-switched transmission of third generation services.

This evolutionary process has already begun, with carriers across the world deploying GPRS, and will be completed with the deployment of the WCDMA and EDGE technologies. The Nokia solution for radio access offers smooth evolution, integration of EDGE and WCDMA with existing base stations, a reduction in rollout costs, and an accelerated shift to an All-IP radio access network.

All-IP Mobility System Based on the Release 4/5 Standard

As a result of upgrading the GSM/GPRS network, the core network is able to continuously support circuit-switching for voice and mission-critical data while providing the benefits of packet-switching for other data services.

As third generation rich call and multimedia services become more widely available, carriers can meet demands for quality, capacity, and profitability by implementing an All-IP Mobility Core.

Upgrades following the 3GPP Release 4 standard allow separation of user and control planes for the Circuit Switched domain, leading to easier capacity upgrades and savings in transport costs.

The 3GPP Release 5 Nokia All-IP Mobility Core will provide the IP multimedia service creation machinery, optimized for the Mobile domain. New platforms are available to support IP multimedia, or, alternatively, Nokia Release 99 and Release 4 elements can be upgraded.

At this point, in areas of high packet traffic, carriers can also choose to migrate to the Nokia All-IP RAN. This will enable optimum support for the growing IP based services and maximize the carriers profit potential by delivering these services at a lower cost per bit.

All-IP Mobility System Beyond Release 4/5

The All-IP network envisages a future in which there is no need for new circuit-switched network elements; circuit-switched traffic will be reinvented as voice over IP or other real-time packet services. The All-IP RAN and All-IP Mobility Core ensure end-to-end transport and control of IP real-time/non-real-time services.

Backward Compatibility

The primary factor determining the speed of transition to an All-IP mobile network without legacy support will depend on how quickly GSM, GPRS and early third generation devices evolve into IP multimedia devices.

As this is uncertain, the multi-phase evolution of the All-IP Mobility System ensures that the flexibility remains with the carrier. Nokia ensures that the All-IP Mobility System remains backward compatible with GSM, GPRS and early third generation devices.

Intelligent Edge and Backbone Neutrality

The focus of the Nokia All-IP Mobility System is to add value to the carrier's business by providing innovative technology. The Nokia focus is not to provide high-speed backbone routers but, instead, to provide *intelligence* in the network through mobility, mobile services and radio access technologies.

In this respect, the Nokia All-IP Mobility System is essentially packet backbone neutral, enabling its seamless integration with the carrier's high-speed backbone. It supports backbone packet technologies (e.g., IP, ATM, MPLS and the Synchronous Digital Hierarchy (SDH)).

Alternatively, if the carrier does not have a high-speed packet backbone, Nokia is ready to provide a complete All-IP Mobility System, including the backbone, as a single supplier solution.

Our global partnering with Cisco ensures that packet backbone products provided in any Nokia All-IP solution will be compliant with industry standards and state-of-the-art backbone technology.

Conclusions

Nokia is able to provide a complete technology solution based on All-IP Mobility. This includes the network, rollout, services and support to optimize the network and introduce new revenue opportunities.

With an active role in the standardization of key system technologies (e.g., IPv6 and SIP), and global leadership in mobility and IP, the Nokia All-IP Mobility System is a complete technology solution, strategy and vision for the carrier.

Nokia has been able to make significant contributions to the relevant fora and standardization bodies with the aim of leading the industry toward a common All-IP RAN architecture and unified mobile IP packet network architecture. Nokia is playing a key role in standardization fora involved in some aspect of the All-IP standardization. Nokia intends to stay at the forefront of the mobile and Internet industries by actively participating in standardization to ensure that third generation products of Nokia are compliant and future-proof.

The All-IP Mobility System can bring significant cost savings to a network. Firstly, ubiquitous access in the core network eliminates the overhead of operating two networks: one for data and one for voice. Additionally, the All-IP Mobility System provides unsurpassed flexibility in allocating bandwidth and QoS for services. This translates into a cost-effective network.

Secondly, All-IP Radio Access offers savings by optimizing the use of resources, particularly in mobile networks where the Nokia All-IP RAN provides flexibility to support changes in traffic composition and is fully optimized to carry IP based traffic.

Finally, the unified network management system provides an end-to-end perspective of the network, which enables easy network optimizations and fine-tuning.

The business model for All-IP networks will be a convergence of Internet, media and wireless communications. Mobile carriers are in a key position to exploit the new business opportunities brought about by the shift toward this IP convergence.

A carrier's key assets in this new business model are: the Mobile Internet; control of the end-to-end quality of service for carrier hosted services; enabling factors specific to the mobile network (e.g., location and presence), the mobile network infrastructure, and, naturally, the subscribers themselves.

The Nokia All-IP Mobility system represents the best technology solution for addressing carriers' future business needs and provides a smooth stepwise evolution path from the mobile networks of today.

Packet Transport in Mobile Networks

Packet Transport Requirements

The protocol to be carried over the packet network of a mobile carrier is IP. However, IP traffic is far from being homogeneous. Different types of traffic cause a variety of requirements for the network. The different applications of packet transport in mobile networks are outlined in the figure below.

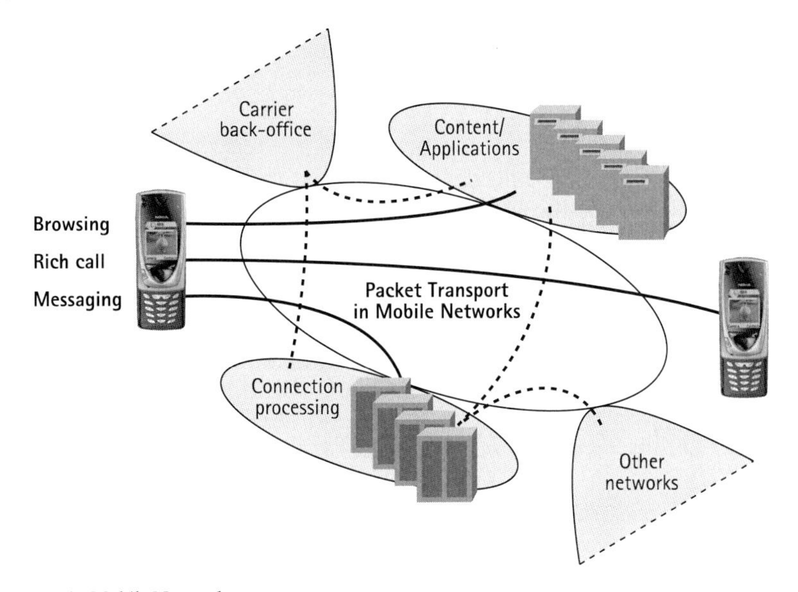

Packet Transport in Mobile Networks

Real-time conversational services set strict end-to-end delay requirements for packet transport. As data processing and media access over the radio network is time-consuming, the delay budget for the packet network is tighter in the Mobile domain than in the Web domain.

Capacity limits of the radio access network and the related access transport highlight the need for Quality of Service (QoS) differentiation. For serving the large number of mobile devices, IPv6 is needed, but the connectivity to existing networks (i.e., corporate intranets) is still based on IPv4. Both protocols have to be supported.

Even though the specifications of the Third Generation Partnership Project (3GPP) are converging to a Mobile Internet architecture with all its transport interfaces intended to be based on IP, there remains a requirement to support other networking technologies that exist today in some parts of the transport network. Frame relay is used in the General Packet Radio System (GPRS) and Asynchronous Transfer Mode (ATM) in the initial third generation networks. ATM also plays a significant role today in alternative broadband access technologies. The non-IP interfaces have to be integrated into the transport solution.

Although the handling of the user data dictates the structure of the transport network, it is important to keep in mind that the network has to carry a multitude of different types of traffic. In addition to the user data, there is operation and maintenance traffic, signaling between the network elements and billing information. Logically, the traffic belongs to several independent networks. These networks all have their own requirements for security, routing resilience and Quality of Service.

Not only do the services and protocols set requirements for the packet transport used for the mobile networks: Geography, the physical structure of the network, the availability of sites and fiber, and security and resiliency policies dictate how the packet transport for the mobile networks is built.

Network Architecture

In the Mobile Internet context, the target is to consolidate all traffic of the mobile networks into one IP network. The network architecture presented here combines the target and the real-life requirements presented above.

Logically, the transport network of a carrier consists of three parts.

- The access network is designed for connecting a large number of individual base station sites. Since, in most cases, fast network rollout to difficult sites (e.g., rooftops and remote masts) is required, microwave radio is the dominant transmission technology. Copper and fiber are used where possible. As building the access network is very expensive, chain and tree structures are commonly used instead of more resilient ring and mesh networks. Today, the access network carries traffic from the base stations toward the core network and back. With the emergence of All-IP Radio Access Networks (All-IP RAN) and the integration of alternative access technologies (e.g., Wireless Local Area Networks, WLAN), routing capability will be added to the access network.
- The regional network connects the access network to the core network. It is fiber-based and contains standard switching and routing equipment for traffic concentration. Today, the regional network carries traffic from the access network to the core and back. With emerging new technologies (All-IP RAN, Mobile IPv6) and alternative access technologies, the regional networks will become truly routed.
- The high-capacity backbone combines the core sites that host the major server farms and the radio network controller sites. This part of the network is typically easy to implement as the number of sites is limited and the connections typically are between cities with several hundred thousand inhabitants. Between large cities, fiber and transport capacity are often available in surplus. Backbone networks are already in many cases router-based.

The structure of a transport network serving both the current (2G) mobile network and the third generation network is outlined in the figure below. The number of sites indicated refers to typical European countries.

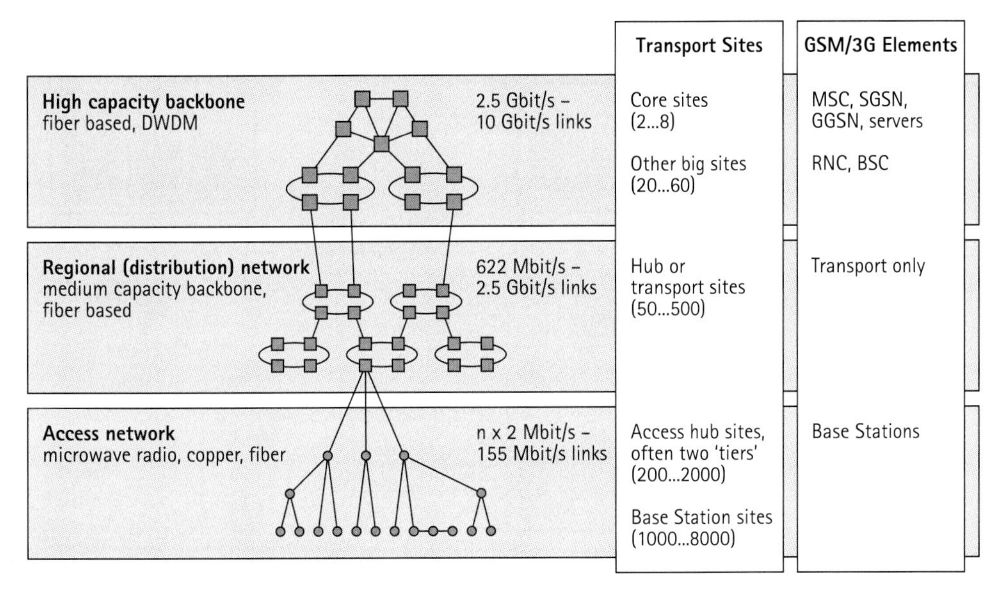

Sites in a typical mobile network

On top of the above physical framework, the necessary logical networks are deployed. For the mobile networks, the deployment of IP transport has started at the core sites, with essentially all network elements being connected to multi-layer LAN switches for connectivity to the operation and maintenance; signaling; and billing networks. Wide area backbone networks covering the packet transport for GPRS traffic and voice over IP between Mobile Services Switching Centers (MSC) are being established between the core sites. With the 3GPP release 4 and release 5 specifications, the IP transport will be extended to the gateway sites that host the Radio Network Controllers (RNC) as well. A mobile network with 3GPP release 4/5 functionality is outlined in the following figure.

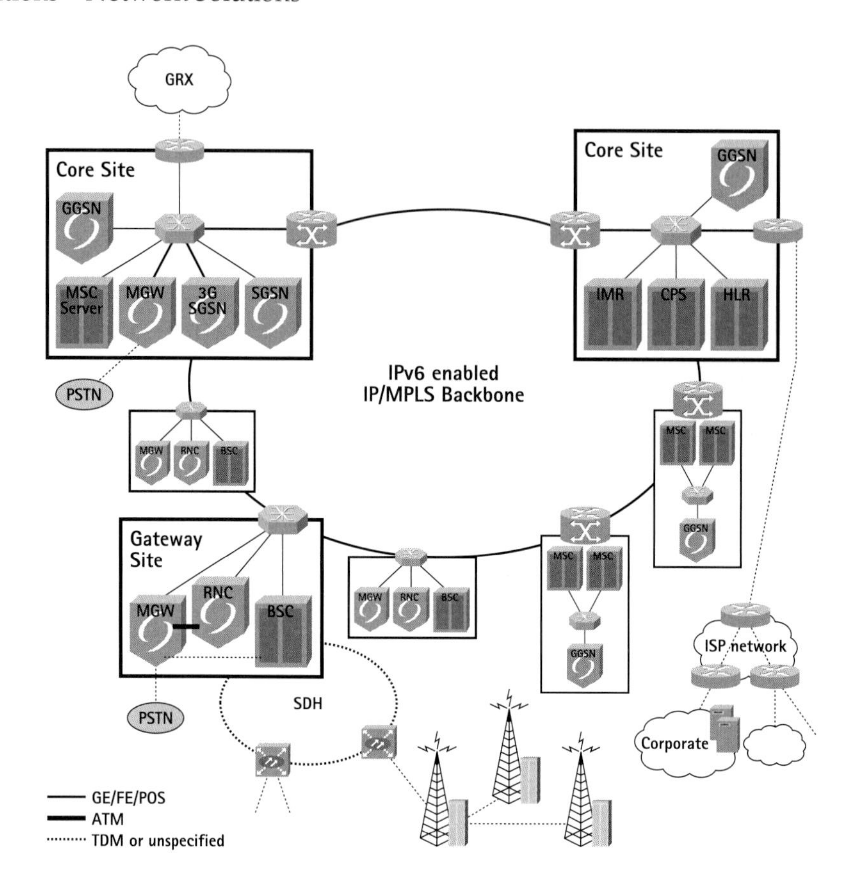

Mobile network with 3GPP Release 4/5 functionality

The above figure shows a network where several systems use the same packet transport:

- GPRS/3G packet switched domain: Serving GPRS Support Node (SGSN), 3G SGSN and Gateway GPRS Support Node (GGSN)
- Circuit switched domain: MSC Server, Media Gateway (MGW) and Home Location Register (HLR)
- IP multimedia subsystem: Connection Processing Server (CPS) and IP Multimedia Register (IMR)

Note that the multi-layer LAN switches that also act as edge routers have essentially taken the role of the distribution frames used in traditional telecom networks. All connectivity of the mobile network elements depends on LAN switching and IP routing. Consequently, special attention needs to be paid to the availability and resilience of the site connectivity solution. In addition to the multi-layer LAN switches/edge routers, a limited number of backbone routers are used to form a stable core network.

In addition to the connectivity within the network, the carrier also needs connections to Internet service provider networks (e.g., for Internet services and corporate connectivity) and to roaming partners. The connections to roaming partners are typically arranged via GPRS Roaming Exchange (GRX) networks.

In today's mobile networks, there are interfaces that are not based on IP (e.g., frame relay based Gb interface in GPRS networks and ATM based Iu interfaces in the initial third generation networks). These interfaces can be initially handled as point-to-point connections the same way as traditional circuit switched interfaces. Over the next few years, circuit switched interfaces are to be replaced or complemented by IP based interfaces (Gb over IP, Iu over IP) in the mobile networks. At the same time, tunneling technologies make it possible to carry legacy protocols over the IP network.

DiffServ based packet prioritization and proper network design are the basic ways to ensure quality of service for the packet transport in mobile networks. While DiffServ is enough in most parts of the network, there may be special requirements that justify the use of other complementary techniques, i.e., bandwidth reservation. It should however be noted that bandwidth reservations dilute the statistical multiplexing gains in the network and may lead to decreased capacity utilization and performance.

In third generation networks, the mobile device requests a specific traffic class for the Packet Data Protocol (PDP) context. For the packet transport, these traffic classes are mapped to DiffServ codepoints. DiffServ can be used across the whole network. Should some parts of the network use other Quality of Service mechanisms than DiffServ (e.g., an ATM backbone), the DiffServ codepoints are mapped to the alternative Quality of Service scheme.

Network security is of key importance when designing the packet transport solution. On the one hand, IP based networks have been targets of a wide variety of attacks from the hacker community and are also known to be vulnerable to configuration errors. Routing protocols are an efficient way to propagate incorrect information throughout the network. To reduce the exposure to attacks and errors, it is good practice to split the network logically per interface (e.g., Gn, Gi) or per function (operation and maintenance, signaling). Communications between the independent parts of the network can be limited or prohibited. Network security can be enforced using a variety of technologies:

- Firewalls at the edge of the network and, for roaming traffic, also firewalls that are aware of the mobile-specific protocols (e.g., GPRS Tunneling Protocol (GTP))
- Virtual Private Networks (VPN) for keeping the different types of traffic apart in the wide area network
- Virtual Local Area Network (VLAN) for keeping the different types of traffic apart on the sites
- Router access control lists for limiting the traffic between the different VLANs
- Security features in the mobile network elements
- Additional systems for key management, intrusion detection and management of the elements involved

VLAN technology allows building several logical networks using the same physical infrastructure. So the size of the broadcast domains can be limited. Using VLANs, mobile network elements can be at the same time connected to several separated networks (e.g., user data, signaling, and charging).

In large backbones, Multi-Protocol Label Switching (MPLS) provides practical tools for the network carrier. MPLS VPNs are a means of separating the different types of traffic in the wide area network. MPLS is an optimal platform for VPN implementations, allowing simple point-to-multipoint provisioning. No point-to-point tunnel configurations are needed since routing protocols distribute the information of a new VPN member to the other VPN sites. MPLS VPN is a promising technology for complementing VLANs in the wide area network.

MPLS traffic engineering can be used for bandwidth provisioning and resilience in selected parts of the network. MPLS Traffic Engineering utilizing Constraint Based Routing enables the provisioning of reserved bandwidth between sites, with the benefits of a connectionless network. Although very useful for problem solving in special cases, MPLS traffic engineering should not be seen as a holy grail. It is not a substitute for proper network planning. It just helps in dividing existing bandwidth.

Any Transport over MPLS (AToM) provides means to consolidate legacy protocols (e.g., frame relay) in an IP based network. MPLS is also a practical way to IPv6 enable existing backbone router networks without changing the hardware, as awareness of the IPv6 protocol is needed only at the edge of the MPLS network.

In some cases, MPLS also makes it possible to extend the IP-compatible control plane to cover existing mobile networks.

Internet Protocol Security (IPSec) provides security for transport of sensitive information over unprotected networks. The traffic can be encrypted. IPSec VPNs are used in the mobile networks for information that requires special protection. Corporate VPN services, billing data and signaling are potential areas of application. Note that IPSec VPNs can be used on top of MPLS VPNs for enhanced security.

The network architecture discussed here is fully applicable to a second or third generation environment that applies to the current and near future specifications and implementations. The evolution toward an All-IP radio access network and the integration of alternative access technologies changes the previous figure so that the IP/MPLS domain is extended to cover the access network.

Conclusions

The network architecture presented here meets the requirements set for future-proof mobile networks. It has a Quality of Service scheme capable of handling real-time conversational services and enabling efficient utilization of the transport link capacity. It also has support for IPv6 and the legacy protocols currently deployed in second and third generation environments as well as for the separation of different types of traffic.

The network consists of the access part, designed for connecting a large number of individual base station sites; the regional network connecting the access to the core network; and the high-capacity backbone connecting the core sites to each other.

Multi-layer LAN switches/edge routers are used for connectivity and providing VLANs at bigger sites. In large backbones, MPLS provides practical tools for the carrier. MPLS VPNs are a practical way of separating the different types of traffic in a mobile network and for complementing the VLANs.

Nokia Operator Wireless LAN

Networks are increasingly being used to store all types of information, which presents its own challenges to the concept of mobility. Consumers are traveling and teleworking more, yet still demand access to their corporate information systems no matter what their location.

The Nokia Operator Wireless Local Area Network (OWLAN) effectively makes a consumer's desktop portable, allowing access to multiple media. Nokia sees this freedom of mobile connectivity as one of the main building blocks of the emerging Mobile World. In this concept, mobile business subscribers will be the first target market to have high-speed, low-cost Internet and intranet access wherever they are. Wireless LAN (WLAN) will be a major access technology providing solutions for high-speed wireless IP laptop and Personal Digital Assistant (PDA) connectivity.

With Wireless LAN, carriers will be able to expand their business to mobile laptop/PDA users. Many Global System for Mobile Communications (GSM) or General Packet Radio Service (GPRS) business subscribers will already have a laptop and will form a ready market for the new service. Offering the fastest wireless indoor data access, up to 11 Mbit/s, Wireless LAN will have a strong attraction. High speed data access will also be extremely convenient for all subscribers to use.

The Nokia Operator Wireless LAN offers Subscriber Identity Module (SIM) based authentication, which is a very simple way to authenticate and provides the means for integration with GSM/GPRS/3G billing systems. The Nokia solution also provides consumers with global roaming for wireless LAN devices.

With the Nokia Operator Wireless LAN, indoor access can be made available in a wide variety of locations, the main ones being hotels, airports, railway stations, business parks, campuses, and corporate buildings.

High-Speed, Low-Cost Wireless Internet Access

One of the definitions of the Mobile World is a world where everyone will have high-speed, low-cost access to the Internet, no matter what their location. However, this access will not be based on a single third generation technology but rather a range of technologies that give people the greatest choice of how and where they get this access. Wireless LAN will be one of these technologies, but it should not be seen as merely a wireless extension of existing Local Area Networks - instead it would be a vital component in the worldwide communication network, providing solutions for high-speed wireless IP laptop connectivity.

Base stations (i.e., access points) capable of providing Wireless LAN connectivity will typically be located at places where business customers, the core potential consumers of the technology, will congregate. They will also be installed in offices. Wireless LAN will allow business customers to check data from their company intranet, send and receive e-mail, save documents and take part in videoconferences, among many other applications.

Mobile GSM and GPRS business customers are expected to form the first target market for the Nokia Operator Wireless LAN. They are already familiar with the convenience offered for voice communication, improved reachability, and, increasingly, data mobility, and they are expected to welcome the opportunity to receive high-speed data directly on their laptops - even when they are abroad.

Reaching the Mobile Customers

Defining the Standard

Although the first commercial wireless LAN systems using the 2.4 GHz frequency band were introduced some eight years ago, the standard defining wireless LAN, IEEE 802.11, has had a difficult gestation period. Many years passed before agreement was reached on the first version of the standard, providing transfer rates of one or two Mbit/s. The standard also approved two incompatible approaches (i.e., frequency hopping and direct sequence), causing many in the industry to lose faith in IEEE 802.11 and leading to the proliferation of yet more incompatible systems.

However, IEEE 802.11 is now enjoying a major resurgence, thanks to the ratification of IEEE 802.11b. This defined a single solution offering 11 Mbit/s wireless data communication. The performance advantage of IEEE 802.11b over all the other wireless LAN technologies in the 2.4 GHz band gave it sufficient advantage to draw most of the industry back to a common approach.

This renewed confidence in the standard was underlined by the introduction of wireless LAN products by industry leading companies and the establishment of the Wireless Ethernet Compatibility Alliance (WECA).

Typically, a Wireless Fidelity (Wi-Fi) certified wireless LAN product provides the following functionality:

- The wireless LAN card is an extended type II PC card with a data rate of up to 11 Mbit/s
- Radio technology: 2.4 GHz, IEEE 802.11b compatible direct sequence spread spectrum, 13 channels
- Coverage area: outdoor max. 400 m radius, office 20-100 m radius (typically)
- Wired Equivalent Privacy (WEP) with up to 128-bit secret key encryption over the air
- SW drivers for at least various Windows® operating systems

Great interest has also been shown in wireless LANs operating in the 5 GHz band. This high-frequency band is able to support even higher data rates than IEEE 802.11b. Two standards are vying for acceptance in this band: IEEE 802.11h in Europe and IEEE 802.11a in the US and other countries. Interest in this band stems partly from the higher data rates available and partly from concerns about cross-interference in the 2.4 GHz band.

However, 5 GHz systems are currently expensive and have high power consumption, and it will probably be some time before 5 GHz products will be comparable in cost to current 802.11b systems.

Making Secure Connections

Security is a major consideration when developing and implementing any mobile system. Potential consumers must know that their information is secure. The IEEE 802.11b standard defines WEP security features, enabling RC4 data encryption with a key length of up to 128 bits. This encryption works over the 2.4 GHz air interface and protects the user data from eavesdropping. WEP security is, however, considered insufficient in the areas of encryption and security key management. The IEEE 802.11 Enhanced Security Task Group (Tgi) is working on a new WLAN security scheme with the following main objectives:

1) To define a new strong encryption method
2) To integrate the new encryption method into access management systems. This can allow practical deployment of systems with thousands of customers

Because today's business customers and companies are very cautious about remote access and data security, it is recommended that the Nokia Operator Wireless LAN customer apply separate Virtual Private Network (VPN) software to create an encrypted end-to-end tunnel between the customer's device and the corporate network. Nokia IP Security solutions offer a comprehensive line of products for security applications, including VPN and firewalls. However, the VPN system is independent of the Nokia Operator Wireless LAN, and any company specific VPN solution can be used.

New Business for Carriers

Charging for Wireless LAN services is another important issue. The Nokia Operator Wireless LAN solution provides carriers with the means to turn a technology into a new business. With the Nokia Operator Wireless LAN, charging is performed in a similar manner to GSM, using a GSM Subscriber Identity Module (SIM) card. The new Nokia Wireless LAN card supporting up to 11 Mbit/s data access offers an integrated SIM card reader. Nokia is the first vendor to introduce this unique feature in the wireless LAN device market. The benefit of using a SIM card is that the identification and authentication of the consumer to the network is automatic and can be integrated into the billing system of a carrier. To support wireless LAN cards without a SIM card reader and laptops/PDAs with a built-in wireless LAN card, Nokia also offers SIM authentication client software. In conjunction with the client software, the consumer needs an external SIM card reader (e.g., plug into the Universal Serial Bus (USB) interface). Secure SIM card based authentication also provides global carrier-to-carrier roaming.

The Nokia Operator Wireless LAN device also uses the SIM card to authenticate the public wireless LAN access network. The authentication information is sent to the carrier core network via a dedicated gateway and verified using the existing mobile functions. Combined with mobile SIM based user authentication and billing characteristics, the Nokia Operator Wireless LAN solution allows the carrier to implement fast Mobile Internet access for roaming laptop consumers.

Nokia Operator Wireless LAN Scope

The Nokia Operator Wireless LAN system consists of two separate parts: the public wireless LAN access zone, which provides the actual radio access network, and the carrier network side, which offers SIM authentication, roaming and billing services. A single carrier will typically have many mobile access zones in different public locations.

The Nokia solution consists of wireless LAN cards for the devices, wireless access points, an access controller and an authentication server.

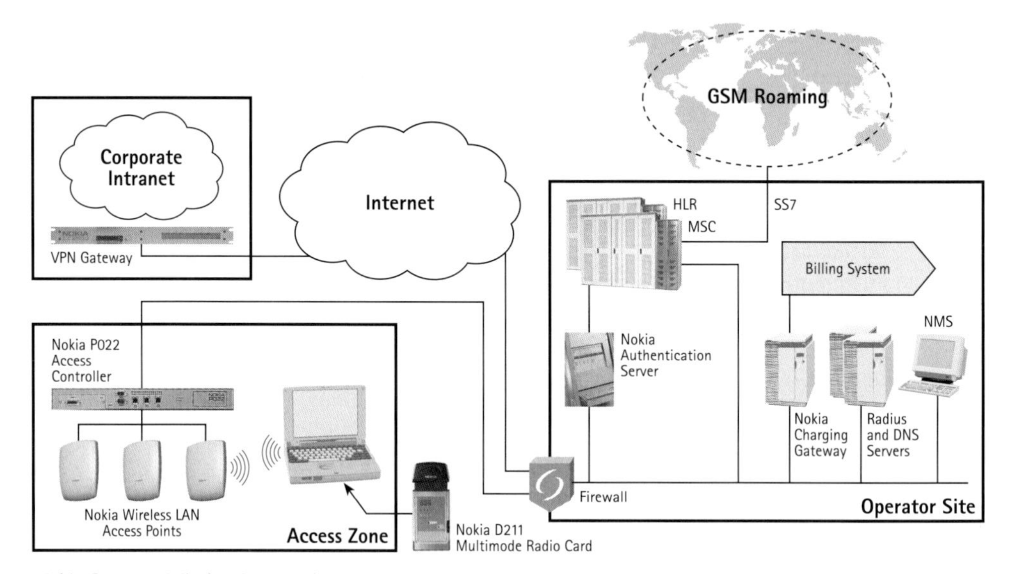

Nokia Operator Wireless LAN architecture

Access Controller

The access controller controls access from the radio access network to the Internet services. It allocates IP addresses to the device and also authenticates the device before the connection to the Internet is established. It relays the authentication messages between the mobile device and the authentication server. It also collects the billing records and sends them to the authentication server.

The access controller monitors each incoming and outgoing IP packet and permits traffic only between the authenticated devices and the Internet. It supports several alternative charging mechanisms (e.g., time based, packet based or flat rate billing).

Authentication Server

The authentication server provides GSM based authentication services to the access controller, as well as collecting charging information. It provides authentication and billing services for a number of access controllers simultaneously. It uses the industry standard Remote Authentication Dial-In User Service (RADIUS) authentication protocol to carry the SIM authentication.

Wireless LAN Access Point

The radio access network is provided using IEEE 802.11b compatible wireless LAN access points, which are connected to a separate public access zone LAN segment. The access points provide a data rate of up to 11 Mbit/s and incorporate advanced management features.

Careful radio network planning ensures good performance and large coverage. For this purpose, Nokia provides dedicated wireless LAN radio network planning software, offering an easy way of performing site surveys and finding the best locations for access points.

Consumer Device

The wireless LAN mobile device inside the laptop consists of a Nokia Wireless LAN card and access software. All the data traffic from the device to the network goes over the wireless LAN link to the public access controller that performs the authentication.

The Nokia access point supports all IEEE 802.11b standard compatible wireless LAN devices. The access software provides the SIM authentication capability that is part of the product.

Seamless Indoor Mobility

The IEEE 802.11 wireless LAN standard supports seamless mobility between different access points that are connected to the same LAN. This feature is also deployed in the Nokia Operator Wireless LAN. In a typical mobile access zone installation, all access points within the same building are connected to the same LAN, allowing the consumer to move freely with his/her laptop inside the building. As the consumer moves to the coverage area of a new access point, the Wireless LAN network automatically switches the connection from the old access point to the new one, and the consumer notices no difference.

Behind the Scenes

The Nokia Operator Wireless LAN solution works in the following way: when the public Wireless LAN service is available, the mobile subscriber simply inserts his/her SIM card into the wireless LAN device and starts the access software. The consumer can also configure the wireless LAN card to automatically log in to the service. For convenience, the carrier can provide the consumer with a separate SIM card for WLAN services.

The Nokia Operator Wireless LAN network components carry GSM SIM authentication messages over the Internet to the mobile core network, which verifies the consumer and grants access. This approach supports normal GSM roaming. After the proper authentication, the Wireless LAN network authorizes IP connection for the mobile device and starts collecting charging information. As the consumer disconnects from the network, the charging information is relayed via the mobile infrastructure to the home carrier, who adds the charges to the consumer's normal bill.

Benefits for the Carrier

- Allows the carrier to enter a new target market and extend its service offering to corporate solutions.
- The Nokia Operator Wireless LAN solution extends the carrier's corporate product portfolio from devices and GSM/GPRS/3G access to mobile broadband laptop solutions and global Wireless LAN roaming.
- Allows carriers to become Mobile ISP type businesses by offering high-speed wireless data access for consumers and corporations.
- Subscriber management and billing based on a SIM card.
- Allows carriers to sell Wireless LAN access as a complementary value-added service for existing customers.
- Seamless carrier-to-carrier roaming utilizing existing GSM core network roaming capabilities.
- The Nokia Operator Wireless LAN solution offers the carrier an easy and cost-effective way to enter the new mobile laptop market.
- A license-free mobile access solution with minimum investment costs.
- As Wireless LAN uses unlicensed frequency bands, it offers a cost-effective alternative for high-speed IP indoor data services in most countries. The solution can be used to offer either new wireless IP services in a limited coverage area or to complement the carrier network in public indoor hot spots.
- Brings significant savings in system investments, as Nokia Operator Wireless LAN utilizes existing mobile core infrastructure functions.

Benefits for the Customer

- Fast and secure wireless indoor laptop connectivity for consumers.
- The Nokia Operator Wireless LAN solution provides mobile professionals with reliable, fast and secure public wireless IP access. This allows them to synchronize their e-mails and establish remote access to their corporate data at access speeds comparable with the fixed Ethernet while travelling. The fast connection brings significant benefits and time savings to the consumer.
- High-speed mobile access to Internet services and corporate data in public places.
- Secure wireless IP access to corporate networks.
- The Nokia Operator Wireless LAN solution supports all legacy VPN solutions, allowing the consumer to establish a highly secure end-to-end encrypted IP tunnel to his/her corporate network via public access zone.
- Can provide a single bill for both GSM and Wireless LAN usage for the customer.
- Significantly improves business performance, while allowing employees to access corporate intranet and e-mail systems from all over the world.

Conclusions

The world of mobile communications is changing. The increased penetration of mobile devices and laptops in the corporate environment, together with the ever-increasing pace of the business world and the increased demand for perfect reachability, has created a new business opportunity for the carrier to cover new market areas with Wireless LANs.

Nokia Operator Wireless LAN technology will allow the carrier to enhance its service portfolio for business users, to generate more revenue, and to enter completely new markets. Early and quick adoption of the Wireless LAN solution is extremely important for the carrier due to the unlicensed nature of the technology and the need to limit the number of radio access networks in the same building.

The Nokia Operator Wireless LAN is an innovative and unique solution. Providing significant benefits for the carrier, it offers a competitive alternative meeting new mobile laptop user requirements and complement public wireless IP service offerings.

The deployment of SIM authentication and existing carrier subscriber management and the billing infrastructure dramatically decreases required system investment costs. Even more importantly, it allows the carrier to sell public Wireless LAN access as an add-on service for its existing mobile business customers and thus increase the revenue from the business market.

Wireless LAN represents a great opportunity for carriers to increase their business growth significantly, while using existing networks. The Nokia Operator Wireless LAN solution is available today and will turn that opportunity into a reality.

Mobile Virtual Private Networks

This chapter describes how Virtual Private Network (VPN) technology in mobile devices enables corporations to extend services to mobile employees and partners without the risk of compromising their existing security standards. It also describes drivers for mobile security, specifically mobile VPNs, and explains some mobile security implementations.

Traditionally, VPN is discussed in the context of a fixed network environment. Often, this consists of placing a corporate VPN gateway at one location and another VPN gateway at a different location to establish a secure tunnel for data to travel through between sites. A VPN tunnel can also be established from a remote worker to a corporate VPN gateway via a local dial-up connection so that corporate resources can be accessed away from the office.

A mobile VPN extends the VPN concept to mobile workers who instead of laptops now carry a mobile device, with common office applications (e.g., e-mail, a text editor and a spreadsheet application). These mobile workers can establish an IP VPN connection from their mobile device over a wireless connection (e.g., the Global System for Mobile Communications (GSM), General Packet Radio Service (GPRS) and Wireless Local Area Network (WLAN)), thus allowing them access corporate applications.

Drivers for Mobile VPN

Mobile VPN technology enables consumers to create secure, transparent connections to secured services. Today, the need for mobile VPN comes mainly from the corporate world, where the number of mobile workers is constantly increasing. Businesses are taking steps to ensure that employees have access to corporate data via devices while out of office range. It is becoming less and less acceptable to be unable to access corporate resources while traveling away from the office. *Anytime and anywhere* connections continue to grow, in concept and in practice, which is changing the employee landscape.

One of the most common applications is a mobile worker accessing the corporate network to retrieve e-mail or get information from the intranet. Additionally, there are a growing number of mobile employees, especially data collectors, who need work-related applications when they are away from the physical office.

Typically, corporations adopt mobile devices for similar reasons: They want to standardize data collection among regions, efficiently serve their customers, and decrease employee workload. For example, if information is entered electronically in the field, it can be fed back to central databases. One of the results is better tracking of worldwide operations, which is an important gauge in determining how different regions are performing. In addition, sending data, be it instructions or orders, allows companies to fulfill consumer requirements more readily. Finally, mobile data collectors used to record data on paper and later entered it in the office or on a laptop from a remote location. Now, they can enter it once in the field and send it to a database, which avoids re-entry of information, thereby decreasing workload and errors.

Mobilizing the Enterprise

Mobile devices are rapidly becoming a centerpiece of business. Corporate e-mail systems have become the foremost communication system in the enterprise, surpassing voice mail in importance. In addition, the number of daily tasks employees are expected to perform is on an upward trend while the time allotted per task is decreasing.

The content being accessed and the infrastructure where it resides are still very much wired and IP based. The same security applied in the wired IP is required for secure communications via mobile and wireless communications, with some additional protocol support, traffic and service awareness, and security vulnerability preparedness.

Extending corporate networks to cover mobile networks creates an obvious security risk; a mobile network is considered a hostile network. It should be treated the same way as the Internet, for anybody can access it. When a corporation decides to opt for using the Internet over private lines and implement fixed-VPNs to protect connections, these connections from the mobile network to the protected corporate network must be protected. An IP-VPN is a perfect solution to address this enterprise level security challenge. An IP-VPN provides a scalable, flexible corporate level security infrastructure on top of which enterprises can build their mobile applications and services.

Virtual Private Networking

A virtual private network is a way to build a secure, private communication infrastructure on top of a public network. VPNs are logical networks that connect physical networks or single hosts to each other by forming encrypted tunnels over public networks. VPNs guarantee privacy and security, allowing companies to communicate information over the Internet inexpensively - regardless of the sensitivity of the data.

VPNs allow companies to communicate with their branch offices, customers, partners, employees and suppliers securely. Through VPNs, the Internet has become a means of providing more cost-effective virtual access to business-critical information from nearly anywhere. VPNs address the following issues in Internet security:

- **Message integrity**: Message integrity means that the recipient is assured that what he/she receives is exactly what the sender transmitted. The messages are protected against any undetected alterations during the transmission, using HMAC Secure Hash Algorithm 1 (SHA-1) or Message Digest 5 (MD5). Message integrity is achieved by digital signing of the messages. If there are any changes to the data, they are detected immediately.
- **Privacy**: Privacy means that, in addition to encrypting the message content to protect it from outsiders, the identities of the sender and receiver are kept secret from anyone observing the transmission. In a mobile VPN, Data Encryption Standard (DES) and Triple DES (3DES) are often chosen as the encryption algorithm.
- **Authentication**: Authentication guarantees that both parties (sender and receiver) have been identified so that they know with whom they are communicating. Common methods of authentication include digital certificates, shared secrets in the form of usernames and passwords and tokens.

- **Replay protection**: Replay protection ensures that the data that was transmitted cannot be captured and replayed at another time.

Most VPN solutions use the IPSec protocol framework, developed by the Internet Engineering Task Force (IETF) because it addresses the issues of interoperability between different vendor solutions. IPSec defines extensions to the IP protocol in the form of two additional headers for IP packets. An Authentication Header (AH) verifies the authenticity of the packet's contents, thus providing authentication, integrity and protection against replaying for the entire packet. Encapsulating Security Payload (ESP) provides confidentiality by encrypting a packet before transmitting it. In typical VPN implementations, ESP is used to secure corporate intranets.

IPSec is policy-based, which allows an administrator to define different security policies. These policies can use different algorithms for establishing different tunnels. For instance, an administrator can enforce different levels of protection depending on whether the tunnel extends across the public network or is contained within a private network.

Site-to-Site VPN

Site-to-site VPNs often replace private lines connecting corporate office networks. These VPNs provide the same or a better level of security but are usually faster to set up as well as being more flexible to use and costing less.

The following illustrates how a corporation can connect a remote office to the company's headquarters. The Internet is used as the transport medium and an IP-VPN solution (2 VPN gateways) is applied to provide the necessary security solution over the public network.

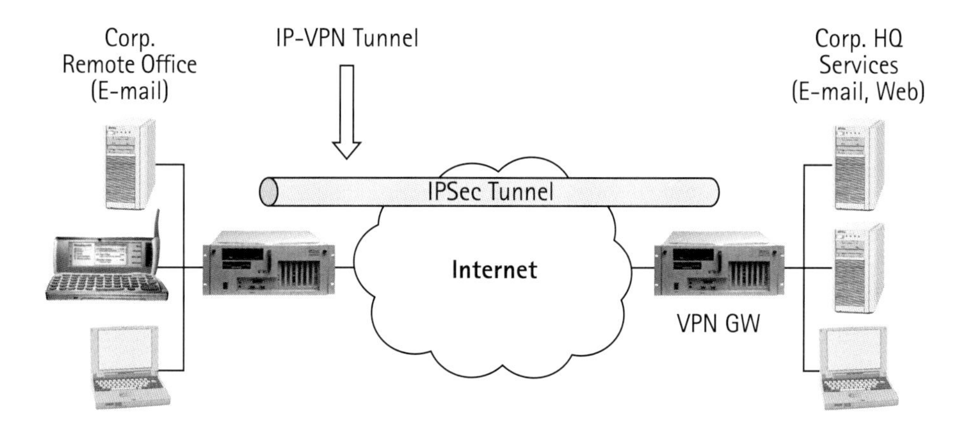

A VPN for connecting two offices in different locations, e.g., Boston and Helsinki

Remote Access VPN

A remote access VPN extends the VPN functionality to cover remote workers (usually equipped with a laptop computer and an Internet connection). Separate VPN client software is installed on the laptop computer. The Internet connection (e.g., dial-up or xDSL) is needed to provide the necessary transport medium. The VPN client software initiates an IP-VPN connection to a corporate VPN gateway. After successful user authentication, the remote user is granted access to the corporate network over a secure (i.e., encrypted) tunnel. The following figure illustrates a remote access scenario.

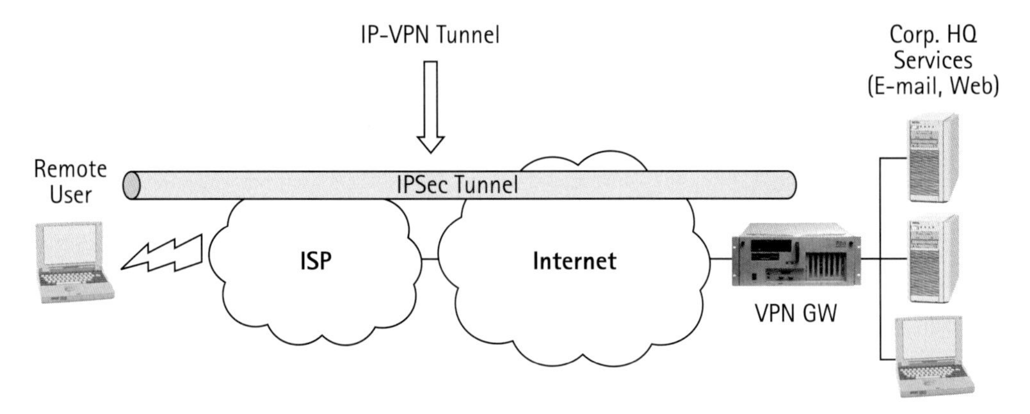

A remote access VPN for connecting a remote worker to corporate resources

Mobile VPN

While the mobile VPN is conceptually similar to a remote access VPN, the mobility of the remote device, the diversity of the underlying network infrastructure, and the availability of device resources introduce many challenges to the VPN solution. In this case, the remote user accesses the corporate network from either on or off company premises by using a mobile connection. Separate VPN client software is installed on the mobile device. The remote user initiates an IP-VPN connection to the corporate VPN gateway. After successful authentication, the remote user is granted access to the corporate network and provided security in the same way as when using a remote access VPN.

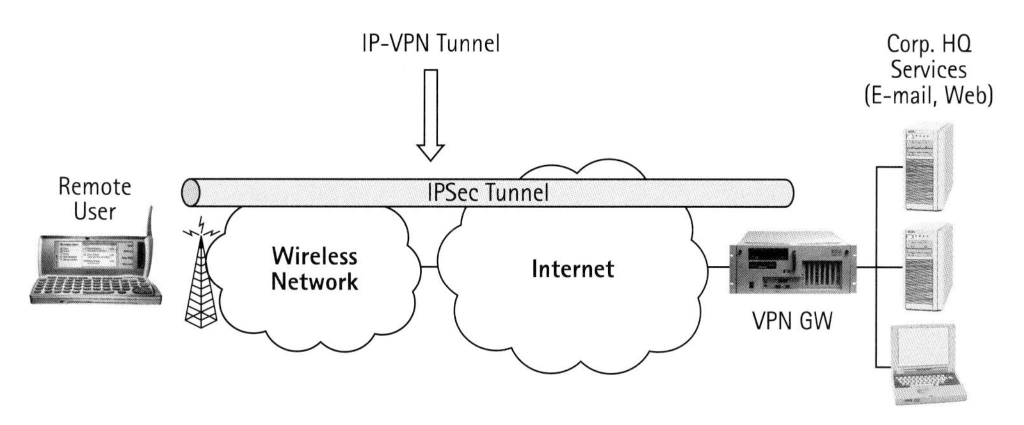

Establishing a secure VPN tunnel between a mobile device and a corporate network

In both the mobile and remote access VPN, remote workers are allowed virtual connections to the corporate network. Remote workers access the same corporate network as they would if they were on-site connecting to the corporate Local Area Network (LAN). To attain this kind of transparency, the network parameters (e.g., internal network address, DNS and WINS information) are negotiated with the remote clients.

SSL vs. IP-VPN

If properly implemented, the Secure Sockets Layer (SSL) and IP-VPN both offer robust security solutions. The main difference between these two protocols is that SSL operates at the application level whereas IP-VPN operates at the network level.

Unlike VPN, SSL requires modifying individual applications on both the client and server end. For instance, in order for a mobile device to use e-mail, the Web browser interface provided by the server would need to be changed. Typically, this requires changes to existing applications or building of a special SSL UI (e.g., a Web browser UI). In most SSL solutions, only the server is authenticated using certificates, and clients are authenticated by applications via legacy authentication. This opens up a possible security risk as the clients can create a tunnel into the secured network before being authenticated.

An IP-VPN offers a transparent solution where the applications do not know about the underlying security solution. In fact, the applications do not even know whether there is a security solution to protect the traffic. Usually, VPNs are more complex to set up, but they authenticate clients at the network edge so attackers cannot access the network. All remote workers are authenticated to gateways using digital certificates, legacy authentication mechanisms (e.g., a SecurID™ card, or pre-shared secrets). Additionally, gateways must authenticate to remote workers. Here, clients cannot get access to the secure network until they are authenticated.

Implementing Mobile VPN

Implementing VPNs in the Mobile domain requires that the challenges and characteristics of mobility be taken into consideration. Some of these considerations are described in the following sections.

Number of Mobile Clients

In the Mobile domain, the sheer number of clients can create problems for the existing infrastructure. The number of clients sets requirements for the number of concurrent connections that the gateway must be able to handle as well as the number of consumers the gateway must be able to authenticate simultaneously. The number of concurrent connections and simultaneous authentication requests must be estimated. Then, gateway equipment that can handle the required load should be installed in the network infrastructure.

Deployment

Mobile VPN client configurations (or policies), certificates and private/public key pairs need to be configured centrally by network or security managers. Mobility presents a special challenge during the deployment of this information to the clients, especially during the initial deployment of the client software and policies.

Additionally, mobile devices are always connected through an unsecured or hostile network, so the deployment needs to be secured. The initial trust relationship between the intranet and the mobile device has to be established prior to downloading VPN-related trust (e.g., certificates) to the device.

Processing Power

Typical devices are powered by a CPU, which provides only a fraction of the computing power of a typical desktop PC. This means that computation-intensive tasks like key material generation and encryption take more time on such a device than on a desktop computer. With slow connection speeds, the encryption is not so much of an issue. However, generating long keys (>128 bit) from equally strong key material can take several seconds.

Network

Mobile networks create some technical issues which need to be addressed when planning mobile VPNs. Mobile networks today, although fast, do have some delay and speed issues, which can lead to timeout problems if applications are not prepared to accept too long delays. Also, because of the vast number of devices that could be connected to the network, private addresses are issued to mobile devices and Network Address Translation (NAT) is used before forwarding IP packets to the public networks.

The sporadic occurrence and nomadic nature of mobile device connections makes the security management of the devices challenging. When the consumer is establishing the secure connection to the corporate intranet, the management back-end needs to make the required checks on the validity of the security profiles. This should be done prior to each connection and without the consumer noticing a substantial delay in the connection establishment phase.

Device Security

Device security is a critical component in a mobile VPN solution. VPNs allow sensitive data to be exchanged between the device and corporate network, which usually means that some of that data is stored in the device itself. Therefore, technologies like file encryption and device lock-up should be in place when sensitive information is stored in a mobile device.

Limited Battery Power

Mobile devices are usually powered by a chargeable battery, which lasts from hours to days with normal usage. Because VPNs usually require heavy computation to do the necessary encryption, they keep the device loaded and hence require more power.

Nokia Mobile VPN Solution

Nokia developed its own mobile VPN solutions to meet the above-listed challenges and requirements of offering transparent IPSec VPN protection for traffic to and from mobile devices. The Nokia Mobile VPN is based on the IPSec protocol and supports the relevant IETF standards.

Operating Systems and Mobile Devices

The Nokia Mobile VPN is designed for smart phones running the Symbian Operating System. The Symbian OS addresses the issues of limited memory and low power consumption at the operating system level. In addition, Symbian OS provides necessary components for building an enterprise level application platform with support for secure computing. The Nokia Mobile VPN Client is tightly integrated with the operating system itself using as many of the available OS components as possible.

Encryption and Authentication Support

Nokia Mobile VPN supports multiple encryption and public key algorithms as well as several key management protocols including the support for industry standard Internet Key Exchange (IKE) protocols. Nokia Mobile VPN solutions can automatically negotiate the strongest possible encryption and data authentication algorithms available between the communicating parties. This includes both DES and 3DES for data encryption and SHA-1 and MD5 for data authentication. In addition, encryption keys are updated frequently, ensuring maximum security.

In large-scale VPN deployments, automated key management is necessary to reduce the number of encryption keys to a manageable level. Rather than issuing a unique encryption key for each pair of VPN connections, the Public Key Infrastructure (PKI) generates a public/private key pair for each individual consumer. One key is publicly known and the other private and accessible only for its owner. Technically, the key pair is mathematically generated so that whatever is encrypted using the public key can be decrypted by using the respective private key. PKI is then used to verify the identity of the communicating parties and create the necessary encryption keys for each session. The beauty of PKI is in the scalability and manageability it offers. There is no need to distribute the secret encryption keys between the communicating parties.

PKI relies on digital certificates to certify the generated private/public keys. Each certificate carries information about a particular VPN consumer, including the consumer's public key, which is used to verify the user identity and to calculate the keys for actual encryption. Nokia Mobile VPN solutions support open, scalable PKI utilizing X.509 digital certificates and Certification Authority (CA) technology. Several CA vendors can be utilized as the trusted CA (e.g., Verisign, Baltimore, Entrust, and Internal CA).

In addition to PKI authentication, Nokia Mobile VPN supports legacy authentication methods (e.g., shared secrets, one-time passwords and tokens). This ensures that corporations are able to utilize the existing infrastructure (e.g., existing SecurID cards and RADIUS servers) to handle authentication. At the same time, Nokia Mobile VPN offers a smooth transition from legacy authentication to PKI authentication.

Internal Addressing and NAT

Internal addressing is a technique where the mobile device is granted a corporate LAN internal address and access to DNS services. Without internal addressing, remote devices could not utilize the corporate internal DNS naming convention, and corporate firewalls might deny access to some corporate servers. With internal addressing, VPN consumers are virtually part of the corporate network. They are provided with the same level of service as they would be if directly connected to the corporate network. Nokia Mobile VPN has also implemented support for NAT so that the existence of public network NAT services can be automatically detected and IP packets can be encapsulated in UDP packets to bypass the NAT service.

Scalability

Extending a corporate network to mobile devices requires an infrastructure that can handle the massive number of new mobile devices that need to be managed and supported. By specifically addressing the issues in scalability, Nokia Mobile VPN provides complete solutions that will scale to meet the VPN needs of corporations, Nokia Mobile VPN gateways can be clustered with load balancing to provide the bandwidth and number of tunnels necessary to support consumers. To manage large numbers of consumers centrally, Nokia Mobile VPN provides a single management tool.

Reliability

The Nokia Mobile VPN provides an infrastructure upon which corporations can base their core services. Therefore, reliability is a key factor when deploying mobile VPN solutions. Nokia uses technologies like IP clustering to ensure that client connections will remain active even if one node in a gateway cluster fails.

User Experience

The ultimate success of deploying mobile solutions depends on how widely the consumers will adopt and accept the mobile VPN solution. By hiding the complex technology involved in the mobile VPN and providing consumers and security managers with intuitive and understandable user interfaces which support the consumer's normal task flow, Nokia Mobile VPN paves the way for corporations to extend services to mobile devices and therefore ensure the success of mobile applications. At the same time, the Nokia Mobile VPN provides consumers with a seamless security experience with secure and reliable access to corporate resources.

Mobile devices present a special challenge in usability because the user interface is limited by the size of the devices. By providing minimal need for consumer intervention and tight integration to the operating system, Nokia Mobile VPN provides an intuitive and easy-to-use user interface.

PART 3.4

End-to-End Solutions

- Mobile Software
- IP Convergence
- Nokia in Messaging
- Multimedia Messaging Service
- Instant Messaging
- Presence
- Multimedia Streaming
- Content Downloading
- Data Synchronization
- Device Management
- Machine-to-Machine

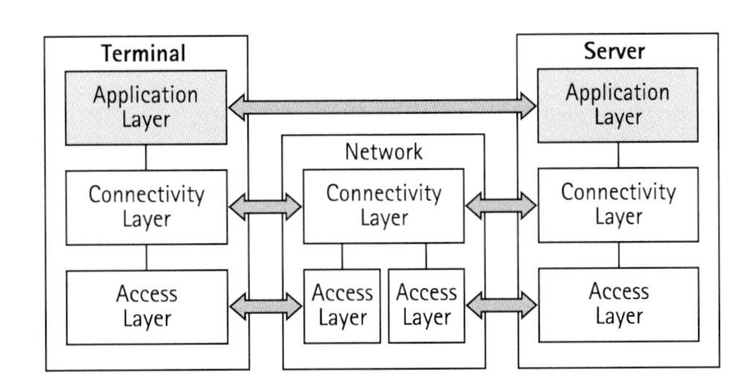

Mobile Software

The Nokia Mobile Software solution consists of three major players:

- o Terminal Software
- o Server Software
- o Forum Nokia Developer Community

Each of these players have a central role of their own in the end-to-end software offering for the other mobile industry players, as illustrated in the following figure.

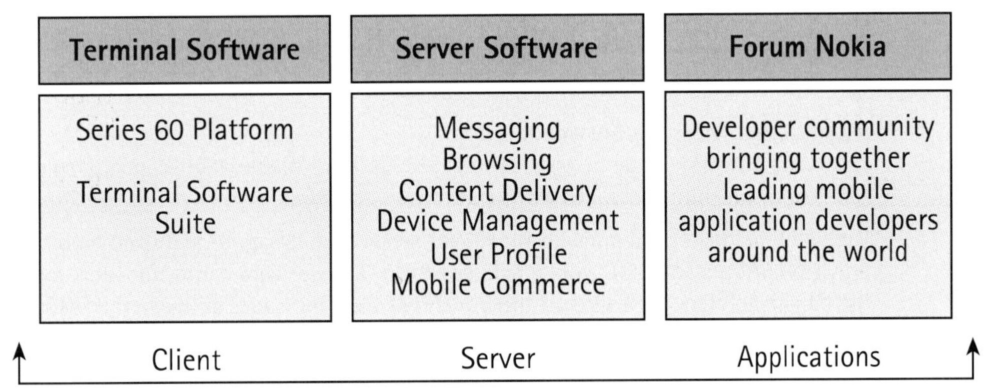

Nokia Mobile Software end-to-end offering

Terminal Software

The Nokia Mobile Software Solution has two products available for licensing to device manufacturers. These products are licensed as source code, giving the device vendor freedom to differentiate and adapt the software for its own device designs.

The Series 60 Platform is a complete Symbian OS based software product for smartphone devices. The large-sized color screen, easy to use interface for single-handed navigation, and suite of applications makes this software ideally suited to support new mobile services (e.g., rich content downloading and MMS). Devices having this software are interoperable with MMS, the Wireless Application Protocol (WAP), Java 2 Mobile Information Device Profile (MIDP), General Packet Radio Service (GPRS), Synchronization Markup Language (SyncML), Bluetooth, and many other open standards.

The Terminal Software Suite is a selection of key mobile application middleware components (e.g., WAP Browser and MMS), optimized for size- and cost-driven mobile devices. No user interface or operating system is included in this license. The Terminal Software Suite allows manufacturers to easily implement one or more technologies on devices with an OS other than the Symbian OS, and on any User Interface (UI).

Server Software

Server Software supports key service enablers for end-to-end mobile services. Solutions based on these enablers are grouped into messaging, browsing, content delivery, device management, user profile and mobile commerce services.

Messaging

Nokia messaging solutions includes servers for the Short Message Service (SMS), and Multimedia Messaging Service (MMS). Together these servers form a complete end-to-end solution for mobile messaging.

Nokia Short Message Service Center

The Nokia Short Message Service Center (SMSC) is a scalable, high-capacity solution for person-to-person short messages and value-added services.

The point-to-point SMS provides means for sending messages to and from mobile devices. The provision utilizes an SMSC, which acts as a store-and-forward center for short messages. Thus, the mobile network must support the transfer of short messages between the SMSCs and mobile devices.

The Nokia SMS Center gives a network the ability to deliver short messages of up to 160 characters to and from mobile devices. The Nokia SMS Center provides capacity, scalability, load sharing and efficient routing and also meets the demand for value-added services. Using a commercial UNIX-based platform, the Nokia SMS Center provides open interfaces to existing data systems, letting the carrier provide a wide range of new, innovative services to consumers.

Nokia Multimedia Messaging Service Solution

The Nokia Multimedia Messaging Service solution is a service platform targeted at GPRS/3G carriers that are looking into offering new, interactive and creative multimedia messaging services. With MMS, it is possible to combine text with richer content types (e.g., photographs, images, audio and voice clips, and eventually also video clips), and send these combinations in the same simple manner as SMS today. Carriers will be able to attract consumers with new value-added services, and to differentiate and enhance their competitiveness by offering Multimedia Messaging. The Multimedia Messaging Service is the ideal way to introduce multimedia services today because MMS messages can be sent over the existing Global System for Mobile Communications (GSM) networks.

Nokia provides a complete MMS solution based on its device and infrastructure expertise. The key element in the MMS network architecture is the MMS Center. The MMS solution also provides permanent message storage with multiple access methods and offers services specially designed for legacy phone users, to enable multimedia messaging between multimedia and non-multimedia devices from day one.

The MMS Center is able to handle several message types from pure text to video clips or any given combination of media types. Support for different media types and formats is being specified in the MMS conformance document, agreed upon by the leading MMS vendors, the aim being to enable interoperability, especially between devices from different vendors.

The very nature of the MMS Center is similar to the SMS Center - it is a store-and-forward platform. Upon receiving a multimedia message, the system will send the device an MMS notification of each arriving message. The result from the consumer's point of view is dependent on the device implementation - the subscriber might be prompted to receive the message, or the whole process can happen automatically, as in SMS. After successful message delivery, the message will be deleted from the database. If the message cannot be delivered successfully, it is stored for later delivery.

The usage of access independent Wireless Application Protocol (WAP) will enable smooth transition from GPRS, where the service will be first introduced, to third generation networks.

The MMS Center has an External Application Interface (EAIF) for application development, allowing service providers to introduce services. MMS is an excellent content bearer for versatile applications.

The Nokia Multimedia Messaging solution offers an enhanced rich set of multimedia services. These incorporate a personal and public multimedia message album, legacy phone support, personalized user profiles, call completion service, multimedia message creation and e-mail filtering, and smart push to device and e-mail delivery, as well as easy content service access, large file download support, receiving MMS settings on the device via Over The Air (OTA) configuration, and end-to-end post-paid and pre-paid charging support.

Browsing

Nokia Browsing solution consists of two servers: Nokia WAP gateway and Nokia Proxy Server. Browsing is one of the key service enablers for end-to-end mobile services.

Nokia WAP Gateway

The Nokia WAP Gateway is a core element of Nokia's browsing solution, but it also plays a supporting role in Nokia's content delivery and MMS solutions. The Nokia WAP gateway supports the WAP stack, WML content fetching from the Internet using the HyperText Transfer Protocol (HTTP), WAP content encoding/decoding, cookie support and Push Proxy over SMS functionality. The supported bearers are Circuit Switched Data (CSD), High Speed Circuit Switched Data (HSCSD) and GPRS - as well as SMS and Unstructured Supplementary Services Data (USSD).

With the WAP Gateway's support for large file transfer, also known as Segmentation and Reassembly, consumers can access rich content (e.g., multimedia messaging, Java games and applications). Large file transfer fragments large messages into a number of smaller data units and selectively re-sends only the failed data units instead of the whole message. This means reduced network load for the carrier and faster services for the consumer.

To ensure data confidentiality, it supports security protocols (e.g., Wireless Transport Layer Security (WTLS) and Secure Sockets Layer (SSL)). Other features include the billing interface, network management system interface, load balancing and high availability support, and subscriber identification.

Nokia Proxy Server

The Nokia Proxy Server is a high performance HTTP proxy enhanced for mobile browsing traffic. Network performance is improved while simultaneously adding value to mobile browsing connectivity. The Nokia Proxy Server handles the connectivity, proxy authentication and caching of WAP requests. Plug-ins can also be integrated, to provide value adding services that enhance service content with profiling and location information. In addition to adding value to the connectivity of WAP requests, the Proxy Server also provides standard Transport Control Protocol/ Internet Protocol (TCP/IP) connectivity for Personal Digital Assistants (PDA), laptops and other devices that run over standard TCP/IP.

The Nokia Proxy Server can connect to subscriber profiling databases (e.g., the Nokia Profile Server), to retrieve profile information that can then be added to WAP service requests. The use of profiling enables both access control and personalization of services. Profile information can be subscriber related, containing security attributes (e.g., authentication and authorization) and subscriber-specific information (e.g., preferences). Or it can be service related and describe request destinations including barring, redirection, delivery rules, and other service related information.

The Nokia Proxy Server provides a service plug-in for fetching subscriber location information from mobile network. Location information is fetched on a request basis of the profile of the service in question. With their subscriber profile, consumers can control which services are allowed to receive their location information.

The Nokia Proxy Server acts as a cache; that is, it locally stores and serves frequently requested content at the edge of the network. This reduces the amount of upstream bandwidth required to serve consumer requests, which in turn lowers consumption of valuable bandwidth. By acting as a buffer between consumers and the inconsistencies of the larger Internet, the Nokia Proxy Server reduces traffic, latency and variability in network response time. This all enables faster access to services and improves the overall user experience of browsing.

In cases where the consumer cannot be identified (e.g., when browsing while roaming in another network), the Nokia Proxy Server can manage proxy authentication. This means that the Nokia Proxy Server can query the consumer for a username and password, which are then checked in the database and matched with the correct Mobile Station International ISDN Number (MSISDN) number before the request is routed. Thus, the consumer can be reliably authenticated.

In the future, the Nokia Proxy Server will also play a key role in mobile browsing as it further evolves to WAP 2.0 environments and the convergence of the Web and Mobile domains. It will also be possible to easily integrate new services including live and on-demand streaming media, filtering, content transformation and billing plug-ins.

Content Delivery

The Content Delivery solution consists of two servers: a dedicated Nokia Delivery Server and Nokia Messaging Gateway. The Nokia Delivery Server is optimized for content download to mobile devices whereas the Nokia Messaging Gateway complements the Nokia MMS solution with more sophisticated content delivery options.

Nokia Delivery Server

The Nokia Delivery Server is designed to perform and control the whole content delivery process starting from the request received from the service portal and finishing with the creation of billing data after a receipt of confirmation of a successful download from the mobile device. During the process, the Delivery Server also implements authentication and device recognition tasks which create an easy-to-download mechanism helping the consumers to personalize their mobile services. The Delivery Server can be used to extend the functionality of a mobile portal or service with a reliable and well-controlled content download service. Typically this could mean a Java™ MIDlet game download as part of a carrier's mobile portal. However, in addition to Java based games, other content types will be appearing in carriers commercial download services. The Nokia Delivery Server follows the Over-The-Air User Initiated Provisioning Recommended Practice for the MIDP 1.0. According to this practice, the delivery of Java applications is separated into two parts: first, the consumer receives the descriptor file that ensures sufficient memory availability in the device; second, the consumer receives the resource file. When both files are delivered to the device, they are compared against each other and a delivery report is transmitted to the Delivery Server, which then reads the delivery report and creates billing data.

The Nokia Delivery server supports delivery of all content types and will provide Content Object Descriptor (COD) support extending today's control of Java applications to all content types. The advantage of adaptation of J2ME™/MIDP based technology for content download, and also for generic content, is that it is an open standard, is easy to implement, and has already been widely implemented. Thus, the defined mechanism both is efficient and ensures a level playing field for a competitive market.

Nokia Delivery Server:

- Offers control for content download and charging
- Offers flexible download pricing and charging model options
- Selects content based on the device type
- Supports various content types
- Allows the evolution of business models
- Is based on open standards

Mobile content downloading starts with content discovery. Multiple methods to discover mobile content are supported (e.g., mobile browsing and SMS-initiated). After discovery, the actual download transaction takes place (e.g., access control, content delivery and billing). The consumer requests a file that points to a specific Uniform Resource Locator (URL). This URL always points to a resource, which is available only through the Delivery Server, regardless of its actual location. One benefit with the Delivery Server is that it includes the capability to direct requests through the Delivery Server and hide the final resource URL. This way, consumers cannot bypass the delivery mechanism, and illegal downloads are prevented. Finally, carriers and service providers can utilize a confirmation message to ensure that the consumer is only charged for successful downloads.

Nokia Messaging Gateway

The Nokia Messaging Gateway enables the consumers to easily access useful information and services with short messages. The Messaging Gateway allows a carrier to create value-added messaging applications for consumers quickly and easily while at the same time expanding their offering from delivering just SMS content to covering attractive MMS content.

In addition to SMS and Smart Messaging content, the Messaging Gateway also supports the retrieval of Enhanced Messaging Service (EMS) and MMS content. With a multimedia device, the consumer can access rich MMS content as well.

The Nokia Messaging Gateway is a comprehensive and robust messaging platform. It links the Internet or company intranets and the mobile network. As a result, information (e.g., headline news, exchange rates, sports results, or stock quotes) can be accessed in seconds. The Messaging Gateway also makes it possible to download ringing tones, graphical logos and icons. The services can be accessed by any mobile device with short messaging or Smart Messaging capability.

With the billing interface, it is possible to implement content-based charging with different tariff classes for different services. Various charging schemes are supported, including hot billing as well as scheduled charging data generation. For the pre-paid customer, in-advance credit checks are also possible.

Device and Subscriber Management

The latest mobile services take advantage of user profiles enabling personalization of the service (e.g., browsing content optimized for consumer preferences and location). Nokia solutions for user profile and device management issues are the Nokia Terminal Management Server and the Nokia Profile Server.

Nokia Terminal Management Server

The Nokia Terminal Management Server allows remote management of the settings in mobile devices and other types of devices connected to the mobile network.

New, powerful mobile devices are able to support advanced mobile services. However, these services can only be accessed when mobile devices are configured with the correct parameters. Many consumers are not willing to spend the time configuring their devices or are not familiar with such parameters at all. With the Nokia Terminal Management Server, consumers can conveniently get the key service settings and start using the services.

The Nokia Terminal Management Server helps carriers and service providers increase the usage rates of advanced mobile services. In addition, it can speed up the rollout of new services and significantly reduce the costs of providing technical support for consumers trying to configure their devices.

Provisioning of the parameters can be initiated in several ways. For example, a consumer may trigger the provisioning by sending an SMS. A self-administration interface of the Nokia Terminal Management Server can be provided via the carrier's portal. Graphical user interfaces are also provided for the carrier's customer service personnel. An application interface is available for integrating the Nokia Terminal Management Server with external provisioning applications.

The Nokia Terminal Management Server provides device management services, which can use standard over-the-air provisioning and management protocols.

Nokia Profile Server

The Nokia Profile Server is a subscriber, device and service personalization server that allows the carrier to easily and cost-effectively manage profiles for WAP, Multimedia Messaging and other mobile services. With access control, the carrier can also define which consumers can access which services.

The Nokia Profile Server enables carriers and service providers to control the flow of information to application developers and content providers. Consumers can guard their privacy by deciding which services can use their information.

For consumers, the Nokia Profile Server provides a self-administration interface for personalizing the WAP services they frequently use. For example, a consumer can set the city in which she lives and for which she wants weather reports. For consumers of the MMS, the Nokia Profile Server gives greater flexibility in deciding how they want to send and receive MMS messages. The Nokia profile Server supports the diversion of MMS messages to an e-mail address or another phone number. This is useful if a consumer prefers not to receive large messages on his/her device, carries a non-multimedia device, or is in a situation where MMS messages cannot be delivered.

Subscriber profiles can also indicate whether or not the consumer is a pre-paid customer. The Nokia Profile Server can also check its service profiles to see which services require an in-advance credit check.

With its interfaces to the customer care and billing system, the Nokia Profile Server enables carriers to easily download existing subscriber data to the profile server database, add new subscribers, and handle mass downloads of subscriber data.

As a network independent product, the Nokia Profile Server supports all major mobile networks.

Mobile Payment

Nokia will provide independent features and solutions based on open standards and technologies for different kinds of mobile commerce needs; mobile commerce supporting features in devices and payment service providers and other involved parties in the business area tools for payment mediation. Examples of the solution offering include the wallet application and Wireless Identity Module (WIM) security element - as device features for easy-to-use and secure online transactions - and the Nokia Payment Solution - as a server based solution for payment service provision.

Wallet Application

The wallet inside a mobile device is one of the most important building blocks for a Personal Trusted Device - offering consumers a visualization of the digital wallet and a trusted user interface. The first release of the wallet application enables consumers to make convenient mobile transactions via WAP browser. The application is capable of storing protected personal information (e.g., notes and cards) inside the device, also making it possible to provide and use virtual cards flexibly. It simplifies the storage and retrieval of personal information in mobile transactions.

The wallet application menu contains three different modules: Cards, Personal notes and Settings. The Cards module is used for storing personal card information, (e.g., payment card, loyalty card) and dispatch note information, for different usage purposes. From the wallet, the consumer can fetch the required information via WAP browser and easily fill in the required fields. The Personal notes module is a notebook where the consumer can store sensitive private information (e.g., passwords, usernames, and account numbers). From the Settings area, the consumer can manage the wallet code settings. The data stored inside the device are securely encrypted and protected with a special wallet code that is used to authenticate the consumer to the application. The wallet application used together with WIM security functions provides an ultimate solution for secure and convenient transactions.

The wallet application is based on existing open standard technologies (e.g., WAP and the Electronic Commerce Modeling Language (ECML)). ECML is an open Internet standard for digital wallets and online merchants that is already commonly used in the Web domain. Its main function is to facilitate the automatic exchange of transaction information from the client wallet to the server application. ECML does not simply transfer credit card information; it can also be used whenever the applications need a common method for transferring (e.g., address information).

WIM Implementation in Nokia Devices

Another important building block in mobile commerce is the WIM security element in the device. Currently, Internet shopping suffers from lack of security when consumers make transactions. The WIM security element enables higher security in mobile transactions and in some cases also provides a solution for higher security in Internet shopping. Through an increase in the level of security, many mobile commerce services will come alive (e.g., banking services), but without long one-time password lists.

The WIM stores and processes information and security keys needed for user identification and authentication. Additionally, it has the ability to perform cryptographic operations. Its main function is to enable digital signatures that are required for authenticated and non-repudiated mobile transactions. Another definite benefit is that transaction fees are lower for digitally signed transactions.

Technically, WIM can be implemented in several ways. The main differences are in business and usage considerations. In current Nokia devices, WIM functionality is stored on the carrier issued Subscriber Identity Module (SIM) card. However, mobile network subscription functionality is separated from the other applications that require authentication and signature capabilities. WIM functionality can also be stored on a second smart card in the device. The Dual Chip approach means that a second smart card is placed semi-permanently in the device. It is removable and issued independently of the SIM card (e.g., by a mobile commerce service provider or financial institution). Its strength is that it separates the network subscription from the other applications, thus creating more latitude in terms of business models. Nokia is committed to providing dual chip devices in the near future.

Nokia Payment Solution

With the Nokia Payment solution, carriers, financial institutions and service providers can position themselves as payment mediators, offering consumers a convenient way to pay with their mobile device, using a wide range of payment methods in a secured environment.

The main function of the Nokia Payment solution is to collect, manage and clear payments from consumers through different payment channels (e.g., network carrier billing and advance payment systems, the virtual purse (i.e., prepaid account within the Nokia Payment solution), credit card institutions and banks). The payment mediator that operates the Nokia Payment solution offers payment services to merchants, content/service providers and retailers, who can integrate the solution into their existing business application. The Nokia Payment solution allows consumers of personal trusted devices to make payments for services, goods, digital content and information.

The Nokia Payment solution consists of three major components: the Payment Server, the Payment Channel Manager and the Virtual Purse application.

The Payment Server manages the transaction flow between consumers, merchants and the clearing channels. The Payment Server records all the events of a payment transaction, validates the identity of the consumers and merchants, and processes the transactions for financial institutions and billing systems.

The Nokia Payment Channel Manager manages the SMS based communication between the customers and the Payment Server. The merchants can initiate the push of SMS payment contracts to the Payment Channel Manager. The Payment Channel Manager sends an SMS payment contract to the consumer. The Payment Channel Manager initiates the payment processing over the Payment Server and returns payment confirmation to the content provider.

In addition, the Nokia Payment Channel Manager analyses HTTP headers in the message flow between the merchant or content providers and the consumers' devices. Whenever HTTP requests for priced content are intercepted, the Nokia Payment Channel Manager initiates the payment transaction and redirects the consumer to the Nokia Payment Server. At the end of the payment transaction, the Nokia Payment Channel Manager releases the requested HyperText Markup Language (HTML) / Wireless Markup Language (WML) page and redirects the consumer back to the merchant application. The Nokia Payment Channel Manager controls the delivery of the requested content and requests the removal of the payment transactions if the delivery of the digital content was not successful.

The Nokia Virtual Purse is one of the clearing channels of the Nokia Payment Server and holds a virtual account for each registered consumer. Consumers can fill their Virtual Purse by using any other available payment methods.

Developer Community

Forum Nokia is offering application developers the opportunity to create, test and market their applications to service providers and carriers. Forum Nokia provides the tools and resources needed for content and application development as well as the channels for sales to carriers, enterprises and consumers.

Developers can stay abreast of news and developments through a subscription to Forum Nokia regional newsletters for Europe and Africa, the Americas or Asia. Subscribing is easy, and subscriber privacy is strictly protected.

Content developers can also download tools and simulators needed for creating and testing mobile applications. Forum Nokia has links to tools from Nokia and other industry leaders including Adobe, AppForge, Borland, Macromedia, Metrowerks and Sun.

Forum Nokia provides also technical support. The support area contains a library of white papers, code samples and FAQs arranged by technology type. The Nokia Knowledge Network enables developers to pose questions to the global developer community.

With the help of Forum Nokia, the application developers test their applications. The Nokia OK program provides the opportunity for a developer's application to enjoy premium placement in Nokia sales channels.

Global and regional channels place the developer's application in front of carriers, service providers, enterprises and consumers.

IP Convergence

In the future Mobile World, we will see the merging of the two most successful phenomena of the last decade - mobility and the Internet. The Internet has given us the ability to access all kinds of services, information and entertainment through one common interface. These services in turn are created and offered by almost endless numbers of service developers, and, most importantly, by the consumers themselves. User-generated content will also drive development in the Mobile World. This is made possible by the open standardized protocols, standard extendable service creation languages, and the modularity of the network. The result is a personalized communication technology that enables people to shape their own Mobile World.

Mobile devices have made us familiar with the concept of being reachable at any time and with the ability to reach other people or services quickly. Combining the freedom of the Internet with service creation, and vast amount of content and services of the Internet with the reachability and immediacy of mobile networks, creates the Mobile Internet - something much more than the Internet of today. The Mobile Internet means personal trusted services, which are available at any place or time, yet are time- and location-aware.

As network systems converge towards All-IP, we will see an even greater multitude of services, as communication services, in addition to other services (e.g., messaging and browsing), will also be realized with IP. Person-to-person communications will still be perceived as the most important service by consumers, but the modes of communication will change.

Service creation for the Mobile Internet and communications services is based on an open content format (e.g., Extensible Markup Language (XML)) and Internet Engineering Task Force (IETF) defined protocols (e.g., the Session Initiation Protocol (SIP)).

SIP was originally targeted for setting up peer-to-peer multimedia sessions, but it has been extended for instant messaging and presence services. The same methods and tools used to create Web services and content will also be used for creating rich call and messaging services.

The creation and integration of these SIP based communication services will be much faster and easier than that of those based on intelligent network protocols. Carriers will be able to create their own service packages and utilize the best of the third-party services.

Applications in All-IP can no longer be viewed as standalone. A rich experience for the consumer is created using several components interacting with each other.

Service mobility means accessibility of a consumer's personalized services through any access network or device. Another aspect of service mobility is reachability: services follow the consumer wherever he/she goes. Reachability is achieved with SIP and mobile IPv6 protocols.

The business model for the future mobile market will be a convergence of the Internet model, the content publishing business, and the mobile information service model. Carriers are in a key position to exploit the new business opportunities brought about by the Mobile Internet. A mobile portal will complement service provision as a consumer interface and also as a marketplace for digital content. As the new roles and competition in the Mobile Internet emerge, there will be a fundamental shift in the ownership of the consumer's business.

In this new business model, a carrier's key assets are: the provisioning and billing infrastructure; control of the end-to-end Quality of Service (QoS) for carrier-hosted services; a large customer base with the subscription and profile data of the consumers; a recognized and established mobile brand; mobile service enablers (e.g., location and presence information); established dealer channels, and, naturally, the mobile network infrastructure itself. Also, carriers have existing working relationships with mobile device vendors, giving them deep insight into the opportunities provided by devices.

In the mobile future as Nokia sees it, consumer behavior is driving the development of applications and services. Nokia will limit the complexity of the technical environment supporting these applications and services from the consumer. Consumers simply do not want to be concerned with the underlying technology. In addition, Nokia supports open technologies, standards and relevant initiatives that support and facilitate the deployment of global technologies and applications and stimulate market growth.

Mobile networks contain a lot of useful information that can be used to make applications more intelligent: location information, presence information and micro-payment capabilities, to name a few. As IP convergence nears, all this will be even more important, as communications services will also be IP based. This, in turn, enables the same success factors that have caused the Internet explosion to blossom further in the creation of communications services. Taking full advantage of these capabilities and making the applications interact and share information with each other with the help of an intelligent middleware platform will enable many new and exciting Mobile Internet applications.

IP Convergence

In All-IP networks, the service creation platforms are IP-based. All services are created with Internet-based protocols and languages. The benefit is that when all services are created with open and standard low-level protocols, creation and integration of services is much faster and easier than with those based on telecoms protocols.

Mobile All-IP Network Architecture

Carriers profit from the endless number of competing innovative Internet service creation companies and developers. The carriers can create their own service packages yet also provide the best services available from small software houses or world-class portals.

Yet, the carriers are in the best position to offer added value to their subscribers. First, they have the subscriptions and profile data of consumers. Second, they own the provisioning and billing machinery. Third, they control the end-to-end QoS for services. And, fourth, they have access to mobile network specific enablers (e.g., location and presence information) with the consumer's permission.

Service creation will occur in three identified domains:

- o Carriers are able to offer services that fully exploit the capabilities of their IP network and the service capability servers integrated with the solution.
- o Third-party service providers or corporations can use SIP capabilities by interfacing with the carrier network server using an external application server. It is also possible for a third-party service provider to operate the SIP application server.
- o Consumers are able to create services by using capabilities offered by a carrier or third-party service providers. For example, a Web interface could be offered to consumers for building services using a simple call processing language.

Since the underlying elements of SIP are similar to those of the HyperText Transfer Protocol (HTTP), creating network-based services (e.g., time-dependent call forwarding) is quick and straightforward. Software developers can design and implement new dynamic SIP-based voice services as quickly and easily as they develop Web pages.

By not requiring major hardware upgrades for application servers but rather enabling new software-based services using SIP, service providers can reduce the time associated with deploying new features from months to days. This means ever improving communications services for subscribers.

Service Mobility Increases Consumer Benefits

Service mobility creates a unified service experience. Service mobility means that a consumer has easy access to personalized services and is personally reachable through any access network or device. User Interfaces and services are independent of time and place, but they are at the same time customized for the device used and are aware of place and time. Nokia vision is that sessions (e.g., a videoconference) can be started on a PC, carried on with a mobile device, and continued with a Digital Video Broadcasting (DVB) screen at home. When all services are IP based, they can be offered through any access network - the carrier can create services on one platform and offer them via multiple access networks, thus greatly increasing the addressable customer base and allowing better service of existing subscribers. Services that are accessible at any place, at any time and through any device will increase consumer loyalty and reduce dissatisfaction.

Service Interaction Opens New Business Opportunities

The convergence of the publishing model of the Internet and the service delivery model of the Mobile Internet will put carriers and third-party service providers in a position where service provision brings new business potential.

Historically, service integration has been rather difficult in mobile networks since they have all required their own protocols, standards and service domains. In All-IP networks, service integration is easy since services are created within one domain. It is easy to integrate location-based applications with mobile commerce applications, mobile commerce applications with calendar applications, calendar applications with location-based applications, and so on. The possibilities are endless.

Voice and data applications have been rather hard to integrate in the same network due to the different standards and bearers. In All-IP networks, the carrier needs to take care of only one network, while SIP remains the enabling protocol.

Service Evolution in IP Convergence

In Nokia view, IP convergence builds on well-established service paradigms (e.g., the Short Message Service (SMS) and Multimedia Messaging Service (MMS)), by adding new functionalities and new content and service types in understandable steps for a consumer. Because consumers can relate to the new services as enhanced versions of the service experiences offered with previous networks, the barriers for adopting them will be significantly reduced, leading to rapid take-off and high penetration.

The market will develop towards All-IP services as an evolution, with some inevitable technological discontinuity occurring between technology shifts. Whereas messaging was introduced as the main application in the 2G era and browsing and rich call services in the 2.5/3G, real-time services will be the focus of attention in the All-IP era. Market development is evolutionary, with some technological redundancies along the way.

In the development of third generation mobile networks and beyond, the focus has shifted towards the IP paradigm. In particular, the work so far has focused on the adoption of IP transport, IP mobility and VoIP protocols (e.g., SIP) in mobile networks.

In future mobile networks, IP will allow the provision of multimedia services as well as other services (e.g., instant messaging and Web browsing), in an integrated fashion. In particular, consumers will no longer be forced to see the mobile network as capable of providing only voice services or as merely bit pipes to access the Internet.

Before we can set the objectives for the new service platform, we must first consider the basic assumptions behind the changing service paradigm. Current service architecture models, as they are evolving at present, do not meet the requirements for service integration, from a technological point of view. Therefore, a more radical and distributed IP-based approach is needed. In practice this means the reuse of existing IETF protocols, when possible, which will allow for easier deployment and acceptance of the service architecture, in both the Mobile and Web domain.

Technology Behind IP Convergence

SIP will be the standard signaling protocol/mechanism to support multimedia sessions in All-IP networks. This choice ensures that future IP-based communication services (e.g., voice services) will be truly Internet based.

Like HTTP, SIP is a text-based client-to-server protocol. SIP was designed to establish, modify and terminate multimedia sessions or calls. However, SIP is different from HTTP in the way that an SIP device may act both as a client and as a server. Therefore, peer-to-peer communication is possible. A text based SIP is relatively easy to implement and debug. SIP is also an extensible and modular protocol. The modularity helps to implement SIP clients in different device categories, from small devices with limited capabilities to full-featured desktop computers.

SIP service architecture follows the Internet design paradigm. Services are developed in the application layer, and the network is used exclusively for data transport. The SIP service architecture also takes into consideration the growing power of the devices by moving more responsibility to communication end-points. The ultimate goal is to push service logic to the end-points, leaving service providers and consumers to develop and control the services. As a consequence, standard interfaces for developing services are needed - and are provided by service development tools familiar from the Web domain, e.g., the Common Gateway Interface and SIP/Servlet servers on the application server side. The XML-based SIP Call Processing Language (CPL) can be used by developers or even by consumers themselves to create SIP services. Actual Web developers will be able to use their experience to develop and integrate new communication services.

SIP also enables traditional telecom-type services as well as user mobility. SIP supports instant conferences. It uses similar Uniform Resource Identifier (URI) based addressing as Internet e-mail (e.g., SIP:user@domain).

Consumers benefit from SIP by having the same address while choosing the most suitable interface (e.g., mobile device, PC or PDA). While SIP is the generic protocol for use over all access networks, consumers may use the most capable access network available, whether in terms of price, bandwidth, usability or some other factor. Services are also personalized, which makes the user experience appealing.

The primary advantage that can be seen with the SIP is the way in which it can integrate voice, video and other interactive communications services with instant messaging and presence information.

SIP will greatly enhance person-to-person communications by combining multiple media types and communication methods with presence and community information.

SIP in Messaging

There are several alternatives for implementing SIP messaging services. SIP provides methods for message distribution for different types of content, which vary depending on the size of the message attachment. SIP can be used for creating separate Transmission Control Protocol (TCP)/ User Datagram Protocol (UDP) sessions for bigger messages. SIP messages can also contain consumer information (e.g., a caller image or ringing tone). This allows the carrier to implement different services around messaging applications.

Messages can be sent in-line using the SIP signaling channel, which is a useful scheme for small messages. For example, a message may include a picture which shows the subject of the telephone call. For large content, this can be enhanced so that small messages are carried in-line and bigger messages are only referenced in SIP signaling. The consumer may have set in his/her profile whether to fetch the content instantly onscreen or to send it to a mailbox for later retrieval.

Another way is to use SIP only to establish a new unidirectional data session. This way, when the messaging server receives a message targeted for a mobile device, it sends an SIP signaling message to the device specifying that a unidirectional data session, is needed.

SIP and IPv6

IPv6 is relatively easy to implement in SIP addressing. Combining the two, highlights personal mobility using a unique user identity, which enables originating, receiving and accessing services from any device and any location. From the consumer's point of view, IPv6 and SIP enable ubiquitous communication in person-to-person, as well as person-to-machine, environments. For services this means increased availability and usage, while more devices are capable of being online.

SIP and Java

SIP and Java are closely linked. Java applications can be transported as SIP payload, and Java applications running on a mobile device can use SIP-based services in communications. A simple case would be distributing a mobile game, checking availability for gaming, setting up the game, and playing against another consumer over SIP. In a game such as chess, the moves can be transported using SIP. In games requiring more bandwidth, SIP may be used for signaling a TCP/UDP connection.

SIP and HTTP

SIP and HTTP stacks have a lot in common. An advanced SIP implementation usually provides a simple HTTP stack. One example of HTTP and SIP cooperation is that after some SIP signaling, a large file is fetched over HTTP using the HTTP GET method. Moreover, an SIP client (e.g., a mobile device) may host a simple HTTP server and offer files and other content so that other parties may download information from the device.

SIP works well in conjunction with the Web (e.g., Multi-purpose Internet Mail Extensions (MIME), URI, and Domain Name System (DNS)). In fact, a lot of SIP services could be originated via Web pages (e.g., click to call, Web phone book). SIP services can also use the resident client Web/ WAP browser to present information (e.g., call presentation service, messages, or pictures). SIP also enables "multicast Web" - which allows (e.g., sending Web pages on top of SIP).

Applications in IP Convergence

IP will greatly enhance person-to-person communications by combining multiple media types and communication methods with presence and community information, not only person-to-person but also instant multipoint-to-multipoint (i.e., conferencing). With IP, adding richer media is made simpler because all the services use the same network and signaling protocols.

Rich Call

Rich call is a voice or video conversation supported with concurrent access to an image, data or other information during a single session. The key in the rich call concept is the consumer's experience: the value and potential of combining telephony with information to provide enriched services.

By joining the Web and Mobile domains, SIP will enable true service mobility and access independence. Its support for rich calls will add *see what I mean* capability for subscribers through a combination of voice, mail, Web browsing, instant messaging, voice over IP and other services. If SIP is the engine for rich calls, presence is the ignition, enabling subscribers to initiate the services and select from a range of different communication modes.

Most of the services do not require voice-over IP or IP telephony service machinery; they can be realized by combining data with circuit-switched telephony or video-telephony. Still, IP telephony or IP multimedia is expected to emerge as the technology of choice for the rich call.

SIP provides essential elements for a rich call before the call, during the call and after the call. With SIP it is easy to implement new features (e.g., dynamic phonebook and click-to-talk), which make it easier to establish a connection. During the call establishment itself, SIP allows for sending a rich clip, which can be a picture with a call subject or a special ringing tone. During the call it is easy to share documents and generally implement information push features. Furthermore, during the session tear-down, the same kind of call termination messages are possible as in call establishment. And, finally, after the call it is still possible to send an associated instant message (e.g., an advertisement of the event).

Presence

As mobile communications become more personal, presence services will add a whole new dimension to staying in touch. Tomorrow's subscribers will know when and how they can reach their friends, even before they make a call.

With presence services, mobile devices will provide dynamic status information about subscribers, including their call/connection status, identities, device capabilities, location and availability. The result will be a visible network personality, one that signals valuable information about the consumer's reachability.

With mobile presence services, consumers will be able to show their status (e.g., busy, away from the desk, or on holiday) to callers and suggest the most appropriate mode of communication (e.g., chat, instant message, or e-mail).

As the rich call is largely about combining different communication modes, presence information should also be seen as a user interface to rich call services rather than just Instant Messaging. Presence is an application in itself, but is also an enabler and enrichment for other applications. Also, a presence service permits call completion in which the caller may choose the best communication method with the callee, thus generating traffic in new cooperative ways that were hitherto not possible.

Messaging

Mobile messaging today predominantly means SMS and voice messaging. As an evolution from SMS, MMS will enrich the messages with multimedia content, boosting mobile-to-mobile messaging to even higher levels. With MMS, it is possible to combine text with richer content types and send these combinations in the same simple manner as SMS today.

Instant messaging is an extremely popular application on the fixed Internet. Enhancing today's SMS, IM enables messaging that is enhanced by presence information. Messages can be sent real-time to the receiving party, whose on-line status can be checked with the presence feature. With SIP, the proven SMS business model may be implemented with new technology.

Mobile instant messaging combines the success stories of SMS messaging, nearly always reaching the recipient, and Internet-based instant messaging, which uses the presence information of the parties. SIP-based instant messaging paves the way for Integrated Messaging solutions, allowing consumers to combine the benefits of e-mail, MMS and instant messaging and choose the appropriate communication method according to the presence information of the receiving party.

Service Enablers for IP Convergence

Quality of Service

In most 2G mobile networks, coverage, price and service rollout were the only way to differentiate between service providers since the services themselves were standardized. Services in the All-IP era are becoming more demanding (e.g., data rates, IP packet delay, and consistent data throughput capacity). Applications have different QoS needs. More often applications are based on quality, reliability and timeliness assurances. In particular, services that use voice and streaming media are quite demanding in this sense. Carriers have the possibility to differentiate themselves from their competitors by offering different kinds of service packages, with different QoS levels. The requirements for transport services vary according to application stream types and consumers.

Examples of these service-level packages are:

- Gold, Silver and Bronze Web browsing subscriptions
- Different QoS for different service providers
- QoS profiles for wireless corporate users

The Third Generation Partnership Project (3GPP) has defined four different traffic classes. Those are conversational, streaming, background and interactive classes. The following table outlines the classes, with service examples.

Conversational	Streaming	Background	Interactive
Telephony	Streaming video	Calendar update	Signaling
Video Telephony	Streaming audio	Mail download	Interactive games
VoIP	Video surveillance		Web browsing

The carrier has the ability to offer different Quality of Service packages for different market segments. The carrier guarantees business customers high bit rate real-time services (e.g., broadband live video) and calendar synchronization, with e-mail download having the highest traffic priority. Further, the free-time consumer package could allow only voice calls (i.e., Voice over Internet Protocol (VoIP)) and the background traffic class. The maximum bit rate could be 64 kbit/s, but the guaranteed bit rate would be slightly lower. Also, only the lowest traffic handling priority would be allowed.

In summary, Quality of Service does not create additional bandwidth. Instead, it manages the existing bandwidth in such a way as to allow for efficient transportation of traffic through the network, with allowance for predictable delays, delay variation (jitter) and packet loss rates.

New Revenue Opportunities

It is important to point out that IP convergence is not a threat to carriers' revenue streams, not now or in the future. The All-IP infrastructure enables new services, as well as new flexible billing models, that were not possible before. The same charging model - price per minute and per message - can be maintained for voice telephony and messaging. Initially, we may see more package-based billing or service combinations. Package-based billing is the most suitable scheme for real-time applications (e.g., SIP-based instant messaging).

The carrier may provide different levels of service packages and combine them with different Quality of Service levels depending on consumer needs. This in turn affords more personalized services, increased consumer loyalty, and decreased consumer dissatisfaction. The service packages may be comprised of the following individual components:

- Store-and-forward extension and storage space
- Quality of Service levels
- Transcoding service in the network
- Voice mail
- Maintaining a presence server and the possibility of creating groups
- Instant messaging
- Offering Mobile Location Services

There is no single billing and charging model available for all carriers. This is one of the strengths of IP convergence. All-IP services enable better and endless possibilities for carriers to set themselves apart from competitors with different service and billing concepts.

The carrier may also offer and charge for SIP CPL services. For example:

- "If the size of the in-line content is bigger than 10 kB and it is from an unknown sender, then forward it to mailto:john@yahoo.co.cx"
- "Attach Star Wars theme as a ring tone for my outgoing call attempts, and me.jpg picture"
- "Pass only urgent priority calls through"
- "If caller is Gregor Schmidt, send soccerresults.html file to him"

It is also possible to charge for maintaining a presence server and virtual groups. Consumers may create their own friend groups or virtual communities.

Conclusions

In the Nokia vision, the future is about seamless connectivity to Internet-based services. This creates an increasing demand for bandwidth, connectivity features and economy that cannot be served by the circuit-switched mobile networks in their present form. The majority of traffic will be packet based in four to five years. Implementing this vision requires knowledge of the mobility business both infrastructure and devices. The third generation is all about services, and Nokia All-IP is about delivering those and more in even better ways.

Applications in IP convergence cannot be viewed as standalone applications. A rich consumer experience is created by using several components that interact with each other. The primary advantage that can be seen with IP is the way in which it can integrate voice, video and other interactive communication services with instant messaging and presence information. In conclusion:

- IP multimedia will greatly enhance person-to-person communications by combining multiple media types and communication methods with presence and community information.
- The key in the rich call concept is the customer experience: the value and potential of combining telephony with information to provide enriched services.
- Presence is a service in itself, if seen externally by others, but also an enabler of and enrichment to other services.
- Instant and multimedia messaging can be seamlessly integrated with conversational communications, thus creating the concept of ubiquitous communications.

Nokia in Messaging

Mobile messaging has emerged as the clear leader in non-voice traffic and revenues. The popularity of the Short Message Service (SMS) has exceeded all predictions and is currently developing into one of the most important revenue sources for many carriers. Despite the limitations of its user interface and technological capabilities, SMS has undoubtedly become the single most important mobile data access method.

Conventionally, SMS has been a major service both in Europe and the Asia Pacific region, and American markets are beginning to see increased SMS traffic. To ensure that SMS continues to develop in the future, the mobile industry has joined forces to produce the next-generation messaging standard: the Multimedia Messaging Service (MMS). For the carrier, MMS gives immediate access to an experienced user group, while for consumers it means the ability to start using new services without delay. The Nokia Picture Messaging concept is a clear evolutionary step from SMS toward MMS, as it teaches consumers to send richer content, beyond simple text.

A strong advocate of open standards, Nokia believes that, by using open international standards, the company can create services that will be widely used. Because of Nokia's involvement, the extensions to the SMS standards need both device and network aspects.

Features of the Enhanced Messaging Service (EMS) (e.g., interoperability) will encourage its use by introducing more versatile services, and Nokia will provide support for EMS in its devices. Furthermore, with the development of content downloading and device management systems, Nokia continues to support and develop Smart Messaging services.

Among the different types of messaging, MMS will emerge as a key technology. MMS enables rich content to be created for messages, while also functioning as a highly versatile platform for many mobile applications and services. To ensure the mass-market adoption of MMS, it will be supported by all categories of Nokia mobile devices.

Instant messaging is moving beyond the legacy Internet, into the Mobile domain. People are no longer tied to the wired environment if they want real-time communication that utilizes presence information. The mobile device will become the preferred method of accessing personalized services, including instant messaging, which will become the main application for group messaging and chat services in carriers' service portfolios.

Instant messaging will also be the first presence-enabled application. As services, instant messaging and presence can be seen as separate, even though in the initial phase they will be bundled into one seamless consumer experience. A presence service is an efficient tool that can also be used for non-messaging services (e.g., multiplayer gaming and directory services).

The combination of instant messaging and presence services offers an appealing business scenario for carriers. Messaging that spans the ever-shrinking gap between the legacy Internet and Mobile domain is appealing to the consumer and, as consumers are already familiar with the concept from the Internet, it should not take long for the service to catch on.

In many ways, IP convergence will bring a new era in messaging. The user experience will remain the same, but the underlying technologies will change. The third Generation Partnership Project (3GPP) release 5 will introduce the Session Initiation Protocol (SIP) as a call control protocol that will also be used in messaging. However, SIP will be introduced in the General Packet Radio Service (GPRS/1xRTT) environment with an adequate quality service level before Release 5, allowing consumers to progress easily to true mobile multimedia messaging.

Short Message Service

The number of short messages being sent in most markets is booming, which brings new challenges for the carrier, such as capacity, scalability, load sharing, efficient routing, and the demand for value-added services. In October 2001, the GSM Association estimated that, globally, the number of short messages sent each day has reached one billion. Nearly 90% of all the SMS messages sent are for person-to-person communication, yet numerous services have been created for application-to-person communication.

SMS Applications

Currently, SMS is being utilized to offer lucrative value-added services. To ensure the continuous development of these services, Forum Nokia works in close cooperation with carriers and third-party designers to develop versatile applications, which include:

- Chat applications
- E-mail applications
- Stock market alerts and other financial information
- Location tracking with GPS equipment
- Distribution management for delivery companies
- Traffic and weather information
- Sports results and instant updates using the push service
- Banking transactions
- Airline information

SMS Extensions

Besides pure text messaging, Nokia has introduced Picture Messaging and Smart Messaging. In addition, EMS, as an extended part of the SMS standards, is fostering open standards, to ensure interoperability across devices. Currently, Smart Messaging is offered to anyone who wishes to implement it, and Nokia has actually offered Smart Messaging to 3GPP to be standardized as another example of enhanced messaging.

Smart Messaging

A vast number of mobile devices support Smart Messaging on the market today. Carriers, content providers and customers have all benefited from this large base of Smart Messaging capable devices and their high-quality content and services, with some of the most popular uses being the downloading of ringing tones and carrier logos. The Smart Messaging specification has been widely accepted by content providers and other device manufacturers. The open Smart Messaging specification includes support for:

- Ringing tones
- Carrier logos
- Picture messages
- Business cards
- Calendar and address book entries
- Caller line identification icons
- Downloadable profiles
- Internet access configuration
- WAP configuration and bookmarks

Enhanced Messaging Service

EMS enables consumers to change typefaces, format text in boldface and italics, and align it as they choose. Additionally, it makes it possible to download and send icons, animations and ringing tones. The EMS standard is part of the SMS standard, and it includes support for concatenated messages.

At present, Nokia sees that multimedia messaging will be available on a large scale next year. Therefore, EMS brings only limited new value to Nokia customers, especially since similar services are already available through Smart Messaging. However, it is good that other companies are moving toward enabling the business potential of mobile services. Yet Nokia is aware of industry dynamics. The following figure represents the messaging migration path as Nokia sees the evolution taking place.

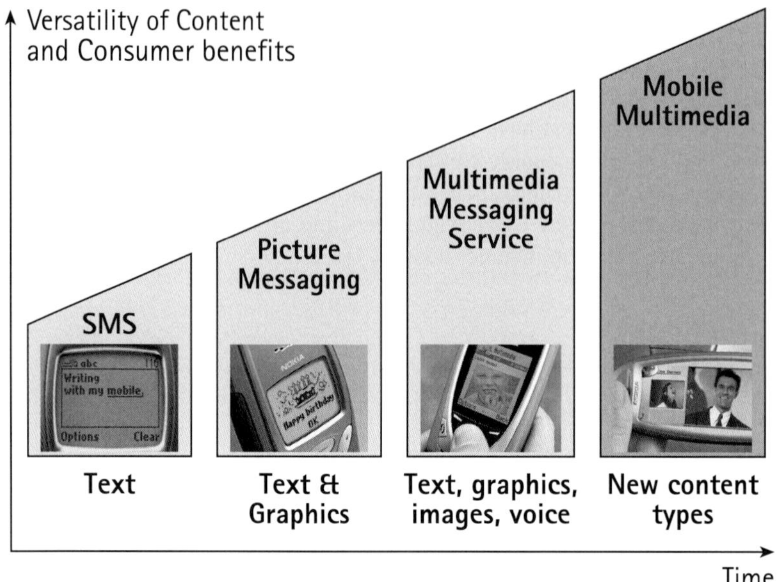

Messaging evolution

Multimedia Messaging Service

Nokia sees MMS as the key application in the company's entry into the third generation device market. MMS is an end-to-end application for person-to-person mobile messaging. It will provide rich multimedia content, including images, audio, video, data and text content, yet will not compromise the ease of use of SMS or its established usage patterns. MMS is a globally standardized service and happens to be one of the first 3GPP standardized third generation services today.

MMS can be used in various situations, whether they are business- or leisure-related, and it meets the needs of many types of consumers. It promotes market development by introducing new customer benefits in understandable steps. The possibility of taking a picture and immediately sending it gives the consumer an opportunity to share an important moment with friends or relatives. This opportunity can be extended for business use wherein a photograph can be annotated with text or explanations and sent instantly back to the office.

From a network perspective, a Multimedia Messaging Service Center (MMSC) is needed for delivery of MMS messages. The MMSC also enables messaging between Internet applications and devices and vice versa.

Nokia MMS solutions support flexible addressing of multimedia messages to both familiar phone numbers - i.e., those with a Mobile Station International ISDN Number (MSISDN) - and e-mail as defined in the MMS standard. MMS messages can be created using either Internet applications or devices equipped with an integrated or connected camera. Also, images can be downloaded using various Internet applications, with which MMS messages can be created, stored and forwarded.

Technology Platform for Services

MMS technology can be utilized as middleware for countless services that will function in the Mobile domain. MMS can also be used as an optional delivery mechanism to download Digital Rights Management (DRM) protected content such as Musical Instrument Digital Interface (MIDI) ringing tones, animated Graphics Interchange Format (GIF) screensavers and downloadable game packs.

One can subscribe to MMS based services very similarly as to the WAP and SMS services today. Both push and pull MMS content are available. These services can include headline news, a daily cartoon strip, or the latest sports news - accompanied by a short audio clip of the excited commentator's report. The messages can consist of pure information or be combined with an element of advertising. MMS adds multimedia content to these messages.

When taking a closer look at global revenues from mobile service spending, one can detect a trend that will lead to a notable decrease in voice services toward 2006. In this following diagram (source: Nokia 2001), the messaging division includes all SMS, MMS and e-mail services counted together, and one should note that the other data services in the bigger pie can include MMS content.

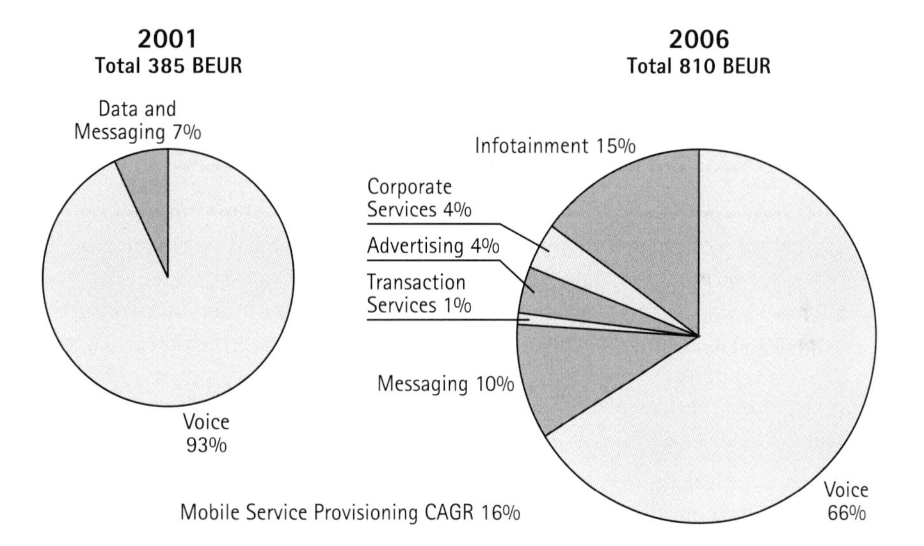

Distribution of revenue in mobile services

E-Mailing with MMS

With the store-and-forward functionalities of the MMSC, message delivery is instant; i.e., the content is directed to the receiver's device, whereas, in the case of mailbox based solutions like e-mail and Unified Messaging the message must be manually downloaded. Accordingly, the obvious benefit with MMS based e-mail usage is that the sender can be confident that the receiver will see the message sent, while the mailbox based solutions can leave a degree of uncertainty as to whether the receiver has downloaded the message or not. Furthermore, with

MMS solutions the sender pays and the receiving of the messages is free of charge, so there is even greater certainty that the receiver will truly get the message.

In Nokia vision, MMS and mailbox services can exist in parallel - just like SMS and e-mail today. MMS will be a service, optimized for mobile messaging, in its own right, and most of the messages will be sent inside the MMS environment, i.e., mobile to mobile, although e-mail connectivity is also provided. So, with the Nokia concept, messages are not sent first to the mailbox. Instead, the messages are pushed immediately to the receiver's device, in an attempt to make the pipe between the two devices as short and efficient as possible.

Message Content

Using e-mail, various kinds of attachments can be sent. Messages in MMS are optimized for mobile use, and only well-defined sets of media formats can be exchanged. Actually, the concept of text and attachments is not a valid one with MMS; the messages are always multimedia presentations, where various message components are displayed in an order predetermined by the sender. So, in practice, the full message opens automatically. There is no need to click on any attachments, since they do not exist.

Thanks to the enormous consumer base of e-mail, it will remain one of the most important and highly used forms of communication. Nokia will also support Post Office Protocol (POP3) and Internet Message Access Protocol (IMAP4) clients in certain devices.

Instant Messaging and Presence

Presence is defined as information describing the status of the consumer. The presence features of Instant Messaging (IM) are a means for exchanging status information with other consumers. Presence information enables a new communications paradigm: see before you connect. With this paradigm, a consumer wanting to communicate with another consumer first checks the status and availability of the other consumer, then, based on the presence information, chooses the most appropriate means of communication. Instant messaging and presence services have existed on the Internet for some time and have given birth to a range of other interesting services and features.

From a messaging perspective, Instant Messaging has been described as a means of sending small, simple messages that are delivered immediately to online consumers. However, this definition has evolved over a period of time, and today's instant messaging services allow consumers to send more than simple text messages. They allow consumers to exchange rich text (e.g., pictures or files; embed smileys; use colored fonts; and even perform video calls). The advanced instant messaging services today also come with a plethora of corporate features (e.g., whiteboards, a scratch pad area and online meeting features). For user personalization, they offer a variety of features (e.g., group discussions, skins, screen backgrounds and privacy features).

In the Web domain, instant messaging services have proven to be quite popular. Now these services are moving to the Mobile domain. The mobile device is becoming the personal trusted device and will thus be the preferred device for accessing one's services. The value proposition of Mobile Instant Messaging consists of two elements - connectivity between the Internet and

Mobile domain for interactive messaging and presence value. In addition, mobility adds new dimensions to these basic value propositions by offering a number of highly attractive features that make the overall value proposition for Mobile Instant Messaging much better.

The main added value of Mobile IM is that access to IM services becomes ubiquitous, meaning that a consumer can access presence information and exchange messages at any time and not only when seated in front of a desktop PC. This will have a profound influence on usage patterns and will also enable presence information to reflect more closely the mood and state of the consumer. The locations and situations, where the consumers are, and the preferred communication method become relevant.

A key aspect of instant messaging and presence services is the immediate nature of the message and presence exchange. The always-on characteristics of the GPRS and 1XRTT services being rolled out today are a perfect complement to an IM service; using a GPRS/1XRTT service, IM consumers can remain connected to their service providers at all times and will thus receive immediate updates as other consumers' presence information changes, and they can receive their messages in real time.

In the early phase of its evolution, mobile instant messaging can use SMS. Naturally, WAP and Web browsing can also be used to offer mobile IM services to legacy clients.

At the moment there are several proprietary instant messaging services on the market that do not interoperate in a user-friendly way. In short, consumers of different services are not able to send and receive instant messages and presence information to/from each other. In order to ensure fast time to market and service adoption, interoperability issues must be taken into consideration. Initiatives (e.g., the Wireless Village) ensure interoperability between different mobile devices, service providers, and the Mobile and Web domains. The more consumers there are using these messaging services, the greater the value added to the consumer is.

At some point, instant messaging will surpass SMS traffic in person-to-person messaging. This scenario will be especially likely when there are devices and networks that enable GPRS/1xRTT always-on connection. However, there will remain a business case for SMS person-to-machine messaging. SMS will also prevail as a primary messaging technology for legacy devices.

Benefits for Carriers

Carriers see instant messaging as an attractive service for several reasons. First, there is a vast base of over 300 million fixed instant messaging users globally. Carriers can connect their consumers to this large base in the Web domain and offer messaging between the Mobile and Web domains. Even in their mobile network, carriers can connect their subscribers using mobile devices and PCs for messaging.

Second, carriers have the opportunity to offer messaging services for different target groups: one-to-one, one-to-many (group communication), and many-to-many (chat). For example, chat services have proven to be extremely popular in the Web domain. Short Message Service Centers (SMSC) are not capable of multiparty messaging; therefore, the network needs an instant messaging server in order to offer IM services. Also, as SMS is restricted to text-only messaging, instant messaging enables richer messaging.

Third, consumers are already aware of instant messaging services in the Web domain and are able to quickly adapt to the mobile equivalent when it is available.

Presence and Messaging

In the Mobile domain, presence services will be richer and even more powerful than what may be familiar from the Web domain. The mobile device is evolving into a Personal Trusted Device (PTD), and presence, among other features, will be one of the main drivers in its movement further in this direction.

Presence and messaging are separate applications or services and can work independently of each other. However, by utilizing the presence service, a consumer has a better idea as to whether a recipient is available to receive messages and is in general willing to communicate. Therefore, the two services are often used in tandem.

Presence services will support all existing mobile communication, not just messaging. Presence information will initiate additional communication in the form of messaging and voice calls. It generates new traffic the same way as Web domain instant messaging has. A change in a consumer's presence information may result in a greeting or another kind of message. Other applications can also be built so that they utilize presence information.

IP Convergence in Messaging

The major cornerstone for IP based communications in messaging will be the introduction of the 3GPP Release 5 specification, which uses SIP as the call control protocol. All the data traffic will be based on packet switched bearers, whereas in previous releases voice and video have been based on circuit switched bearers. The major change will be the use of SIP, which will be used for all session set-ups as well as messaging services. From the messaging point of view, 3GPP Release 5 will enable easy integration of all messaging into true mobile multimedia messaging where video, voice content, pictures, and other types of multimedia components are created, sent and received in a simple and efficient way. Boundaries between different messaging technologies will disappear. But the key promise of IP convergence for consumers is that applications work together.

IP convergence will happen in small steps, with the introduction of GPRS/1xRTT being one of the first ones. Standardization efforts will drive the market towards All-IP devices and networks from the services point of view. Through these industry initiatives, service providers are able to start offering interoperable messaging services to their customer base and get on the learning curve.

Conclusions

Messaging on mobile networks is dominated by SMS today. However, the nature of mobile messaging is quickly evolving from a pure textual base to a visual base and developing from the popular SMS to the more advanced MMS. The mobile industry is evolving from a voice-driven form to a personal multimedia form with text and image driven intermediate steps.

SMS was the first mobile service to provide a serious financial boost in carriers' revenues, and multimedia messaging will clearly lead the way to more profits for carriers. Another aspect of the mobile communication evolution that was learned from the success of SMS is the demand for the instant creation and consumption of content. Multimedia messaging applications are the essential drivers of continuous growth in new services beyond voice, promising increases in airtime, revenue, service differentiation and consumer loyalty.

Instant messaging and presence services will add another dimension to the mobile messaging. They will offer popular Internet services in a mobile context, raising the value of communication in general and blurring the boundaries of Mobile and Web domain messaging paradigms.

In the future, all the different messaging technologies will serve a valid function and will be justified in coexisting. SMS is superb for quick and pithy communication, while MMS is an excellent way of sharing richer content in person-to-person communication. Moreover, MMS can also be used as a bearer for content in general. Instant messaging enables simple and appealing consumer services in the group communications area as well as in person-to-person messaging. Furthermore, presence will be the glue that combines all the messaging technologies into a package that is easy to understand and use.

From the consumer's point of view, presence services will combine all messaging technologies into one seamless messaging experience. Presence-specific applications (e.g., presence-enabled phonebooks) will be one central element of the communication experience. Presence information will initiate the messaging experience. In addition, a well-designed presence service can be seen as the UI for messaging. The following figure about IP convergence in mobile messaging illustrates these aspects.

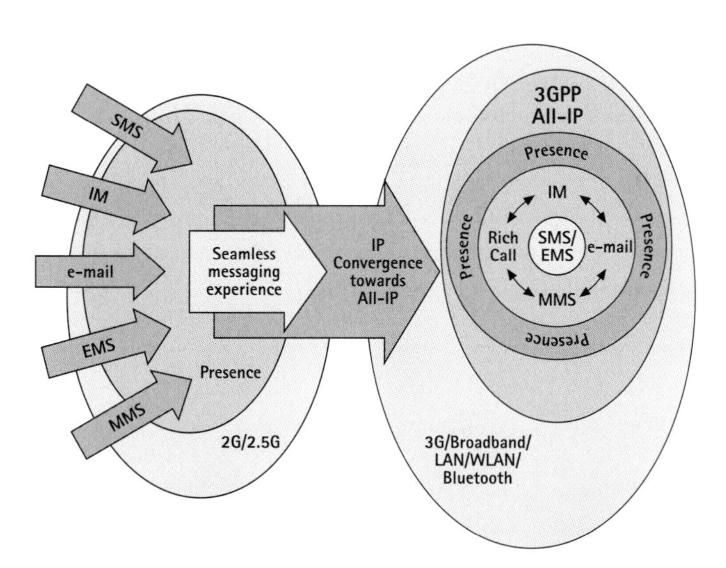

IP convergence in mobile messaging

IP convergence will have a major impact on how mobile services, messaging services included, will be delivered and consumed. For a 3GPP Release 5 solution, Nokia is studying various alternatives for implementing MMS and other messaging technologies. Nokia sees that MMS will evolve continuously along the path started by the Nokia MMS solution, based on 3GPP Release 99. Also, Nokia sees that MMS is in line with its plans for an All-IP service platform.

In the quest to further develop and facilitate the next generation of products and services, Nokia is developing an open technical architecture that enables seamless interoperability between key applications, network environments and user identity/addressing. Additionally, the complexity of the technical environment supporting applications and services will be limited from the consumer's viewpoint. Consumers want seamless messaging experiences; i.e., they are not interested in whether the message being sent is an instant message, SMS, MMS, e-mail or something else. Accordingly, Nokia supports open technologies, standards, and relevant initiatives that support and facilitate the deployment of global technologies and applications and stimulate market growth.

Multimedia Messaging Service

This section presents ideas for carriers who intend to enter the Multimedia Messaging Service (MMS) arena. A number of the most important issues are highlighted to give an understanding of what is required for MMS and how the Nokia MMS solution currently fulfills these needs.

The MMS concept builds upon the success of the Short Message Service (SMS). Hence, this section presents a way to enter the MMS market using an evolutionary approach. This protects the carrier's network investments. The MMS concept is discussed, and the required hardware and software are described. Finally, recommendations on the basic steps to prepare for entry to the MMS market are presented.

Technology Concept

The MMS is a messaging service for the mobile environment that is standardized by the WAP Forum and Third Generation Partnership Project (3GPP). To the consumer, MMS is very similar to the Short Message Service (SMS): it provides automatic and immediate delivery of user-created content. The primary addressing used is recipient Mobile Station International Integrated Services Digital Network (ISDN) Number (MSISDN), and the bulk of the MMS traffic goes from device to device. MMS also provides support for e-mail addressing. Hence, messages can also be sent from device to e-mail and back.

MMS messages can contain still text, images, voice or audio clips, synthetic audio, video clips and a multitude of other presentation formats. A multimedia message is a presentation created by the sender using, e.g., predefined templates. Alternatively, the content can be obtained ready-made from a third-party content provider. The message is delivered using a WAP push service to the recipient's device. The receiving consumer is notified only after the whole message has been received.

MMS transport is carried out using Wireless Application Protocol (WAP) protocols, and any bearer capable of supporting WAP can be used. Thus, MMS is access independent; i.e., MMS is not limited to only the Global System for Mobile Communications (GSM) or Wideband Code Division Multiple Access (WCDMA). The Wireless Session Protocol (WSP) is used for message transport from device to a MMS Center (MMSC) and from MMSC to device. MMS is an independent application (e.g., independent from the browser).

Hardware and Software

MMS Center

The MMS Center (MMSC) is the store-and-forward network element that delivers the MMS messages from the sender to the recipient. The MMSC concept is similar to a Short Message Service Center (SMSC); (i.e., the server stores the message only for the time that is required to find the receiving device). After the receiving device has been found, the MMSC immediately forwards the multimedia message to the recipient and the message is deleted from the MMSC. Thus, the MMSC is not a mailbox server since it does not store the message if it can be delivered. The existing SMSC cannot be upgraded to an MMSC in terms of software, as the capacity and interface requirements are different.

The MMSC hosts a number of interfaces for connecting to other networks, e.g., the Internet, and an external application interface to enable the delivery of value-added services. The MMSC may also have an interface for e-mail.

The Nokia MMS Center provides interfaces for an external WAP gateway and the billing system as well as an External Application Interface (EAIF) for MMS applications.

WAP Gateway

MMS content is not transmitted in the SMS transmission channel. The SMS transmission channel is too narrow for transmitting multimedia content. Examples of MMS transmission bearers include single slot GSM data, High Speed Circuit Switched Data (HSCSD) and General Packet Radio Service (GPRS). Other protocols and bearers can also be used. MMS is actually the first third-generation service that can already be offered with the current networks.

On the protocol level, MMS messages are transported using the Wireless Session Protocol (WSP). In addition, the lightweight MMS protocol data units defined by the WAP Forum are used. The WAP browser is not involved in MMS transport - only the WAP transport protocols are used. To enable the use of the WAP protocols in MMS message transfer, a WAP gateway is needed to connect the MMSC to the WAP network.

The Nokia MMS Center uses an integrated WAP interface to connect to the mobile network. In addition, the existing WAP gateway on the carrier network can be used initially, while the service is new and traffic is still low. To ensure sufficient capacity for increasing MMS traffic, Nokia suggests that a dedicated WAP gateway is used for MMS traffic. However, a specific GPRS access point should be used for the MMSC and other WAP services. This ensures that low-end devices with only one PDP context can use MMS and other WAP services simultaneously.

Segmentation And Re-assembly (SAR) is a software feature in the Nokia WAP gateway. It enables large messages to be sent in small packets, reducing the re-transmission time for lost packets. SAR also reduces the network load, due to use of more efficient re-transmission schemes.

Profile Server

Personalization is the key to any mobile service; consumers desire and expect to control their messaging domain. Profiling will enable consumers and carriers to effectively supply, control and manage value-added services. The profile server should be fast, with a high-capacity network element optimized for read requests, ensuring that MMS network elements share an equal view of user profile information.

The Nokia Profile Server provides vital information for MMS solutions about consumers' mobile device capabilities, the storage and processing of consumers' preferences, and information about their subscription details. In addition, consumers get greater control and flexibility in deciding how they want to send, receive and filter MMS messages. For example, pre-paying subscribers can be barred from accessing high-value services if they have reached the limit of their pre-paid account threshold.

Value-Added Services

The combination of high-capacity multimedia messaging and applications provides a comprehensive multimedia solution. The applications will complement person-to-person messaging. Two MMS features that are invaluable in any carrier service are provided: support for non-multimedia devices and message storage. Legacy phone support will be crucial to the initial deployment of MMS services. This will increase the number of subscribers who are able to send and receive multimedia messages, thus enabling MMS to reach an important mass adoption status. The other main feature, permanent message storage with multiple access, allows all consumers to store and manage messages, therefore providing additional network storage to supplement existing storage on the consumer's device.

To seamlessly combine the Internet and mobile messaging, format conversions are required. The MMS solution converts between messaging formats that are supported on the Internet and mobile networks. Text, pictures and audio clips can be converted from the Multi-purpose Internet Mail Extensions (MIME) formats to formats specified in the 3GPP standards.

The demands and needs of subscribers who desire comprehensive applications and content services are met by a content application gateway between the mobile network and applications on the Internet and corporate intranets. Content can be provided in standard HyperText Markup Language (HTML) and Wireless Markup Language (WML) formats and adapted by the application gateway in order to make it suitable for mobile devices. The messaging platform enables carriers to develop new multimedia messaging services and enhance the existing SMS services, moving them toward MMS. Services that are provided by the messaging platforms are accessible using MMS and SMS.

For the carrier to be able to offer more than a plain person-to-person MMS service with user-created content, the following value-added service platforms can be considered:

- Multimedia Terminal Gateway
- Multimedia e-mail Gateway
- Messaging Gateway
- Multimedia Voice Gateway.

Multimedia Terminal Gateway

The Multimedia Terminal Gateway offers the possibility of supporting non-MMS enabled devices as part of the overall MMS service portfolio. Subscribers who do not own MMS devices will receive an SMS notification that an MMS message has been sent to them and that they can view the message by logging on to their carrier's Web site. For security reasons, they will need to supply the username and password that were sent to them in the notification message.

Another value-added service offered by the Multimedia Terminal Gateway is a Message Album for long-term storage of the subscriber's favorite MMS messages. The consumer can compose, delete and forward messages directly from the Multimedia Album.

Subscribers with non-MMS devices can also subscribe to the Message Album as a MMS subscriber and get their own personal inbox for MMS messages and be able to create and send MMS messages from the Web. This possibility enables easy familiarization with the service and increases the likelihood of the consumer upgrading to a MMS device.

Multimedia E-Mail Gateway

The Multimedia e-mail Gateway enables the Smart Push of e-mail messages to devices, allowing subscribers to receive important e-mail messages and enjoy multimedia content from the Internet. The Nokia Multimedia e-mail Gateway provides the carrier with the possibility of sending MMS messages between MMS devices and e-mail accounts. Message routing, spam filtering and call detail record creation are some of the features provided by the Multimedia E-mail Gateway. By expanding the MMS market to cover e-mail accounts, the carrier is effectively creating a larger target market.

Messaging Gateway

As MMS device market penetration will be very modest in the beginning, it is essential that the carrier be able to offer ready-made MMS content to subscribers. By partnering with third-party content providers, the carrier can stimulate MMS usage by offering attractive MMS content. The Nokia Messaging Gateway offers an open service creation interface through which third-party content developers can create HTML-based MMS services and offer these services to MMS subscribers.

The Nokia MMS Solution enables carriers to offer consumers easy access to useful services via the use of short messages. Interesting MMS content stored on the Internet can be accessed in seconds and can range from headline news or cartoon-of-the-day content to movie reviews and real-estate pictures with floor plans. With consumer self-provisioning, consumers can even subscribe to personalized push services via SMS or WAP on their mobile device or via any standard Web browser. Different charging schemes are possible, including content- and advance payment based charging.

Multimedia Voice Gateway

With the Nokia Multimedia Voice Gateway, Nokia offers voice clip call termination that will be a pioneering service in multimedia call answering. It is a call-answering service that is based on a store-and-forward application. It features voice call termination and instant delivery of voice messages to the subscriber's multimedia device. The voice message is sent as a voice clip in a multimedia message. The subscriber can also record a personal greeting over the device. Callers can now maintain the convenience of leaving voice messages with the added confidence of knowing the message will be received, increasing call completion and, therefore, voice minute revenue. Furthermore, storing voice messages on devices simplifies additional actions taken on reply-and-forward messages.

Mobile Devices

To launch the service, the carrier has to ensure that attractive MMS capable mobile devices are available on the market. Nokia offers the Nokia 7650 imaging phone as one solution for MMS services. In addition to the 7650, there are other models, such as the 7210 and 3510, that support MMS as well.

The MMS functionalities of the Nokia 7650 include an integrated digital camera with a Video Graphics Array (VGA) resolution, picture taking and sending capabilities, a photo album for storing pictures and a large 176 x 208 pixel color display. The device allows consumers to combine audio, graphic, text and imaging content in to one message. The advanced graphical user interface and joystick with 5-way navigation add ease and speed to the use of this new device.

With the Nokia 7650, the connection to WAP services using GPRS is always activated, so it is quick to connect to the WAP homepage or a bookmarked page. GPRS makes it convenient to use many mobile services, including MMS. The Nokia 7650 works at three data transfer rates. At default data transfer rate, it sends and receives data at up to 14.4 kilobits per second.

Carrier Service Concept Development

MMS provides a versatile development platform for all kinds of Store and Automatic Forward services. History has shown that, for various reasons, it took three to five years per market to make SMS successful. SMS has proven to be a very profitable business for the carriers, and Nokia sees that the SMS traffic can be gradually migrated to MMS, potentially making the service learning period, or chasm, shorter for MMS. Therefore, it is reasonable to state that MMS has good business potential for carriers in the person-to-person messaging area.

MMS is already an excellent transport mechanism for digital content. Nokia can see that MMS together with mobile commerce solutions forms a versatile platform for future content delivery business. Hence, the carriers need to explore the degree to which they want to partner with content developers (e.g., digital image libraries, e-postcard providers and auctioning services), and, together with them, launch content services that are optimized for MMS devices.

Service Concept

Before the service launch, a carrier-specific MMS concept needs to be prepared. MMS and the Nokia MMS solution provide a flexible platform that enables the carrier to develop a competitive MMS proposal to attract the mass market. A number of ways to market MMS are presented below.

There is no other store-and-forward service capable of dealing with multimedia content, which is optimized for the mobile environment. Therefore, the carrier with MMS can differentiate itself from those carriers that only offer SMS and e-mail services. Furthermore, the Nokia MMS Center has an external application interface allowing use with any application.

With the non-multimedia device support offered by the Nokia Multimedia Terminal Gateway, the carrier can increase the number of subscribers who are able to send and receive multimedia messages and enable MMS to reach critical mass. This way the carrier can offer an MMS service, which is available for all subscribers independent of their device capabilities and differentiate itself via the richness of the service offered.

MMS is a store and forward service, which by its nature does not offer long-term storage for messages. The Nokia solution includes a message storage facility that makes it possible for the carrier to offer a storage service that is customized to consumer's needs. Now the carrier can offer a storage service, provide a Web and WAP user interface, and differentiate itself from the competition, for example, by offering storage space.

Since MMS includes interoperability with e-mail, carriers can offer an e-mail interface concept (e.g., address, billing, spam filtering and message routing), and stand apart due to the flexibility of its service offering. Additionally, Nokia offers the next generation of call termination in a multimedia environment, making it possible for the carriers to offer an enhanced voice messaging service with immediate message delivery to the device.

Charging Concept

Consumer confidence is vital when defining the pricing structure of multimedia messaging services. If the consumer is unsure of the cost, it is likely that he/she will not send messages at all. If this reaction is widespread among consumers, ultimately it will result in very low MMS revenue.

The carrier should ensure that the consumers feel that the impact of MMS on their phone bills is predictable and that they can safely use the service. Nokia recommends that the carriers deploy an MMS charging model similar to the one used in SMS: transaction-based billing, i.e., billing based upon the number of transmitted messages. However, due to the variations in size of multimedia messages, from a few kilobytes to several megabytes, this may require further adjustment in order to reflect the cost of delivering the message. Nokia is currently analyzing the solutions proposed by standardization bodies.

To avoid the message recipient switching off his/her MMS application to avoid unwanted costs, receiving MMS messages should be free of charge. Using the familiar SMS billing model where the sender pays all costs per message will lower the barrier of entry for consumers. The exception to this rule would be some application-originating, mobile-terminating services where the recipient has ordered the content or has subscribed to these kinds of value-added services. In this case, the recipient would pay for the multimedia message.

Initially, Nokia does not suggest introducing a subscription fee or monthly fee, as these may add to the barriers of entry for new MMS consumers. However, as consumer acceptance grows, this model may be desirable for certain services. For example, access to value-added services (e.g., Web mail accounts like Yahoo) could successfully be provided as a subscription-based service.

Charging Solutions

The technical realization of the *sender pays all costs per message* charging model requires some integration. For example, a device-to-device multimedia message sent via GPRS creates not only a charging record at the MMSC but also a record for the SMS notification and a GPRS record for the access to the MMSC. If no further action were taken, the subscriber would be charged for the total cost of all these records. This is not an attractive charging model from a subscriber point of view, as the consumers do not have a clear idea of the cost of sending a multimedia message. Furthermore, it would not be allowed in countries (e.g., Germany) where the total price of a service including access must be advertised.

Another consideration is the support of the specific requirements of pre-paying subscribers. Pre-paying subscribers form a significant percentage of the carrier's customer base. However, they bring extra complexity to the carrier's network in terms of service status management, which is required to provide the necessary revenue assurance. For this purpose, Nokia recommends the Nokia Charging Center.

Any solution for the charging of multimedia messaging services must address both of the previous issues. To reiterate, the consumer must only be charged for the advertised cost of the multimedia messaging service, and the charging solution must take this into account.

Generally, there are two types of charging records: access records, produced by the Mobile Services Switching Center (MSC) or Gateway GPRS Support Node (GGSN), and content or messaging records, produced by the MMSC and application gateways (e.g., the Nokia Multimedia Terminal Gateway).

Market Making

To increase the awareness of MMS, the carrier will not have to rely solely on user-created content to fill their networks. By offering third-party MMS content services through the carrier's portal and by offering Multimedia Album types of services, the carrier is able to offer a wide variety of MMS content from the start and therefore demonstrate to the market how much richer and more versatile MMS content is compared with SMS. As an example of third-party MMS content, Nokia is partnering with companies (e.g., eurosport.com and Lycos Europe) to ensure that there is enough attractive MMS content when the service is launched. Through attractive content services, the market demand for MMS is created, and once MMS device ownership increases, user-created content will start filling the carriers' data network capacity.

Conclusions

When preparing the MMS service launch, Nokia recommends that the carrier follow the SMS format. The same service pricing principles, where the sender pays a fixed fee per message sent, should apply. The consumer experience should also be the same as with SMS - the message is instantly delivered to the recipient's device, with automatic presentation. In short: MMS should be the same as SMS except for the richness of the message.

To stimulate the market and to ensure a rapid uptake of MMS from the day of launch, the carrier needs to offer value-added services that can be enjoyed by subscribers who still do not own an MMS device.

The MMS service should be immediately ready to go when the MMS device is purchased. The required service and device settings need to be in place when the subscriber exits the shop with the brand new MMS device.

The MMS service rollout has already started. The carriers should commence the MMS trials using the commercially available Nokia MMSC and MMS devices to ensure that the customer care, provisioning and billing systems are prepared for the service launch.

Instant Messaging

Instant Messaging (IM) is a way of sending short, simple messages that are delivered immediately to online consumers. Combining two key technologies - instant message delivery and presence information - IM is an attractive messaging service that has already proven popular with consumers.

Presence information describes the status of the consumer. Using it in a mobile application expands its usefulness beyond merely knowing whether consumers are online or not - it can be used to indicate their location, their need for privacy or willingness to communicate, and a rough idea of their moods and sentiments.

It introduces the *see before you connect* idea - a consumer wanting to communicate with someone first checks the status and availability of the other consumer and then chooses the most appropriate way to communicate.

Presence and instant messaging features are separate and can work independently of each other. However, a presence service gives a consumer a better idea of a recipient's ability to receive instant messages. The two services are often used in tandem and are marketed as instant messaging services on the Internet, and now also in the Mobile domain.

One can assume that instant messaging services will always combine instant message exchange and presence features. Therefore, in speaking of an instant messaging service, both aspects of the service are considered.

Mobile Instant Messaging

The main added benefit is that access to IM services becomes ubiquitous, meaning that a consumer can access presence information and exchange IM messages at any time, not merely when seated in front of a desktop PC. This will have a profound effect on usage patterns and will also ensure that presence information better reflects the mood and state of the consumer. In fact, in the Mobile domain, being online or offline becomes largely irrelevant since consumers are essentially always online. Much more important is the location and situation of the consumers and the communication method they prefer.

In addition to widened presence, the growth of mobile instant messaging services is driven by a number of other technological factors. A key aspect is the immediate nature of instant messaging, which is supported by the always-on characteristic of the General Packet Radio Service (GPRS).

Such packet services will give IM consumers a continuous data connection to their service providers, providing immediate updates on the presence information of other consumers and bringing them their messages in real time.

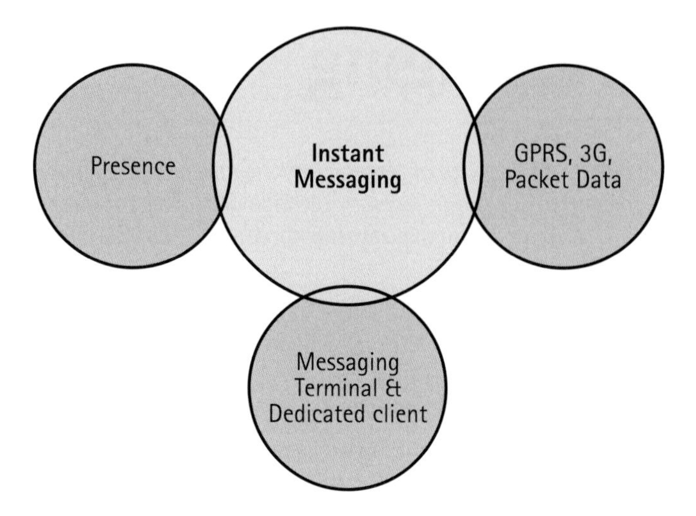

Core enablers for instant messaging

In the early stages, standards based mobile IM will be a new feature in devices from major device vendors. In order to ensure quick growth and acceptance among the consumers, the Short Message Service (SMS) and Wireless Application Protocol (WAP) access, can also be used to offer mobile IM services.

The key is not the technology used, but the connectivity: all consumers can exchange messages with each other regardless of what bearer they use as the access method.

Another key aspect is the increasing ease of use of mobile devices. Consumers have already accepted SMS messaging with predictive text input, proving that keyboard size is not an issue. New devices will also have bigger, color screens, making it more natural for consumers to carry on longer discussions and follow them more easily on screen.

Benefits for Consumers

Nokia expects that in five years, there will be very few consumers who prefer instant messaging from a PC - using a mobile device to access IM services will predominate.

The list below shows the main reasons for the success of instant messaging in the Mobile domain:

- The screens of mobile devices are large enough for the basic mobile IM and presence features (e.g., reading and writing messages, maintaining a contact list and viewing the status of contacts).
- User interface improvements (e.g., predictive text input in mobile devices), will be a further boost for mobile IM services.
- Instant messaging and presence services benefit from the evolution of the mobile network; for instance, using GPRS as a means of access allows flexible billing methods.

- Mobile IM services are available for the traditional circuit switched GSM network.
- Compared to a desktop IM client, the mobile device is always with the consumer, enabling constant updating of presence information.
- The mobile device is becoming the personal trusted device, used not only for communication but also for contact management, identity and time management, providing an appealing platform for IM and other presence enabled services.
- The amount of data actually transferred is relatively small and does not require much bandwidth, hence allowing inexpensive services that will appeal to a mass market.

Presence Allows Continuous Mobile Bonding

Presence helps strengthen the bonds between consumers, as well as allowing them to communicate more effectively and appropriately with each other.

Because consumers are almost always online, presence will be used to indicate user availability for communication. Consumers will also be able to define how they wish to be contacted: in some situations, a voice call is not appropriate but a text message is.

To ensure effective communication between friends, presence services must offer a means of controlling privacy. While there is likely to be some presence information that can be shared with all consumers, an individual consumer must have strict control over all sensitive information, particularly that concerning location. Consumers are the ones who control their presence - they decide what others can see and when they can see it.

Mobile devices are developing to allow rich communication

Market Potential

The success of text messaging and related services, as well as the increasing numbers of subscribers to desktop instant messaging, indicate that consumers are ready for mobile instant messaging and presence services.

Young people are generally impatient when it comes to communication - they need to be reachable constantly and also be able to reach others all the time. If they do not receive a reply, they need to know why they are not being answered and when the person will be available again. This continuous sharing of availability, whereabouts and intentions, as well as constant monitoring of the mobile device, are typical of young consumers today.

Because mobile IM services are based on presence information and a mobile device is the ideal and preferred device for managing presence, the market opportunities of these services are huge. This potential has been verified by research. A recent survey [1] indicated that IM has become a huge phenomenon in Europe, the USA and Asia. The Spanish in particular spend as much as 10.6 days per month on IM services, with similarly high figures of 10 days per month for Germany, 8.5 days per month for the UK, and 8.4 days per month in France.

In the US, consumers spend an average of 8.9 days on instant messaging per month. In the Asian market, IM is again the number one messaging service used on the Internet, with usage as high as 32% in Hong Kong; 11% in South Korea, Taiwan and China; and 22% in Singapore.

Cahners In-Stat [2] found that more than 80% of the 10- to 17-years-olds surveyed said that they would like to use instant messaging on mobile devices.

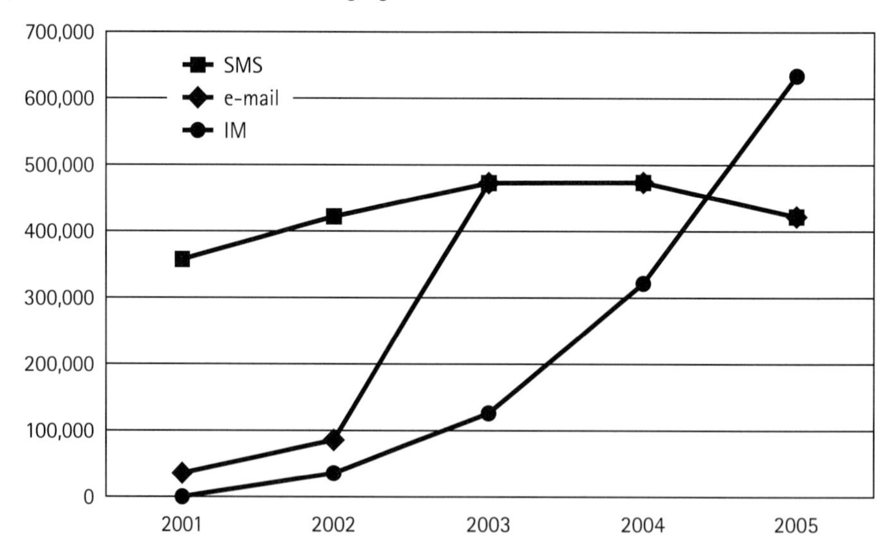

Worldwide Wireless Messaging Subscribers: User forecasts [2]

For the business sector, it is forecast [3] that 90% of companies will use instant messaging by 2003. In terms of revenue, another study [4] forecast that instant messaging services will have a monthly Average Revenue Per User (ARPU) of about US $4.5 by 2004. It predicts that IM will contribute nearly 20% of global carriers' messaging revenues by 2004.

Instant Messaging Appeals to All Users

The heaviest consumers of mobile IM and presence services will be young people, as they tend to use these services to keep in touch with their friends. This is something they have become used to through using SMS messages, and, in fact, young people can feel cut off from their friends if they do not own an SMS-enabled device.

Consumers who have adopted text messaging services enthusiastically are also likely to adopt mobile IM services. Also, users of Internet-based IM will find mobile IM to be a big improvement, with its lack of limitations on location and the freedom it brings from a fixed connection.

Also important is the corporate sector. These consumers expect to work more efficiently, have more control at work, save money and be able to transfer data. They will use presence services to keep up-to-date on events. Time is of the essence for these consumers, and presence awareness will help them save time and communicate more efficiently.

Carriers will also benefit through the ability to offer connectivity to all fixed instant messaging services, allowing their offering to stand out in the market.

The Winner Owns the Customer Base

In the early stages of mobile instant messaging, gateways to fixed instant messaging services will allow early adopters to communicate with any fixed instant messaging users.

Some carriers may opt for simply providing a gateway to existing instant messaging services. The financial risks may be lower, but the carrier may lose the opportunity to build its own customer base and to take advantage of the benefits mobility offers for presence services.

This gateway mode of operation will be useful in promoting mobile IM to fixed service consumers. However, as the number of mobile IM consumer increases, carriers can host a totally mobile customer base.

Carriers and other service providers have a central role in the mass adoption of instant messaging and presence services. Presence services have a central role in carriers' service portfolios since other services and applications can also be built on them.

Standardization

As IM and presence services improve, more consumers will start to use them. The main fear among consumers, and the main barrier to IM acceptance, is the walled garden phenomenon - the inability to communicate with consumers who are with another carrier.

To ensure that the IM systems of different carriers in different countries can work together, Nokia has joined forces with other important industry players to create an open global standard for a mobile IM and presence service.

Future of Instant Messaging

Based on analysis of mobile device usage and desktop IM services, we can make some predictions about what consumers will want from their services in the future.

Carriers with their own IM and presence service consumers will be able to learn from them and develop other value-added services related to instant messaging. Examples include extending into the corporate sector, creating new advertising possibilities and initiating sponsored instant messaging services. Customer Relationship Management (CRM) may also benefit from mobile IM and presence services because they can be integrated with other applications in the corporate environment. Also, presence information can be used to enhance other services (e.g., gaming and directory services).

In the future, IP Convergence will bring about a new era in messaging. The user experience will remain the same, but the underlying technologies will change.

Conclusions

We are at the beginning of a fascinating evolutionary path: we can now offer basic IM and presence services for consumers in the Mobile domain. As mobile devices and networks develop to support them, services will become richer. The presence system in particular is expected to evolve into content rich services that use the full potential inherent in mobile communication. In addition to being an attractive service, it will enable and enrich other services, IM being the obvious first one. Carriers need to play a part in this development to avoid missing the opportunities in related value-added services.

Above all, perhaps, is the importance of using open interfaces - only this way can we ensure a successful, global mobile instant messaging and presence system that provides a good consumer experience.

References

[1] Survey by NetValue

[2] Cahners In-Stat Group; Wireless Messaging Fusion. August 2001.

[3] Gartner Group

[4] Strategy Analytics

Presence

The mobile device is becoming a very personal device, even an extension of the user identity. This applies to the look and feel of the device itself as well as to how it is used and for what purposes. Applications and services that further this evolution and support the consumers' natural commutation patterns and individual needs in a fun and efficient way will be the most popular and sought after. Presence will be one of these services.

Presence as such is a familiar concept to those using instant messaging services in the Web domain. In the Mobile domain, presence information will not only enhance messaging but will become a service in its own right, one that can be leveraged in numerous types of applications and services. Presence will be the hub for all communication. Mobile telephony will benefit from presence information just as much as messaging.

Presence services will provide an appealing business opportunity to both, carriers and service providers, with many opportunities for leveraging. These in turn will bring forth more enriched applications with a personal look and feel, in the end resulting in increased revenue and reduced customer churn. A presence service is a tool with which consumers create their own content, so to speak, and share it with others. Presence is a way to make not just technology, but also services and communication itself more sensitive and personal.

Emerging Consumer Trends

Consumer behavior demonstrates a change in how people communicate and what they expect from communication devices. Until today, communication with mobile devices has been mostly driven by the need to communicate. Now, mobile communication is becoming more and more emotional and expressive.

Mobile communication is broadening and becoming a visual, emotional and interactive way of sharing one's presence. Therefore, presence itself, in this sense, will form a central part of the communication culture, technology and products.

Presence services support the consumers' need to continuously share their availability, whereabouts, intentions, preferences and even emotions. Even today, consumers are interested in what the party with whom they wish to communicate is up to before they place a call or message. Presence information addresses this, enabling the caller to see what the other person is up to.

Presence makes for a more refined means of communication. It shows the initiating party whether the person at the other end is available and willing to communicate. Presence information can also be used by any party to communicate information on when, with whom and by what means he/she is able or willing to communicate. This will allow consumers to control their own communication more effectively.

Availability sharing may raise some security and privacy concerns for some. These are delicate issues and are addressed differently by those of different cultures and with other differences in viewpoint. As consumers own their specific presence information, they are the ones to make these judgments. They have the final say in how the information is used.

Presence will be a key enabler and enrichment to multiple applications and services. There will also be many different categories of consumers, each of which will use the presence information for slightly different purposes. These groups will range from corporate business users to today's youth market. In the corporate environment, presence information is likely to be used more for rational availability management, whereas young consumers are constantly seeking new ways to express themselves and build identity in a fun and visually rich way. Successful presence services will be customizable to different needs of varied consumer groups and market sectors.

Concept of Presence

The modern concept of presence has its roots in the fixed Internet and PC environment. Instant messaging is a popular service, especially in North America. In the PC environment, it is the main and most popular tool for interactive communication, consisting of an intelligent friend directory and message management. Until recently, presence has been tightly combined with instant messaging, where it has been used mostly for availability management. The value in presence has been in knowing if friends are online, at their PCs. Instant messaging services on the fixed Internet have been a powerful tool for service providers to build a loyal customer base with minimal churn.

One definition of presence is: a perception of a human being that some other human being is close or nearby, mentally or physically. It is a perception held by person with a special bond to someone. According to these definitions, presence is tightly bonded to the human context. However, things and places may also have presence. And the transmission of presence information over longer distances can be viewed as an extension to the human senses. Carrying this further, network elements may utilize consumers' presence information in creating and providing more personalized services as well as deduce details on consumers' presence from raw presence data provided by various sources.

According to another definition of presence, it is a dynamic variable profile of the user, one which is visible to others and used to represent oneself, share information and control services. In essence, presence is two things: a person's status to others and the status of others to the person. Status may involve related information (e.g., personal and device status, location or context, device capabilities and preferred contact method).

Presence in the Mobile Domain

In the Mobile domain, presence will be a richer and even more powerful service than what many consumers have become used to in the Web domain. The mobile context will expand presence from being online for instant messaging into a powerful tool of self-expression and continuous mobile awareness. The mobile device is evolving into a Personal Trusted Device (PTD), and presence, among other features, will be one of the main drivers in this evolution.

Reasons why the use of presence will enhance mobile communications and provide an appealing service are easy to find: the mobile device is often already the primary means of storage for contact information and is carried along all the time. It follows its owner everywhere. Mobile communication is by nature very personal and person-to-person oriented. This, Nokia believes, will make the mobile device the de facto device for publishing and managing presence information.

Presence services will support all mobile communication, including real-time and delayed text messaging and relayed and delayed speech. Presence information is not restricted to named persons but can also refer to unnamed persons and even groups and intelligent devices. Presence information will initiate additional communication in the form of messaging and voice calls.

Mobile presence enables a new delicate background communication layer and continuous mobile bonding with the aid of 24/7 up-to-date presence information. It also enables emotional bonding for virtual groups and acts as a tool for a mobile virtual identity. People have the ability to create content that they actually know is useful to others.

When presence information is combined with contact information stored in the device (i.e., the phonebook), it will create a dynamic entity that naturally extends and enriches the static representation of contacts. Presence services enable more sharing of private information within small trusted groups as well as sharing availability information with a wider audience in order to enable more appropriate and effective communication. As mentioned earlier, presence information can serve rational as well as emotional and expressive needs.

A mobile presence application is a useful tool for creating mobile awareness of close contacts. Consumers are always online and therefore it is not worth announcing that in the similar way as in the PC context. The context for mobile presence is real life, not something artificial that one must log into. This is the fundamental difference from fixed Internet instant messaging.

In the Mobile domain, presence information is likely to also include information from the network (e.g., location), which has little meaning without mobility. Further, devices in the Mobile domain differ from each other in terms of display capabilities. For example, when networks and devices enable true mobile multimedia, it is also important to share information about device capabilities as one of the presence attributes. As there are legacy devices that do not support the latest features and functions, this information is important.

One clear consumer need is the ability to share different status information with different groups. This leads to multiple layers of presence depending on the type of people who are viewing the information. While there is likely to be some very simple presence information that can be shared with anybody, consumers are not willing to share everything with everybody. Also, information which applies to one group may not be detailed enough, appropriate, or even correct for another. For example, consumers' availability might be different for co-workers and family. Further, location information is a typical example of information that consumers are likely to share only with limited and user-selected contacts.

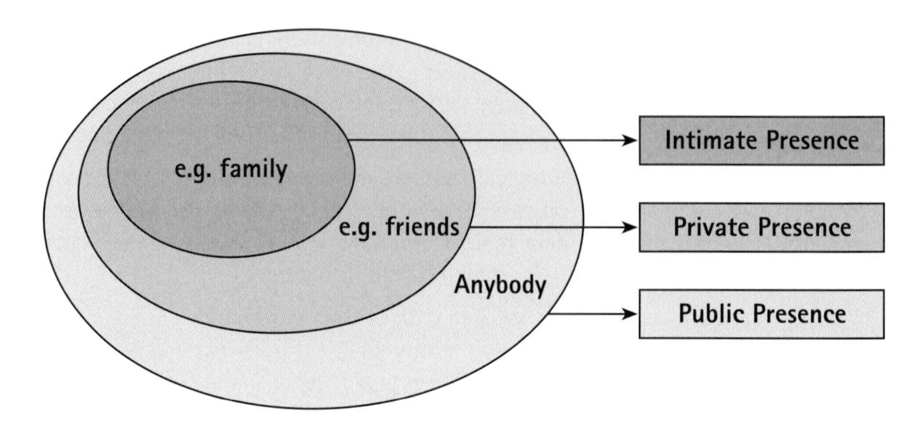

Multiple layers of presence

Mobile Presence Use Cases

Mike and the Problematic Valves

Mike has recently started working at Pipemaster & Co. Today he is in the Haga district heating center for the first time. A valve control unit there looks extremely strange to him. More experienced people must have fixed these in the past, so Mike decides to call for help. He looks at colleagues' presence information to see who is available for a quick consultation.

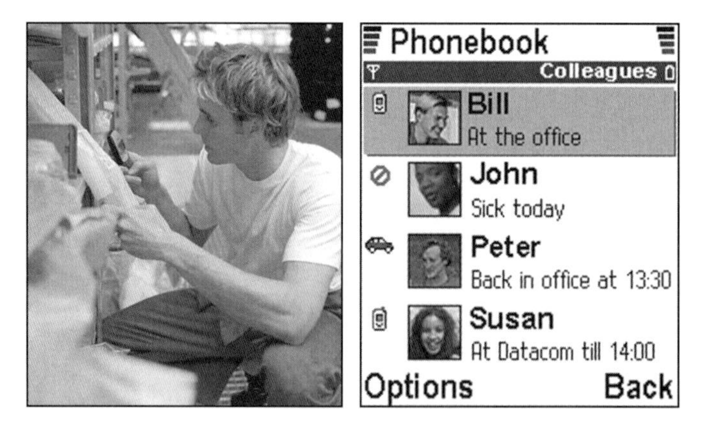

Mike with problematic valves and the device's presence display

Mike starts to go through his colleagues' information in his device. He has subscribed to all his co-workers' presence information in his dynamic phonebook. Once somebody changes his/her presence information, it is automatically updated in Mike's device in the background as well. This way he always has the latest presence information available. John seems to be sick today,

Peter is on the road, but Bill seems to be at the office and available. Mike decides to make a quick call to him. Normally, he would have just sent a text message, but this time the problem is a bit more severe than usual.

After the job, Mike marks the task as completed in the shared to-do list that is part of his presence information. He also checks his boss's information for any new urgent assignments. There are problems again at the Ferry Island power plant. He takes action and heads there right away. At the same time, he changes his preferred communication method to voice calls since it is hard to read text messages while driving. With his hands-free set, Mike can still handle calls. Now people know not to send him messages while he's driving to Ferry Island.

Lisa Connecting with Family

Lisa's mother is a busy professional woman who has plenty of meetings every day. Still, she and Lisa want to keep in touch. While she is in a meeting, Lisa's mother checks up on Lisa's presence information from her mobile device. The presence information is always up-to date. Lisa's school day is over, and she has switched on her mobile to be reachable by her mother and friends. Mother smiles as she notices the image she and Lisa created the evening before and uploaded as her presence information.

Lisa connecting with the family and displays for her parents' devices

Lisa checks whether it would be a suitable time to call Mom. From her phonebook she notices that her mother is in a meeting and wishes not to be disturbed. Lisa knows that she can always call her but decides not to disturb her so she sends a text message. She knows that her mother will call her later when she's out of the meeting.

Lisa also checks her father's status. Usually, he puts something funny in his presence information on Fridays, an amusing picture and a slogan to match. She guesses that he is a bit stressed today and decides to surprise him by baking a pie, so she heads for the grocery store. Lisa updates her presence to "Shopping", which is automatically sent in the background to both her parents' devices. Lisa knows that all her family members check the others' presence information on their way home. One can see if others are late for dinner, working late or already at home. Lisa decides to bake an apple pie, her dad's favorite.

Presence as an Appealing Business

The Mobile domain, now reaching almost a billion subscribers worldwide, is a lucrative platform for new consumer services.

Presence can contribute to existing businesses and create a business area of its own. There will be basic presence services for consumers, new presence-enabled services, and various content and infrastructure options as part of the presence business.

A basic presence service for the consumer establishes basic publish/receive features for presence information. This could be the core competence of carriers in the Mobile domain, as they have the opportunity to fetch various infrastructure related attributes (e.g., location), from their networks.

New presence-enabled services refer to several new services which use presence information in dedicated application areas (e.g., stock market alarms). This is a big opportunity for innovative, entrepreneurial companies. Another example is network gaming services.

Carriers and other service providers have a pivotal role in the mass adoption of presence services. Basic mobile presence services can have a central role in the carriers' service portfolio since other services can build on the basic presence service.

A presence service increases consumer loyalty, as shown by instant messaging over the fixed Internet. The implementation of the basic presence service can also be a competitive advantage over other carriers not implementing it: by binding presence information to other services, a carrier gives consumers high-value services that other carriers may not be able to offer without that information. There is a very strong personal channel to personalized services through presence information. A carrier may also decide to sell presence information to other service providers, with consent from the consumer.

As mentioned earlier, presence services generate new traffic in the form of messaging instead of unanswered calls. It also generates new voice and messaging traffic the same way as fixed Internet instant messaging has proved - changes in a consumer's presence information may result in a greeting or other kind of message.

The spread of consumer services, i.e., maximizing the penetration of presence-enabled services in the consumer base, can be achieved with great success by carriers. Key elements here are: implementing open presence technology standards, promoting service sales, signing carrier to carrier agreements regarding presence information exchange, and promoting innovative new presence-enabled services. The visibility of presence information across carrier boundaries is very important, as an average consumer has communication partners in many different carrier networks.

The pricing of presence services needs to be considered carefully. Carriers must ensure with their charging schemes that consumers are willing to take up the services and use them in a rich and expansive way. Nokia believes that there is considerable market potential in the presence area, comparable to SMS, should the price setting party in the value chain implement a moderate approach in this. Completely free presence services would neither enable nor support a healthy presence industry, nor would they enable quality of service or the offering of new innovative presence services to consumers in the long run.

Service Interoperability

The more presence capable devices there are and the better the communication network coverage is for presence service, the more useful presence will be for consumers. Nokia believes presence will be pervasive in the future. Therefore, it is imperative to ensure interoperability between different device manufacturers, presence servers and carriers, as well as Web and Mobile domains.

Instant Messaging and presence services are moving from the desktop to the Mobile domain. To support this, the Wireless Village initiative was set up by Ericsson, Motorola and Nokia, to build a community around new and innovative mobile Instant Messaging and Presence Services (IMPS).

As technology standards and delivery platforms mature, new standards arise and become de facto. It is important that the infrastructure offering comply with these new standards. Third generation networks and All-IP based mobile presence services are clearly a natural extension of the current presence infrastructure offering.

The availability of presence information will change mobile communication fundamentally. Consumers will be in touch with each other prior to initiating communication. Communication will become more effective and appropriate as consumers are able to share with others how and when they wish to be contacted.

Presence services will also offer a personalization opportunity as mobile devices become an extension and representation of one's identity and social network. As the mobile device continues to evolve into a personal trusted device, it will play a more significant role in consumers' lives. Applications and services that enable consumers to express their emotions and aspirations have true success potential, given a rapid implementation of the presence infrastructure, open technologies, and information sharing by carriers. With all these elements, they can boost third-party software development and moderate consumer pricing. With presence services, every consumer becomes a content creator as well as a publisher. Personality enters communication.

Multimedia Streaming

Enabling the Mobile Internet requires that the most successful mass-market services from the legacy Internet need to be accessible via state-of-the art mobile devices. Multimedia streaming is an appealing service that faces heavy technological competition on the Internet. This service is also technically applicable over evolving second- and third-generation mobile networks; thus, streaming clients will soon be deployed in advanced mobile devices.

Usage of streaming services on the Internet is booming. With these services going mobile, consumers' favorite animations, music and news services will be available independent of location and time. Accompanying this promise, the forthcoming multimedia services are also setting new challenges for the Mobile domain. Streaming technology is one way to meet these challenges. Streaming provides consumers with an end-to-end application that allows them to enjoy multimedia content when desired.

Nokia sees that core multimedia services must be based on open standards, in order to enable interoperability between devices and services as well as allow content and service creation by other companies. The current proliferation of proprietary streaming systems on the Internet is something we need to actively avoid in the Mobile domain, where there are already several application and equipment interoperability issues, with numerous device and network providers in place.

Evolution in radio access technology enables streaming to mobile devices even before the mobile industry welcomed transition to IP convergence with conversational mobile services over IP transport. The take-off of multimedia streaming is related to the overall development of the market.

Introduction

In the past, to view multimedia content on the Internet, consumers had to download the entire clip or file to their local hard disk drive before watching it. During the last couple of years, streaming has matured and gained high consumer acceptance, especially among users of Internet-enabled PCs. This technology is also seen as one of the new value adding Internet services, and competition in this area has been and continues to be challenging.

As an overall concept, streaming technology can be seen as pseudo-real-time consumption of multimedia content. With streaming services, a media player client opens a connection to the content server and starts to stream the media content at a payload rate. Then, the client starts to play the content immediately.

Multiple Benefits and New Experiences

Streaming does not just free valuable device memory; it also enables the distribution of larger media files as well as live services. The increasingly important issues related to illegal copying of content are also taken care of, for the content does not remain in the device after the streaming session is over. Content access, digital copyright management and streaming can be handled together, allowing a flexible and reliable way to distribute digital content in the Mobile Internet era.

The consumer needs a player, which is a special program that decompresses video and audio data. This client application must be able to control the streaming flow (control plane) and manage the media flow (user plane). In addition, the client also has to interface with the underlying transport network technology and the specific protocols and data bearers dedicated to the service.

Now, as access to Internet services is moving rapidly to mobile devices. The available computing capacity in devices is increasing, and data rates for consumers are approaching those of wired devices. Hence, streaming services are also technically feasible in mobile devices.

The first commercial streaming services may well utilize existing circuit switched bearer services, but the third generation network will see such services being offered over packet switched bearers.

Generally, multimedia streaming is, by definition, seen as including one or several forms of media, which are streamed or transported to the client over the network. Some example services are listed below.

- Audio streaming
- Streaming with an audio and a video component
- Audio streaming with a simultaneous visual presentation comprising still images and/or graphical animations, video clips presented in a pre-defined order

To give an overview of streaming as a technology, a framework of a typical multimedia content creation and retrieval system is presented in the next figure. The content creation system has one or more media sources (e.g., a camera and a microphone). To allow the creation of a multimedia clip consisting of different media types, the raw data captured by the various sources must be edited.

Typically, the storage space required for raw media data is huge. In order to facilitate an attractive multimedia retrieval service over generally available transport channels (e.g., low bit rate modem connections), the media clips are also compressed in the editing phase - after which the clips are handed to a server.

A number of clients can access the server over the network. The server is able to respond to the requests presented by the clients. The main task for the server is to transmit the desired multimedia content to the client. Then, the client decompresses and plays the clip. In the playback phase, the client utilizes one or more output devices, most often the device screen and speaker.

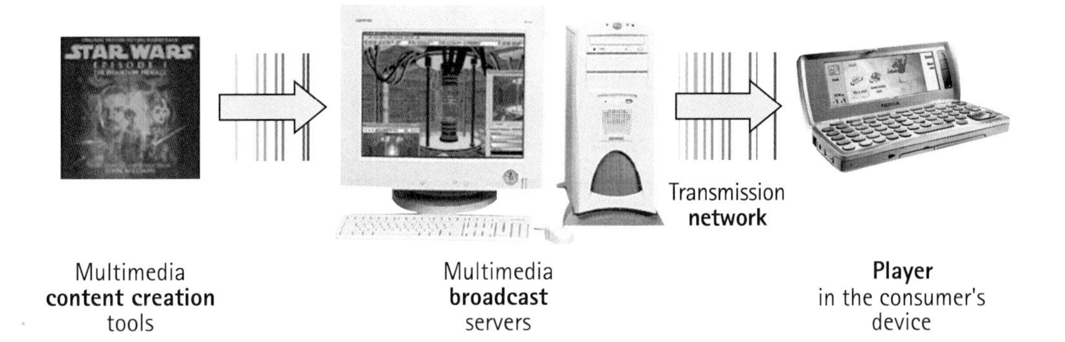

Nokia streaming solution

Nokia Streaming Solution

In order to meet the multiple challenges related to implementation for the streaming market, Nokia has entered an alliance with RealNetworks, the leading provider of digital media technology for the Internet, with more than 250 million registered users of its media player products, including its new RealOne Player. This alliance enables faster market take-off by already working to move much of the already existing content from the Internet into the Mobile domain and at the same time offering a solid path for evolution toward an open standard based streaming services solution. This provides attractive business models for all the stakeholders of the value system: many content owners and broadcasters can utilize their existing packaging systems and yet get access to the new mobile market. At the same time, carriers can provide faster take-off for new services for consumers.

Nokia will include the mobile version of the RealOne Player as a standard feature on those of its mobile devices that use the Symbian operating system. The RealOne Player, with support for Third Generation Partnership Project (3GPP) media formats, RealAudio and RealVideo, will be included as a standard feature on the Series 60 Platform. Nokia will also offer RealSystem Mobile, the RealNetworks delivery platform, as part of its infrastructure solution.

Evolution of Streaming Services

Early applications over High Speed Circuit Switched Data (HSCSD) bearers will likely consist of concise content, preview or pre-listening applications, and audio content accompanied by still images. The challenge for streaming over the General Packet Radio Service (GPRS) is Quality of Service (QoS). Alternative technologies for technical architecture (e.g., progressive downloading), are also being evaluated.

The keys to economical service provisioning in mobile streaming will be the QoS mechanisms brought by third generation network evolution in releases 4 and 5, the creation of a Packet Switched Streaming (PSS) system compliant content server infrastructure and content creation tools in carrier networks and on the public Internet, the necessary application-aware firewall systems, and the application of flexible charging mechanisms in the carrier's service infrastructure.

PSS can be deployed as a downlink transport mechanism for Multimedia Messaging Services (MMS), which will enable a new set of MMS-originated service possibilities. It will also remove obstacles posed by limited memory storage in devices, as the streaming content does not need downloading and storage prior to playback by the consumer.

New features standardized by PSS will enable services that will include vector graphics animations, subtitles with formatted text and synthetic audio in Musical Instrument Digital Interface (MIDI) format. There will be tools to optimize the service provisioning from servers to clients based on devices' media capabilities. With 3GPP Release 6, the multimedia services will have the standardized Digital Rights Management (DRM) tools to also provide highly copyrighted content for mobile streaming service subscribers.

New Services and Business Opportunities

Thus, the technical architecture becomes linked with the business architecture, as new streaming applications are challenging not only from a technological perspective but also from a pricing model and value chain perspective. In the packet-switched networks, the pricing models have to be flexible enough, with, e.g., content-based pricing or access to a certain amount of content for a flat fee. Value chains are getting more complex as different business models from the Web domain, content creation and Mobile domain are converging.

From the carrier service perspective, streaming is one of the key areas differentiating the third generation from the second, as it enables new, attractive service concepts. The most promising service concepts/use scenarios for mobile streaming include:

- **News and Information Services**: Streaming hotlines, sports broadcasts, news - audio, still images (e.g., Synchronized Multimedia Integration Language (SMIL)) video
- **Entertainment**: Streaming trial use of a game before downloading, music previews, movie previews before buying tickets, Internet radio, Web cam content, previewing of digital content
- **Communication and Messaging**: Viewing video content after the whole message has been received, *see what I see* concept, Session Initiation Protocol (SIP) voice mail control, talking and sharing video content by streaming

Multimedia streaming is also enabling an entirely new market channel to the Mobile domain for many content providers. By virtue of having only a small amount of content in the client at any instant, streaming offers a relatively secure means of content distribution and complements well the offering of downloading. Moreover, if the content is never actually stored in the device, the copyright issues regarding illegal use of the content are already addressed.

Standardization

Nokia sees that basic multimedia services must be based on open standards, in order to enable interoperability between devices and services as well as allow content and service creation by other companies.

In the area of mobile streaming, Nokia has been actively participating with 3GPP, which has been standardizing a network transparent PSS service. It was done the first time for 3GPP Release 4 and later in Release 5. 3GPP and Nokia will keep enhancing existing service features with additional ones in later releases. Nokia believes that a successful open standards based IP multimedia service will thus develop. And as a Release 4 service, it will offer a gateway to packet switched multimedia services prior to the SIP based IP Multimedia Subsystem (IMS) architecture of 3GPP releases 5 and 6. Nokia has also been active in the Third Generation Partnership Project 2 (3GPP2). The target is to harmonize the standards defining the streaming services.

Packet Switched Streaming Standard

The 3GPP packet switched streaming service is being standardized based on control and transport parts by the Internet Engineering Task Force (IETF) protocols Real Time Streaming Protocol (RTSP), Real-time Transport Protocol (RTP), and Session Description Protocol (SDP). A protocol stack for standardized streaming services is presented in the following figure.

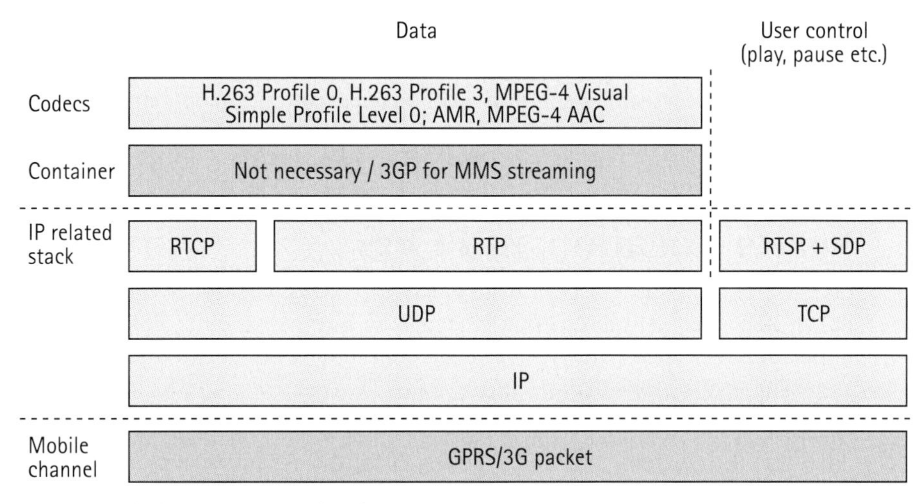

The packet switched streaming protocol stack

Codec standardization has not evolved far from the codec set already defined for multimedia services in 3GPP Release 99, as harmonization with existing 3GPP codecs is listed as one major goal of this work. 3GPP finalized a basic version of the service for Release 4. The next 3GPP milestone, PSS Release 5 frozen in March 2002, adds some new media types, additional presentation and layout features, support for subtitling and karaoke options, and a framework for enabling device capability based content adaptation in streaming servers.

Digital rights management for streaming services has been left for a later 3GPP release, which aims to generate a general DRM framework for all third generation services.

Nokia supports this approach, as the technical benefits in this approach are clear. They include the low license costs of implementations, protocol convergence with regard to IMS services, and WAP and Extensible HyperText Markup Language (XHTML) browser evolution in devices.

For example, the robust mobile Real-time Transport Protocol/User Datagram Protocol/Internet Protocol (RTP/UDP/IP) header compression will benefit only IETF standards-based media types, as it provides optimized spectral efficiency for streaming and conversational class multimedia services. In networks and devices, this meets the specifications of 3GPP Release 4 and onwards that specify the robust header compression functionality to radio access networks.

Other Streaming Standards

The 3GPP2 is in the process of completing a baseline video streaming service. Currently, definition of a new, broader Multimedia Streaming Service (MSS) comparable to PSS Release 5 is in its early phase. This service control and transport rely heavily on existing IETF protocols and will be compatible with the existing IP protocol stack. Relevant IETF protocols suggested in the latest contributions to 3GPP2 include specifications for control (RTSP), packetization and transport (RTP) and are thus similar to the 3GPP suggested specifications.

Mobile Streaming Server

A mobile streaming server has a key role in the streaming solution. It brings new business areas for carriers, media-rich services for consumers, and the development of more versatile applications. The streaming server also has an important role in optimizing quality of service for the customer. The streaming server consists of state-of-the-art functionality for video and audio streaming, and it also has media caching servers.

Server Location and QoS

Carriers need to provide access to streaming content hosted on the Internet and also have the option to host content locally that is specific to their subscribers. Both scenarios require that infrastructure software will be deployed within the carrier network to achieve a high-quality streaming media experience.

The delivery of streaming media in the Web domain has evolved to where high-quality packet delivery is usually accomplished by moving content close to the consumer - to the edge of the network - thereby minimizing the network path between content server and consumer. This so-called edge delivery architecture is used to reduce packet latency, allow audience scalability, minimize bandwidth consumption, and ultimately improve quality for the consumer. Applying the same edge delivery approach to the Mobile domain simply means that the carrier offers an additional node in a distributed delivery network.

The benefits of edge delivery in the Web domain are realizable in the Mobile domain, if not required. Deployment of replication technology within the carrier network must support caching of static streaming content and splitting of live content.

In addition, the deployment of a dedicated server and proxy within the Public Land Mobile Network (PLMN) also provides the opportunity to integrate QoS and billing mechanisms that are supported in the network so they are tied directly to the delivery of streaming content. This provides greater flexibility in tiered-service access plans for consumers.

Mobile Streaming Use Case

Here is an example of a service taking advantage of the streaming server. The consumer is checking cinema offerings with a mobile device and is offered preview clips of the films:

- After a movie clip is selected, a streaming request is authenticated and the service authorized before the clip is served
- The streaming server begins transmission of the clip and generates accounting information
- Transmission quality is monitored and, if network congestion makes it necessary, an adjustment is made to optimize the quality of the playback
- At the end of streaming, accounting information is updated and the session ends

Digital Rights Management and Streaming

Since streaming technology involves the content not being saved in the device after the streaming session is over, the increasingly important and complex issues of illegal copying of content are hence taken care of. Moreover, a flexible and reliable way to distribute digital content over the Mobile Internet is achieved as content access, DRM and streaming can be handled together. Mobile DRM provides the infrastructure for the usage and transaction control of content delivered over the air.

Conclusions

Streaming is an increasingly popular technology with which to view and listen to multimedia content. Now, streaming services are entering the mobile networks and offering new services and usage possibilities.

As a technology, streaming offers pseudo real-time service, which means that the consumer can play the multimedia content without downloading the entire file. This creates multiple benefits as it frees valuable device memory and enables the distribution of larger amounts of media content to a device as well as live services.

Additionally, streaming also prevents illegal copying of the content because the content is not saved in the device but is instead consumed on the spot, making it a secure way to distribute digital content over the Mobile Internet.

The actual consumption of streaming services requires a streaming server for content storage and delivery and a media player for content viewing.

Like most new technologies, streaming enables attractive new service concepts. The most promising early applications can be found in the fields of information, entertainment and person-to-person communication.

Streaming provides multiple benefits. Consumers can enjoy multimedia content when they desire, even when they are on the move. Carriers can have new and differentiating service concepts. Content providers will have a new market for their Digital Rights Management protected content.

Content Downloading

Almost everyone has downloaded ringing tones and screen icons to a mobile device. Now, more services are entering the market. Consumers can enhance their devices with interactive, dynamic applications, downloaded and stored in their devices for use when they want or need them. And when they are no longer needed, it is easy to delete them. The time for mass-market content downloading is now.

Examples of downloadable applications include interactive games, life management services, Musical Instrument Digital Interface (MIDI) ringing tones, Symbian applications, travel-related services and information tools. The possibilities are limitless, and hundreds of thousands of developers around the globe are gearing up to unleash their creative potential for downloadable applications.

For carriers, downloadable application portfolios provide better ways to stand out from the competition and to offer personally relevant services to consumers - increasing customer loyalty and Average Revenue Per User (ARPU).

Protection of downloadable content and applications through Digital Rights Management (DRM) technologies ensures that content developers' rights are respected and their products are not illegally copied, distributed or otherwise misused by consumers. On the other hand, DRM can also enable new, secure and consumer-friendly preview and superdistribution services. Both, the protection of distributed content and increased consumer satisfaction are also beneficial for carriers offering download services.

Establishing a solid download business requires carriers to implement certain components in their network infrastructure. This includes connectivity products (e.g., Wireless Application Protocol (WAP) and Messaging gateways, delivery mechanisms integrated with the billing system, service portals and content storage). Nokia is committed to providing a solution with all components necessary to start the business as well as fulfilling the crucial requirement of simplifying the downloading process for consumers.

More Freedom for Personalization

Mobile devices have become very personal for many of us. We carry them with us, just like we carry a wallet and keys. Just like we would hate to lose wallet and keys, the loss of a mobile device would make us miserable. All these items are needed daily, and often they are personalized in one way or another: a wallet could have family pictures inside, a key chain has distinguishing items hanging from it, and mobile devices have color covers and personalized ringing tones. Recognizing the personal value of a mobile device helps us to understand the value of content downloading - it simply allows us to personalize our daily lives even more.

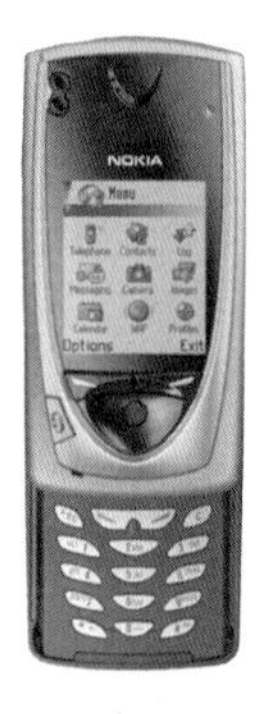

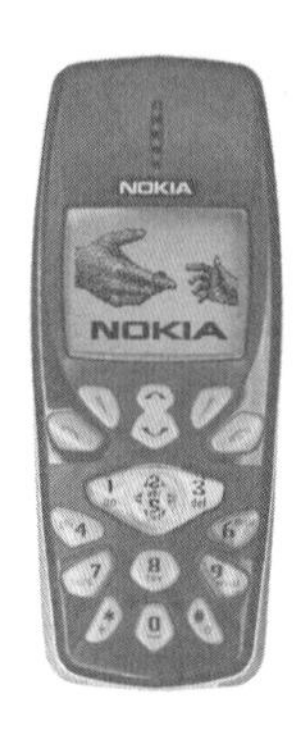

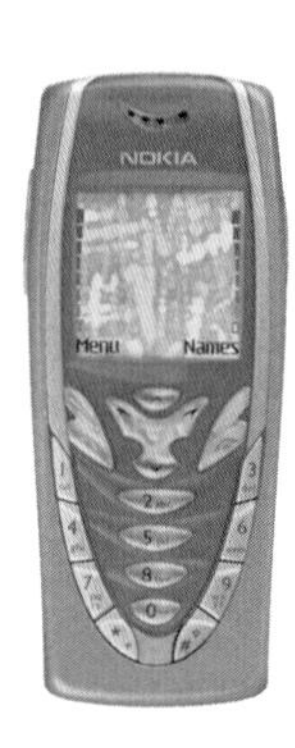

Downloading provides personalized services on demand.

Content Download Over WAP Session

There are several ways to receive content in mobile devices, including messaging (SMS, smart messaging and MMS), streaming, downloading and loading via a connection with a PC. Content download means transferring non-markup content from a server to a device, over the air (OTA), for more than a single use.

Currently, the WAP Session Protocol (WSP) provides the most efficient way of delivering files or applications to mobile devices. A WAP Session provides a reliable connection between client and server, allowing the delivery of fairly large files and enabling efficient re-transmission in case errors occur during the delivery process.

Downloading Java Applications

Wireless Java™ is a great example of content downloading. The download process of Java content has gained momentum in the mobile industry, resulting in standards and recommended practices for over-the-air delivery of Java applications. Wireless Java provisioning is also setting the standard for the download of generic content types.

Java technology is a key enabler when developing downloadable stand-alone and online applications for business and entertainment purposes. When the user downloads Java 2 Micro Edition (J2ME™)/Mobile Information Device Profile (MIDP) content, the actual download is performed as specified in "Over the Air User Initiated Provisioning Recommended Practice for the Mobile Information Device Profile 1.0". This is an appendix to the MIDP 1.0 specification defined by the Java Community Process (JCP) and widely accepted by the industry.

Device Type Recognition

The most distinctive difference of the delivery of Java applications from that of other content types available today involves device type recognition and confirmation of successful downloads. Device type recognition ensures that the requested Java service actually runs on the device and is optimized for the device's capabilities. Customers need not worry about the content selection because the delivery platform will request the right content type for the device. Device recognition utilizes the user agent information that is found in the request header. The user agent information holds the device type and configuration details of MIDP and CLDC versions.

Confirmation of Successful Downloads

A confirmation message allows carriers and service providers to ensure that only successful downloads are being charged to the consumer. Dividing the delivery of Java applications into two parts enables confirmation.

In the first part, the user will receive a Java Application Descriptor (JAD) file containing the Uniform Resource Locator (URL) of the resource file, content creator, name of the application and file size. Transparent to the user, the JAD file determines the size of the memory of the mobile device, ensuring that the device can store the requested application in memory. The JAD also specifies the server address to which the application connects for information updates. After these routine checks, the consumer can continue, to retrieve the actual Java Application Resource (JAR) file.

In this second part of delivery, the resource file is delivered to the mobile device. After the whole JAR has been delivered, it is checked against the JAD to ensure that transmission was successful. If the data match, the device will auto-install the application and send a confirmation message to the server. In the event of a mismatch, the user is given a failure message and installation is not implemented; neither will the server receive confirmation.

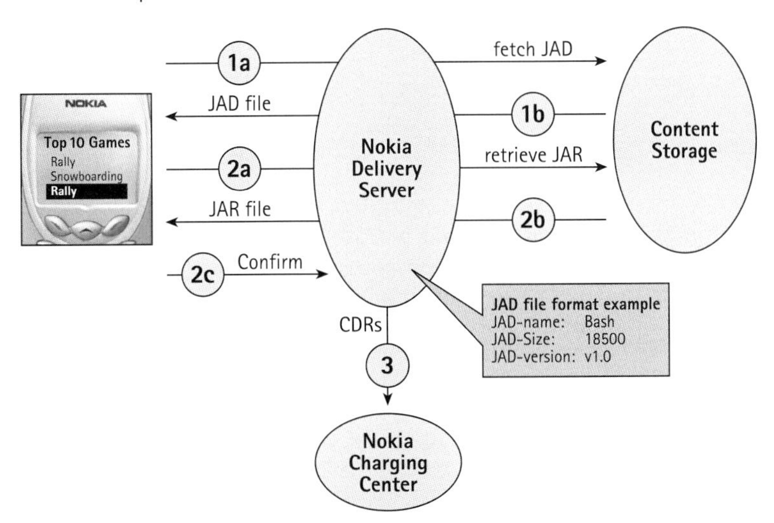

Delivery process flow after the content download link has been selected

While Java applications are the first content type following the industry defined process, other content types are starting to follow the same principles in order to provide more control for content downloading.

Downloading Generic Content

Content delivery should not be restricted to Java applications. Rather, the platform should enable download of various content types, including polyphonic MIDI ringing tones, screensavers and more.

The specification for over-the-air download of generic content defines a mechanism for reliable download of non-Java content. The concept is derived from the open solution defined by the Java Community Process (JCP).

The specification defines a Content Object Descriptor (COD) content type, which is almost identical to the JAD media type in syntax and semantics. The COD content type adapts the JAD media type to fit generic content.

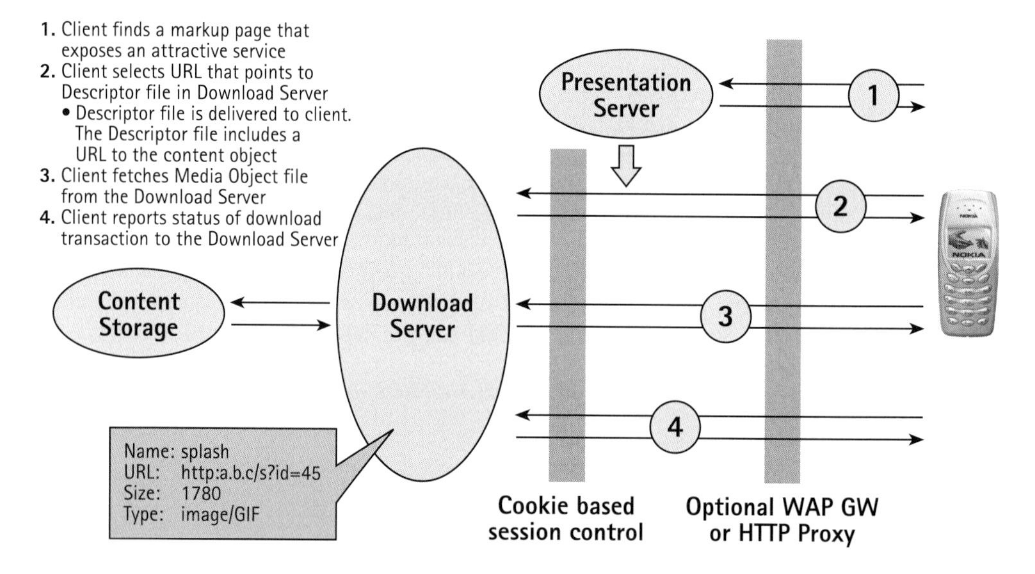
1. Client finds a markup page that exposes an attractive service
2. Client selects URL that points to Descriptor file in Download Server
• Descriptor file is delivered to client. The Descriptor file includes a URL to the content object
3. Client fetches Media Object file from the Download Server
4. Client reports status of download transaction to the Download Server
Presentation Server
Content Storage
Download Server
Name: splash
URL: http:a.b.c/s?id=45
Size: 1780
Type: image/GIF
1
2
3
4
NOKIA
Cookie based session control
Optional WAP GW or HTTP Proxy

Content delivery flow for generic content

The biggest benefit of descriptor file usage includes verification that requested content could be interpreted and used in the consumer's device and confirmation of successful downloads. Additional benefits include assurance of sufficient memory on the receiving device before delivery of the resource file.

Authentication with JAD and COD

In order to perform financial transactions related to download, the download server must have knowledge about the authenticated identity of the client.

In the ideal case, this is implicitly available (e.g., as a Mobile Station International ISDN Number (MSISDN) extracted from the mobile network (from the access router or GGSN)). If the MSISDN is not available, the client connects to the download server and identity is requested.

The HyperText Transfer Protocol (HTTP) provides a simple challenge/response authentication mechanism that may be used by a server to issue a challenge in response to a client request and by a client to provide authentication information.

This exchange can be performed within the context of the download transaction. It is also an authentication method where the client clearly is aware of the authentication process, and the identity of the server with which the authentication is performed can be displayed to the consumer.

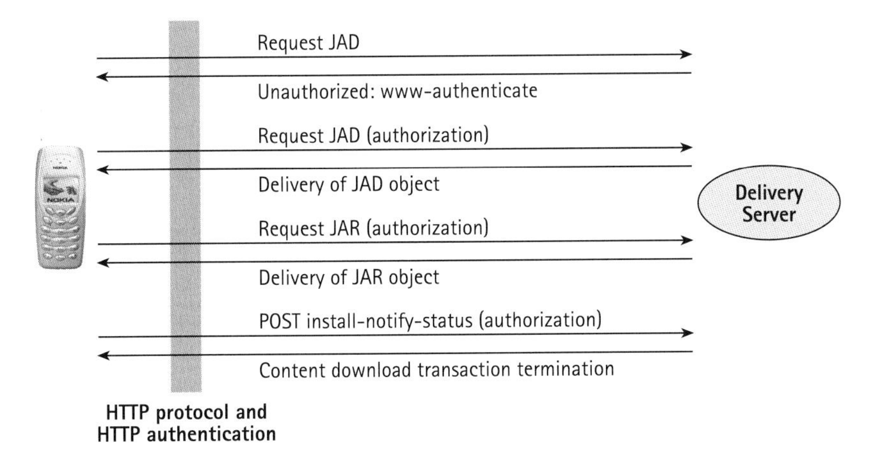

Authentication process when MSISDN is unavailable

One can conclude from the preceding paragraphs that usage of a descriptor file and resource file provides enhanced control of delivery mechanisms. The material which follows examines the whole end-to end delivery process and its main features.

Content Delivery Process

Nokia has a strong commitment to content downloading. This involves wide developer support with software development kits, documentation, application examples and commercial support - all helping the markets to experience innovative applications and services offered by Nokia partners. Second, Nokia continues to lead the mobile markets with feature-rich and well-designed devices capable of storing applications locally, in memory. Third, Nokia is building an open, standard-driven network architecture with server products enabling over-the-air downloads.

To understand the different steps in the content delivery process, it is necessary to examine the basic features of Nokia's solution for content downloading.

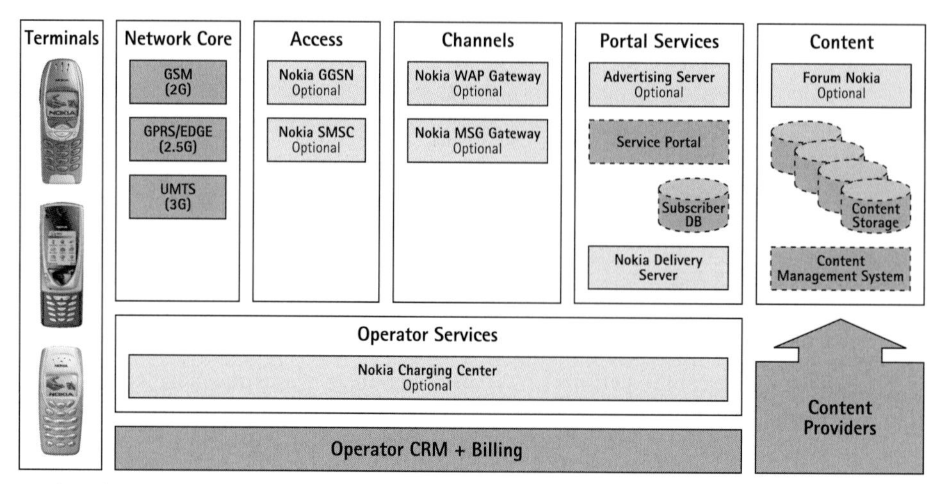

Sample configuration of Nokia solution for downloading content

Content Discovery

Every download process starts with discovery of the content. The consumer can initiate download using three methods: SMS messaging, WAP and legacy Internet browsing.

Today, most people send a keyword in an SMS to a service number in order to receive desired content (e.g., a ringing tone or logo). Having gained wide acceptance among consumers, pull initiation via SMS is a basic feature of a content downloading platform.

The second option is WAP browsing or Extensible HyperText Markup Language (XHTML) content with a mobile device. Here, the consumer can utilize either pull or push initiation to find the content and download it to the device's local memory.

The third option for content discovery is legacy Internet browsing with a desktop computer. The consumer utilizes convenient input and display features to find desired content and identifies the mobile device number where actual content will be delivered.

All three scenarios utilize different initiation methods while actual delivery is then provided using the WSP. SMS and legacy Internet initiations trigger a WAP-push message response from the service portal. The consumer receives a description of the object to download and a link for continuing the download transaction. The consumer follows the link, and file transmission begins.

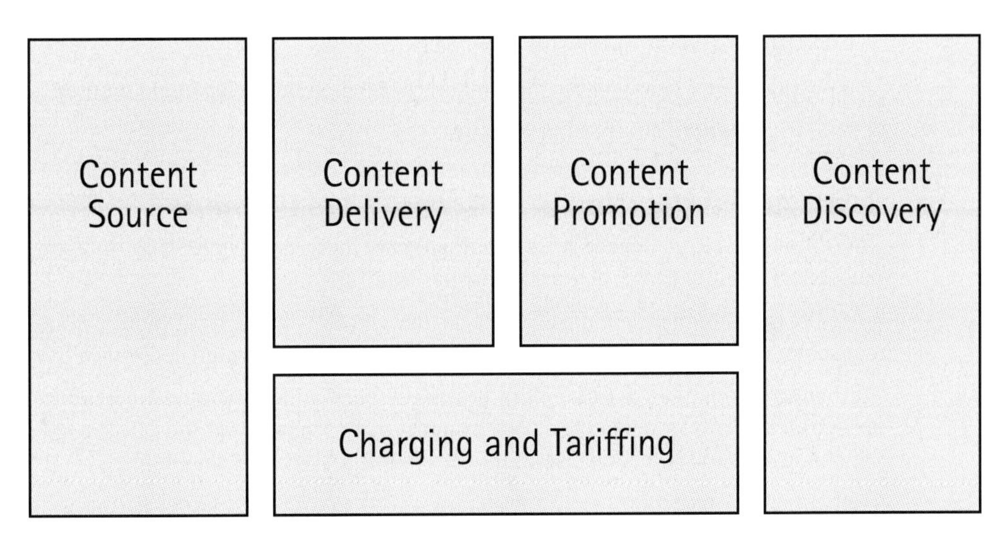

The downloading process can be divided into five logical steps.

Content Promotion

There are different media and channels to help consumers to find content. Carriers and service providers are encouraged to use innovative ways to promote applications, in addition to their service portal.

Printed media have had an impact on the ring tone and logo business, encouraging carriers to utilize this established channel in the future for other applications. Radio and television are starting to merge with mobile communications, using SMS voting and other interaction methods to affect the selection of programs and music. Service providers and carriers should consider taking advantage of these media, if not through direct marketing, then with sponsorship. The most lucrative channel may still lie in subscription-based notifications. Benefiting from existing Customer Relationship Management (CRM) databases allows service providers to send weekly notifications to consumers and to explain the latest service offerings.

Combining the promotion channels with sensible marketing messages and cost control can lubricate service discovery and encourage consumers to download applications that are relevant to them.

Content Delivery

Content delivery starts at the point when a consumer selects a link for downloadable content. From that point on, the Nokia solution for content downloading takes care of the following tasks:

- User authentication and access management
- Service authentication being requested
- Device recognition

- Confirmation of successful downloads
- Support for charging for the content, depending on the charging method
- Log creation for reporting purposes

User Authentication and Access Management

There are three recommended ways to authenticate the subscriber: MSISDN, International Mobile Subscriber Identity (IMSI) and username/password pair.

MSISDN based authentication refers to action wherein the carrier's mobile portal checks the consumer's phone number and determines if the consumer has paid in advance or will pay later.

Authentication based on IMSI refers to device-specific identification wherein the consumer's device identifier is stored in the carrier's database. This means that the device owner will always be charged even if someone else's SIM card is being used with the device.

Authentication based on username and password can be used either as the primary method (e.g., with the consumer always asked to input these identifying details) or secondary, used only when MSISDN/IMSI is not available.

Service Authentication

When the consumer selects a link for downloading an application, there is a small risk that an unauthorized party might try to push illegal content to the consumer. Therefore, Nokia's solution ensures that only the requested service from the authorized provider is delivered. This security can be implemented different ways, but one of the most commonly used is to manage the access authority of pre-defined IP addresses. The carrier managing the delivery mechanism specifies the IP addresses that can push content to its delivery system. Often firewalls and leased lines are used to enhance the security. This approach seems simple but is very effective.

Device Recognition

Today, services can be based on multiple formats, not all of which are supported by all mobile devices. Furthermore, devices have different capabilities and configurations. In order to optimize services offered to consumers, application developers must manage device capability and content format fragmentation issues (e.g., display sizes, tone generation support and vibration features). At the same time, carriers and service providers must be able to provide an easy-to-use download mechanism with as few clicks as possible for the consumer. Therefore, transparently identifying the device type is extremely important.

Many devices available today are capable of attaching user agent capability information to the request header. In simple terms, the mobile device sends an identification string which explains its basic capabilities to the server.

The delivery platform reads the user agent capability information provided in the request and makes an Extensible Markup Language (XML) request to content storage. Content storage holds XML documents for every application variant, and each of these documents includes information about the target device for which it is designed. When the delivery platform finds the correct application variant, it responds to the consumer with a descriptor file and the delivery process continues as described earlier.

Confirmation of Successful Downloads

The confirmation message has importance for two main reasons: first, it allows carriers and service providers to ensure that they charge only for successful download and, second, a download can be automatically retransmitted in a cost-effective manner, if unsuccessful.

When descriptor-based content (e.g., JAD or COD) is delivered, the device can compare the descriptor against the resource file, generating a status report. In the event of an unsuccessful download, a segment corrupted in transmission can be re-sent to correct the error. For successful status, the mobile device sends confirmation to the delivery mechanism. Confirmation then triggers the charging transaction.

Charging for Content

Many charging methods are available. The most common of these are pre-paid and post-paid accounts. A pre-paid account often involves an In-Advance Credit Check (IACC) to ensure that the account has a sufficient balance. Carriers can also choose to reserve or deduct money before the delivery of the application. The post-paid method is most commonly used with small payments (e.g., for ringing tones, logos and Java applications). Post-paid charges should utilize a confirmation message so that the delivery mechanism creates a Call Detail Record (CDR) only after verification. The charging system will then periodically collect the CDRs using a File Transfer Protocol (FTP) request and forward them to the billing system.

Log Creation for Reporting

The Content Download platform should enable tools for analyzing market behavior. Therefore, the service portal should be able to request log data from the delivery mechanism and collect information about the most wanted applications, as well as consumer behavior.

The Nokia Content Downloading solution supports log requests, to provide the information necessary for carriers and service providers to adapt their service strategies appropriately.

Content Protection

For the delivery of digital content to be beneficial for all parties concerned, solid methods for managing the use of the content need to be in place. To ensure profitable business, content providers' copyrights need to be protected so that they will continue to publish good digital content. From the consumer's point of view, content protection can be used for enabling new features (e.g., previews and superdistribution). These requirements can be supported by Digital Rights Management (DRM) technologies, which will offer methods for content protection and add new dimensions to content discovery.

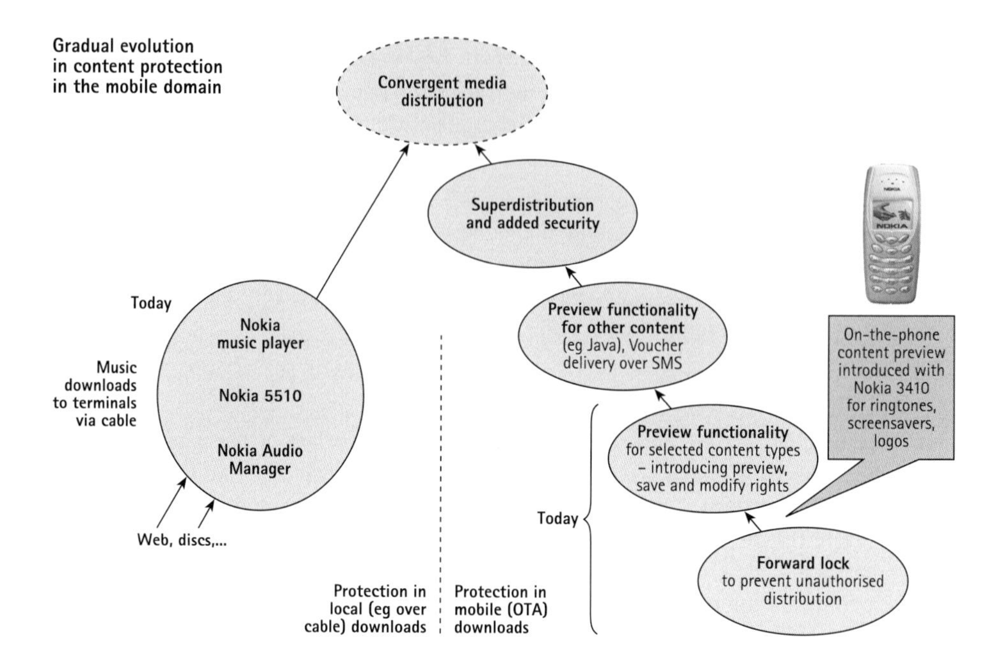

Evolution of content protection in the mobile domain

Nokia views content protection in the mobile domain as evolving in two parallel tracks, which will converge later as technology and standardization matures. The left-hand track in the picture above describes solutions for downloading content over the Internet to mobile devices through PCs, and the right-hand side describes evolution in the Mobile domain.

Conclusions

Mobile devices are an important part of our daily communication. As technology evolves, it brings more services and personalization capabilities for consumers. Content downloading began with icons and ring tones and is now moving toward more advanced applications. At the same time, the mobile industry must ensure easy-to-use processes and profitable operations. This means that content downloading involves not just the simple delivery of applications or files but the charging and copyright issues. Nokia has committed to standardized solutions in order to provide a beneficial business ecosystem for all parties. Through the standards, consumers can enjoy interoperable services over multiple carriers' networks, using various device types. The Nokia solution for content downloading is in line with this commitment, enabling all parties to enjoy the evolution of mobile communication.

Data Synchronization

Having your personal information and data always available and up-to-date is mandatory for the contemporary consumer, and even more so for corporate citizens. Consumers are, to an increasing extent, keeping their key data with them in electronic devices (e.g., laptops or mobile devices). As these devices are nowadays only intermittently connected to the network, consumers are, in practice, forced to maintain several copies of the same information. As the magnitude of the data grows, maintaining current information on each device becomes an ordeal. The process of comparing databases and making them current and identical is called data synchronization.

The importance of a convenient tool for data synchronization has created a myriad of prospective solutions from different vendors. Unfortunately, these solutions have simultaneously created a synchronization challenge for the consumers. The solutions have been based on proprietary protocols, each of which has supported only a limited number of applications, operating systems and transport protocols. As a result, keeping the information current on separate devices is, at best, quite inconvenient and is, at worst, impossible.

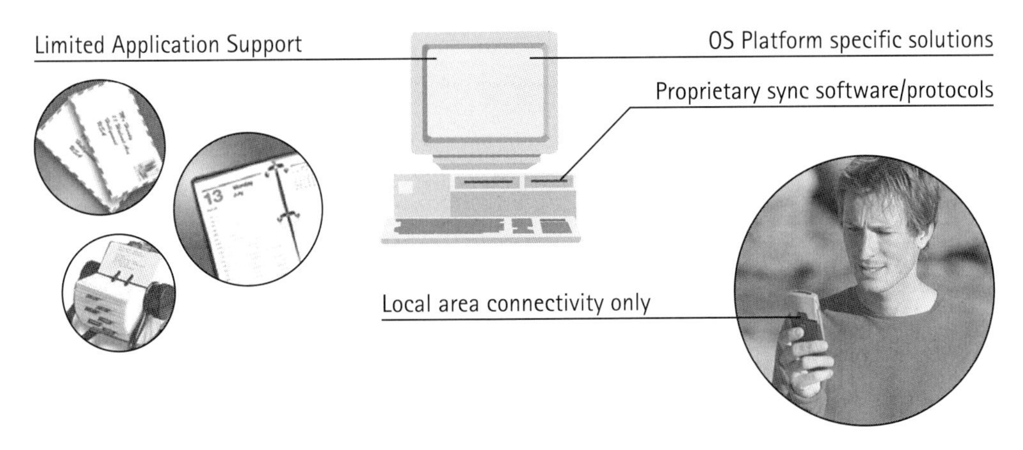

The synchronization challenge

The SyncML Data Synchronization (SyncML DS) protocol is an open industry specification for keeping data up-to-date between different devices. In short, SyncML DS is the common language for data synchronization, allowing convenient and seamless data synchronization between different kinds of devices, regardless of the vendor, operating systems and/or connection network.

In more technical terms, SyncML DS supports a variety of transport protocols and arbitrary networked data. It is easily expandable and based on eXtensible Markup Language (XML), which is widely considered a future-proof choice. SyncML DS effectively addresses the resource limitations of mobile devices and has been optimized to work with a variety of applications and devices. At the moment, SyncML DS is the only available synchronization protocol that can deliver this kind of universal connectivity. SyncML DS technology has firm industry support, and it is the protocol of choice for universal data synchronization.

SyncML DS Technology

SyncML DS is based on the server/client architecture, where a SyncML DS server handles the synchronization session between two databases. As illustrated in the following figure, a user connects with a SyncML DS enabled device to a SyncML DS synchronization server. The SyncML DS server is connected to the remote database. The SyncML DS server handles the resolution of conflicting entries and updates the information on both the device and the remote database. The information in the device and the remote database is thus made identical.

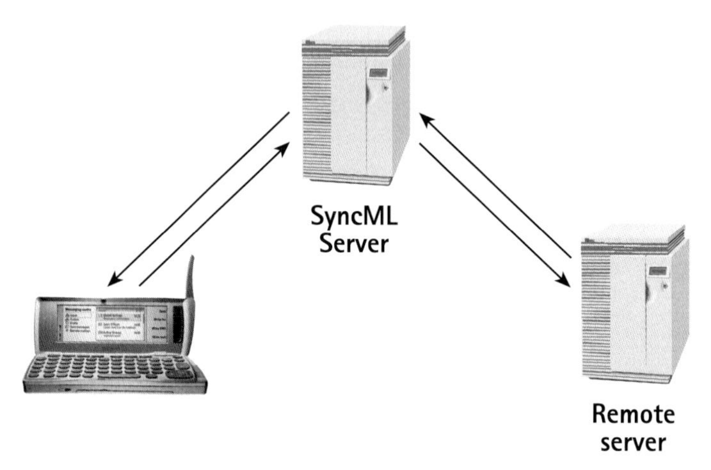

Client/server architecture

SyncML DS is transport independent and, thus, capable of synchronizing data over many different protocols used by mobile and networked applications. It works smoothly and efficiently over the HyperText Transfer Protocol (HTTP), the Wireless Session Protocol (WSP), Object Exchange (OBEX), the Simple Mail Transfer Protocol (SMTP), Post Office Protocol (POP), the Internet Message Access Protocol (IMAP), Transmission Control Protocol/Internet Protocol (TCP/IP) networks, and other transport protocols. The most commonly used protocols are HTTP, WSP and OBEX.

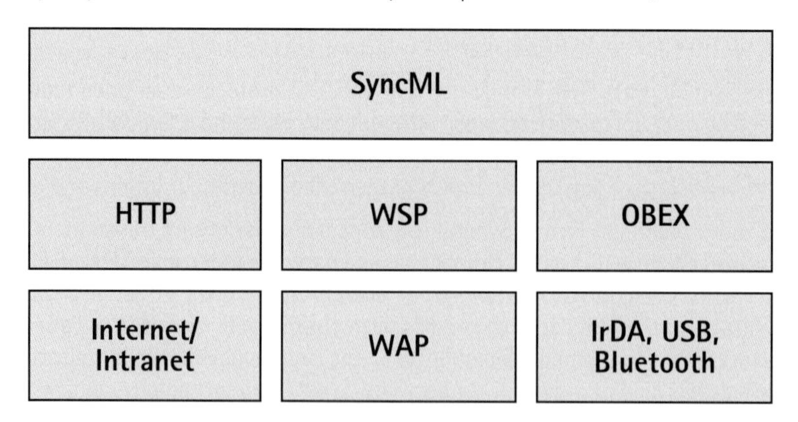

SyncML DS in protocol stacks

In short, SyncML DS offers a versatile tool for integrating data synchronization capabilities into any service concept. The protocol does not mandate how information is represented or organized in the device or within the networked data repository after synchronization is complete. As SyncML DS enables mobile devices to communicate with a vast range of data, the protocol also supports simultaneous synchronization with multiple network data stores.

In the first phase, SyncML DS enabled devices synchronize Personal Information Management (PIM) data (e.g., contact information and phone numbers, calendars, to-do lists). This provides carriers and service providers with an opportunity to offer new services where the personal information of consumers is stored and synchronized with their system. By combining SyncML DS and time-critical content, calendar management can be turned into a valuable service wherein interesting events and time-critical information are fed into mobile devices. The consumers will receive the information they need and want at any time and any place.

Security

The SyncML DS specification uses the security mechanisms of the underlying transport media. Thus, no restricting security schemes have been defined. SyncML authentication is based on basic or digest access authentication defined by the Internet Engineering Task Force (IETF): Base64 encoding and MD5 are used, respectively. Authentication can be performed on several levels: between the synchronization server and a client, on the database level and on operation levels. Other authentication schemes can be specified by prior agreement between the originator and the recipient.

Interoperability

To ensure interoperability, the protocol defines how common data formats are represented over the network. To ensure extensibility, the protocol permits the definition of new data formats as the need arises. In addition, the protocol allows implementers to define experimental, non-standard synchronization protocol primitives. The most commonly used data formats that the protocol supports from the outset include vCard for contact information and vCalendar for calendar, to-do list and journal information.

Interoperability is ensured by a specific interoperability testing procedure determined by the SyncML Initiative, a non-profit organization developing SyncML DS technology. Currently, the SyncML Initiative has made available a self-test for testing specification conformance and held a Syncfest event for interoperability testing with other vendors' and manufacturers' products.

SyncML Evolution

SyncML is rapidly evolving into the de facto standard in universal data synchronization. SyncML DS is thus the protocol of choice for data synchronization in the Mobile domain.

The first services will concentrate on offering personal information synchronization and combining the information with interesting content. In the future, SyncML is going to be expanded to support new data types (e.g., images, files, and database objects). Expansions will build and offer vertical applications for corporate users (e.g., company files, sales data, SCM, and fleet management), and consumers (e.g., information services and interactive games).

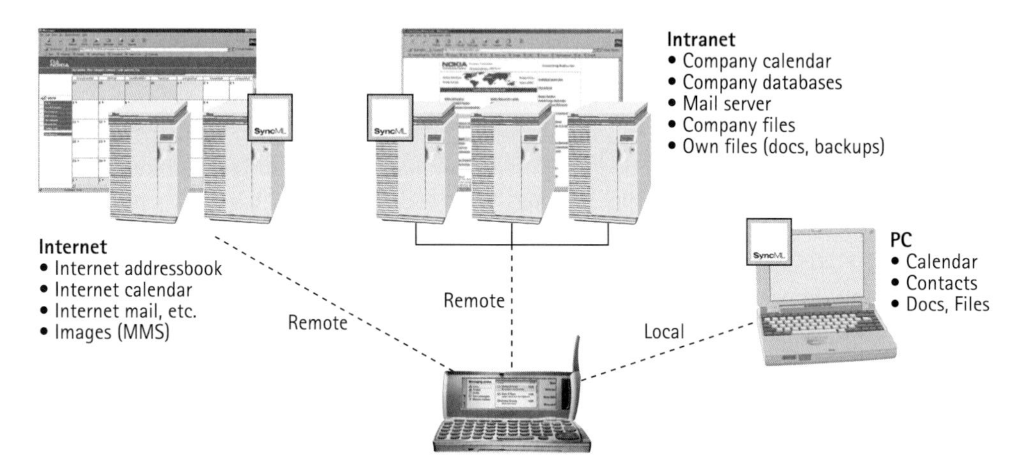

SyncML enabled services

Carriers and service providers are naturally best positioned to offer and benefit from data synchronization services. By offering these services to corporate users and consumers, carriers have a viable method for generating concrete revenues and for reducing churning via creating sticky services involving the critical information the consumers are interested in.

Conclusions

SyncML DS is the protocol of choice for universal data synchronization between devices from different vendors and systems. SyncML DS has comprehensive industry support and is supported by several mobile device vendors. By enabling convenient and seamless data synchronization between any devices and over any kind of network, SyncML DS benefits both consumers and carriers/service providers:

- **Consumers** - they can finally have their data with them. Any time. Any place.
- **Carriers and service providers** - they can easily create solutions for all SyncML enabled devices using one enabling technology, without interoperability constraints.

Carriers and service providers are playing a crucial role in the deployment of the technology. They are in the best position to offer and benefit from synchronization servers and services. By offering the service to corporate customers and consumers, they have the opportunity to reap concrete revenues and reduce churning via enhanced services.

Device Management

As the functionality of mobile devices grows at an increasing rate, the consumers of these devices have less time to spend on configuring and maintaining the devices. This development is leading to a perilous situation, into which a third party (e.g., a carrier or service provider) must step to alleviate the consumers' problem by managing the devices for them. Device Management (DM) is a generic term for technological tools used in provisioning, managing and updating the mobile devices on behalf of the consumers. The management operations to be supported are:

1) **Remote Parameter operations**: Provisioning key parameters to enable key services (e.g., browser settings)
2) **Remote Diagnostics and troubleshooting**: Identifying and remedying parameter-related error situations on the device, remotely via the mobile network
3) **Software Operations**: Updating part(s) of the software on the mobile device or installing new software packages.

Device management development is legitimately driven by business concerns. Even in the short term, device management will enable concrete competitive advantages via parameter provisioning, service activation, keeping track of device fleet capabilities and direct cost savings. This is illustrated in the figure below.

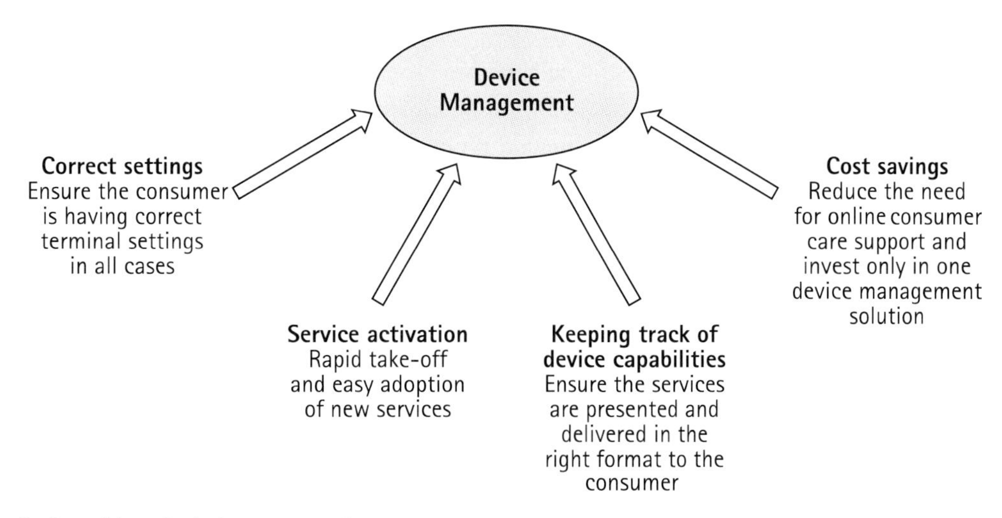

Business drivers for device management

Device management technology is increasing in importance due to the immediate need for a convenient tool for provisioning services and for a credible growth path for enabling technology for the advanced functionalities of the future. Nokia believes that the majority of the mobile devices launched after 2003 will support a standards-based device management solution. A solution based on open standards will enable the management of a multitude of devices with only a single infrastructure investment, also sidestepping any possible infrastructure lock-in.

Market Forces

A critical impediment to the adoption of value-added services in the Mobile domain has been, and continues to be, the convenient and simple provisioning of parameters to actually enable the services on mobile devices. The average consumer finds the manual configuration of Wireless Application Protocol (WAP) parameters very inconvenient and, in the worst case, impossible. This translates directly to a considerable amount of lost revenues as well as consumer dissatisfaction concerns for carriers and service providers. In short, there is a direct need for a technological tool for convenient provisioning of the key parameters today.

In the short term, the nature of mobile devices is dramatically changing as their functionality increases with the addition of new, more powerful and richer applications. At the same time, these increasingly advanced devices remain in mass-market environments to be used by consumers with minimal technical interest or skill. This development is leading to a situation where external parties locally or remotely maintain or configure the computers for consumers.

Device Management can be used to manage very different data objects. Some of the data objects are simple numeric or textual parameters, while others are more complex binary data structures. Numeric objects may include connectivity parameters (e.g., access point addresses and proxy configurations). Binary objects may be security keys or even displayable content (e.g., animations, screensavers and caller identification animations). In the future, the DM system could even be used to distribute and install software.

Device management also enables carriers to serve their consumers better and more efficiently. On top of conveniently provisioning the services, carriers can enhance their service level by maintaining a database of the services used by the consumers. With their knowledge of services used, they can offer similar services that are likely of interest to the subscribers or use the information for other kinds of marketing planning.

Over the longer term, the functionality of mobile devices is verging very close to that of personal computers. This will also introduce the need for software upgrading and patches. For corporations and carriers, this means an immense fleet of mobile devices, each comparable to a personal computer, to be managed and maintained.

To recap, there is a direct need for a device management solution that a) offers a tool to meet the current need for provisioning the key parameters and b) has a realistic technology growth path so the consumers can be served efficiently also in the future.

Management Framework

In practice, the market needs an open standard based device management solution. The following arguments support this conclusion:

- **Interoperability**:

  Practical interoperability (e.g., across product lines and between different vendors) can be achieved only through common agreement on appropriate technology and mechanisms. Utilizing the carefully planned interoperability processes and requirements of standard building organizations, the industry can more quickly reach full interoperability.

- **Industry adoption**:

  A solution supported by only a limited number of industry players is not valuable for carriers and service providers. By supporting an open standard solution, carriers, service providers and equipment manufacturers are ensuring true end-to-end interoperability. The result is a usable solution and for the consumers as well.

- **Only one infrastructure investment**:

  Carriers and service providers need only invest in one open standard based infrastructure solution to support the multitude of devices and services. Even better, they are not locked in with the infrastructure in the future, as any solution supporting the open standards can provide them with similar functionality.

Device Management Architecture

The Device Management process can be divided into two separate parts, the bootstrap process and continuous provisioning. This architecture and accompanying terminology have been put forward by the WAP Forum. The division and key points of the architecture are highlighted in the figure below.

Nokia believes in an open technology device management architecture, as defined by WAP Forum

The architecture is based on establishing a trusted relationship between the device and the management server

The architecture has two phases
- Bootstrapping
- Continuous Provisioning

Bootstrapping provides the terminal with
- Trusted Relationship with the device management server
- Provisioning of key parameters

Continuous Provisioning, e.g. repetitive management actions can be done only by a trusted device management server

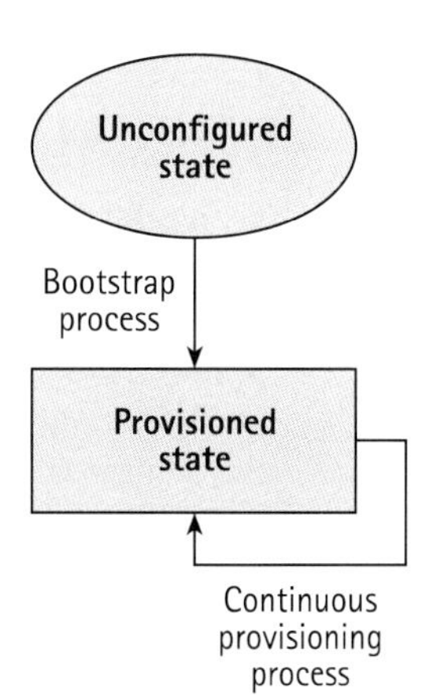

Device Management Framework: key points

Bootstrap technology is used to

a) provide mobile devices with essential parameters to enable *out-of-the-box* functionality, and

b) enable the initial settings and a trusted relationship for continuous provisioning. After the bootstrap phase, only continuous provisioning is needed between a mobile device and a device management server. In general, the bootstrapping is done using unsolicited message functionality (e.g., WAP Push over Short Message Service (SMS)).

Continuous provisioning is used for all the repetitive management actions performed for the mobile device. This includes parameter modifications, diagnostics and troubleshooting. Continuous provisioning requires a two-way connection between the device management server and the device being managed. Also, to ensure security, continuous provisioning requires a trusted relationship between the DM server and the device to be managed. This trusted relationship is to be established within the bootstrapping phase.

Nokia believes in the open device management framework that utilizes WAP 2.0 provisioning for bootstrapping and Synchronization Markup Language (SyncML) Device Management for continuous provisioning. These are the only available open technologies that can offer the functionalities required to meet the market's requirements.

WAP 2.0 Provisioning

The WAP Forum 2.0 provisioning specification provides for the initial provisioning of key parameters to the devices. WAP Forum bootstrapping enables carriers to initially provision key parameters and to enable continuous provisioning by establishing a trusted relationship between the managed device and the SyncML Device Management server. By provisioning key parameters during bootstrapping, carriers can enable full functionality of key applications for the consumers at the point of sale. By using the WAP Forum mechanism and security features, bootstrapping is secure and safe.

SyncML Device Management

The SyncML DM protocol closely resembles the one-way synchronization defined by the SyncML initiative for data synchronization. Instead of databases being synchronized, management objects are synchronized or transferred. A management object might reflect a set of configuration parameters for a device. Actions that can be performed on this object might include reading and setting parameter keys and values. Another management object might be the execution environment for software applications on a device.

The SyncML DM protocol is designed to work well in the mobile environment and is transport independent, making it possible to utilize virtually any kind of transport mechanism for device management sessions. It also provides an extensible, mature and flexible security model and the independence afforded by execution at run-time.

An important characteristic related to the nature of DM is the differentiation of the paying party, depending on the service. Some management operations are initiated and desired by the service provider, and they should not typically cause costs to the consumer, while the consumer directly triggers other operations and should thus be charged for them.

Conclusions

Device Management is the generic term used for the technology that allows third parties (e.g., mobile carriers, service providers, and corporate IT departments) to remotely provision and configure mobile devices on behalf of consumers. This includes remote provisioning of new services, configuration and management of device parameters, and settings and remote device diagnostics and troubleshooting.

Device Management technology is a key enabling feature for

1) Permitting value-added services in the Mobile domain
2) Enhancing the service level of carriers via service provisioning and troubleshooting
3) Causing direct cost savings in customer care and management
4) Collecting and utilizing customer care information

In order to offer true value to the market, an open technology solution is needed. Nokia believes in an open standard framework that consists of two phases: bootstrapping and continuous provisioning. The WAP Forum 2.0 provisioning specification for bootstrapping and SyncML Device Management for continuous provisioning fulfill the criteria for openness and offer sufficient flexibility and extensibility to become industry standards.

Device Management technology offers services to other applications (e.g., providing them with configuration data). It cannot be classified as a standalone technology or application but, rather, is a very important and vital enabler for mobile devices with a large set of mobile applications.

Machine-to-Machine

We have recently witnessed a series of fundamental changes in the communication culture and technologies. Almost twenty years ago, the introduction of mobile devices freed personal voice communication from location. Subsequently, consumers learned to satisfy some of their other communication needs using data services on their devices. A mobile connection to the Internet was introduced to consumers, expanding their communication options even further.

The next step in the evolution of communications is extending this connectivity beyond human beings. To allow the vision of a Mobile World and true independence of location to become a reality, we have to enable communication between individuals, devices and systems. In the context of wireless data, Machine-to-Machine (M2M) solutions are an ideal bridge from 2.5G business to the third generation. The service-focused business models of tomorrow may already be here in the form of M2M solutions. Together with mobile devices targeted for personal communication, Nokia also offers a platform for creating and operating M2M solutions, thereby enabling the true exploitation of the opportunities offered by wireless data.

Nokia supports open technologies in M2M business and will actively drive the market toward global M2M standards. Our partners in the M2M business will benefit from our long experience and competitive position in the mobile marketplace. Furthermore, the highly advanced Nokia M2M Platform, consisting of Nokia GSM Connectivity Terminals and Nokia M2M Gateways, will benefit corporate customers, carriers and application developers as well as service and solution providers in creating and maintaining industry-leading M2M solutions.

Introduction

Connecting People, Devices and Systems

M2M stands for machine-to-machine, man-to-machine and machine-to-man and is often related to the concepts of telemetry and telematics, which can be considered as subsets of the overall business scope of M2M. In the Mobile World, M2M is about combining telecommunication and Information Technology (IT); wireless data is used to establish a link between remote devices or locations, systems and consumers. M2M broadens the scope of communication from how we are used to perceiving it - it is not only consumers that utilize telecommunication and Internet technologies to communicate but the machines around us as well.

The M2M business is about creating solutions aimed at improving existing business, creating totally new opportunities, and essentially making daily life easier. By means of M2M solutions, which are often tailored to meet the specific demands of each situation, companies can automate their processes and integrate their assets with their IT systems. The goal is to increase the performance and competitiveness of the company through increased efficiency, cost savings, additional revenues or better service levels. It is rather typical that the rationale for utilizing M2M solutions is the avoidance of physical visits (e.g., meter reading visits), and the cost savings that can be attained through exploiting the real-time information provided by the wireless data connection. Furthermore, through M2M solutions, companies can better analyze their current business and processes and thereby detect the areas that can be further improved.

Machine-to-Machine Applications

M2M solutions are typically created for collecting information, setting parameters, sending indications of unusual situations, or taking care of an online transaction by means of a wireless data connection. There are several different application segments in which these data links can be exploited. New M2M applications are continuously emerging, and they may serve almost any business area and physical environment. It is fair to say that only imagination limits the range of M2M applications. However, in order to give a concrete picture of the total business potential, some of the recognized M2M applications are presented and grouped according to their uses and application environments in the following figure.

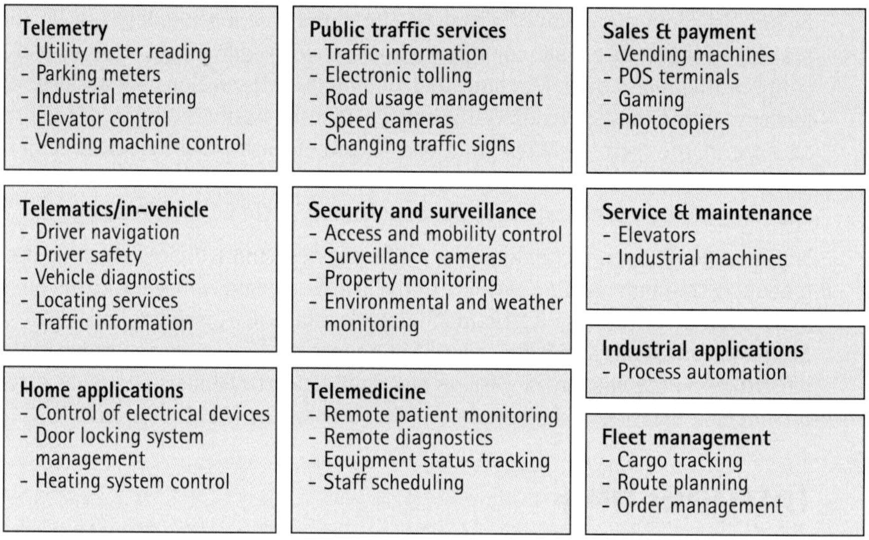

Telemetry
- Utility meter reading
- Parking meters
- Industrial metering
- Elevator control
- Vending machine control

Public traffic services
- Traffic information
- Electronic tolling
- Road usage management
- Speed cameras
- Changing traffic signs

Sales & payment
- Vending machines
- POS terminals
- Gaming
- Photocopiers

Telematics/in-vehicle
- Driver navigation
- Driver safety
- Vehicle diagnostics
- Locating services
- Traffic information

Security and surveillance
- Access and mobility control
- Surveillance cameras
- Property monitoring
- Environmental and weather monitoring

Service & maintenance
- Elevators
- Industrial machines

Industrial applications
- Process automation

Home applications
- Control of electrical devices
- Door locking system management
- Heating system control

Telemedicine
- Remote patient monitoring
- Remote diagnostics
- Equipment status tracking
- Staff scheduling

Fleet management
- Cargo tracking
- Route planning
- Order management

Examples of M2M applications

An ever growing number of M2M solutions aim to serve the customer base of the company by offering value adding services to them. Virtually, all the machines can be networked into the Internet. Later, these networked machines provide a number of local information points and services for consumers. Thereby M2M can be seen as the entity creating information and content that is needed in the fulfillment of the Mobile World vision.

M2M solutions should be designed to grow along with the company and its needs. Technology development or changes in the business environment may create a need to introduce new applications or services. The following example illustrates an M2M solution that develops over time and that ultimately combines both company internal applications and consumer services. It even generates new business.

Vending Business Use Case

The first target of the solution is to minimize the costs of vending machine operation by using remote monitoring, data collection and configuration of the machines. Maintaining optimum stock in each machine, undertaking proactive maintenance, immediately fixing malfunctions and changing prices remotely are just a few of the options for improving efficiency that this M2M application provides.

The M2M solution in the vending business may be expanded by providing consumers with the possibility of mobile payment. In addition to getting rid of the trouble and cost of handling coins, mobile payment increases sales. The mobile payment solution can be implemented today in cooperation with a carrier, and the evolution of mobile devices will enable new concepts to be applied in the future. Creating a direct link to the consumer through his/her mobile device will for the first time make it possible to build consumer profiles and provide personalized services and offerings to consumers based on their individual needs.

The next step of the M2M solution in the vending business could be to expand the business scope of a vending operator. The M2M-enabled machines could be used to providc information or content (e.g., news or games) that are financed by a third-party content provider. The same content might also draw consumers to the machine and make them spend an extra dime for a snack or a beverage while there.

Similar types of opportunities as in this example can be found in almost any sector or operating environment. The solutions just have to be tailored to serve the needs of each specific business. M2M solutions should not be seen as merely narrow vertical applications, isolated from the external world, but rather as a tool to integrate devices, various applications, consumers and companies so they become interactive parts of the Mobile World.

Machine-to-Machine Requirements

The requirements of a successful M2M solution are reliability, upgradeability and affordability. Today, it is not always easy to meet all these requirements, and even though M2M business is in a phase of rapid growth, even more efforts will be needed to fulfill these three basic requirements. As the number of different M2M solutions is high and the requirements presented by customers are case-specific, application development and system integration are often described as the most problematic areas of M2M solution creation. So, developing and utilizing efficient tools for this area is one of the key issues in meeting M2M solution requirements.

M2M solutions will typically link a company's remote assets (e.g., game machines, vehicles and traffic signs) to its existing IT infrastructure. Therefore, expertise in both mobile and Internet Protocol (IP) technologies will be required for effective application development. The reliability of a solution can be guaranteed only by taking an end-to-end approach to the development work. In addition, some applications (e.g., mobile payment or transferring price information) set higher requirements for security than others. Efficient information security measures (e.g., data encryption and authentication) are needed to provide adequate security.

Upgradeability means that the customer must be able to take advantage of the latest technology, whether in terms of lower equipment costs, higher data transmission rates, or more affordable operating costs. However, solution upgrades cannot lead to expensive re-development cycles because this is likely to lead to the loss of much of the benefit achieved with the solution.

Therefore, easy upgradeability of both software and hardware components is one of the key elements of an M2M solution.

The factors affecting the affordability of a solution are the costs of application creation, system components, operation and upgrades. The optimum cost can be reached only by considering all these factors; optimizing only one of them could be achieved only at the expense of the others. One can minimize the application creation and upgrade costs by selecting reliable products with efficient development tools and standard, open interfaces. Operational costs might be minimized by, for example, using different data bearers flexibly.

Machine-to-Machine Solutions

As we move rapidly toward the third generation networks, more attention than ever is being paid to the wireless data market, particularly to the service offering aspects of it. While the core of the communication business remains in the increasingly saturated and very competitive voice market, there is a constantly growing demand to look for alternative revenue streams (e.g., generated by the utilization of wireless data). In order to achieve growth in the diversity of data business, completely new strategies and business concepts are to be conquered. The Short Message Service (SMS) has already evolved from a means of personal communication to a popular service delivery medium and a real revenue source for innovative carriers; it is a good example of how technological innovations influence the process of service evolution and thereby offer new possibilities to enhance customer satisfaction.

But only the first steps have been taken toward the Mobile World. The wireless data market is continuously growing; it would be shortsighted to believe that Web browsing is all that the wireless data business will be about. As the number of different consumers and applications increases, it gets rather challenging to come to grips with the full variety of these applications. By analyzing wireless data services and applications through looking at user identity, network environments, access methods and interaction modes, the complex field of wireless data business can be clarified.

When concentrating on communication and the means of data access, one can identify three types of wireless data service demands: messaging, browsing and M2M. Each of these has its unique requirements for service creation and strategy development. It should be noted that M2M applications may be combined with applications from the other two areas in order to create solution packages that best satisfy overall consumer needs.

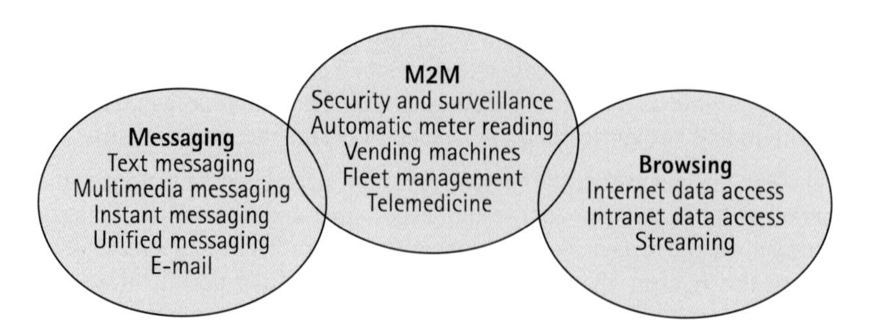

Wireless data segments

Content is the real driving force behind the wireless data business. Also, strong service and application concepts must be present as a foundation for successful business before the data market will really take off. By means of M2M solutions, the desired content can be created in a bi-directional manner. M2M applications enable meaningful, interesting and tangible content for professional third generation applications in real time.

M2M solutions will be a significant sector of the wireless data business, as they enable mobile connectivity and Internet access everywhere. As noted, the importance of wireless data is increasing rapidly. Nokia will provide a full product portfolio for exploiting wireless data business opportunities.

Technology for Machine-to-Machine Solutions

It is obvious that solution functionality and consumer experience are the things that really matter to consumers; they simply do not want to be concerned with the underlying technologies. But when designing an M2M application or a solution, the question of what technology is most suitable is to be considered carefully. This decision could have a far-reaching impact on operational costs or the possibilities for expanding the solution. It has become rather evident that, where available, the Global System for Mobile Communications (GSM) is most often the optimum technology for M2M solutions.

The history of openness and standardization of GSM enables the creation of global M2M solutions. In the future, with the introduction of the 850 MHz band beside the 1900 MHz band, widespread M2M solutions will became a reality also in the Americas. Therefore, it is not an exaggeration to state that GSM technology enables the creation of truly global M2M solutions. GSM technology roadmaps are created jointly with all the major players in the GSM industry, to guarantee the same level of stability and global compatibility in the future.

The GSM market has faced huge growth during the past decade, and the growth is continuing. Consequently, the prices of GSM technology and communication are decreasing, benefiting M2M solutions from the beginning. In addition, the high number of GSM product and communication providers enables the fulfillment of various customer needs. That there are multiple providers also guarantees the continuity of GSM technology - no single player can bring down the GSM market.

A great benefit of GSM technology is the high-level data services, with security features, that are already available with GSM networks and products. GSM networks usually offer several bearer options, including the General Packet Radio Service (GRPS), High Speed Circuit Switched Data (HSCSD) and SMS. The data services are continuously being developed further, which enables a long life cycle for M2M solutions built on GSM technology. The future development path is essential, as M2M solutions are often long-term investments.

A GSM solution is easy to install. No cabling is needed; equipment with GSM connectivity can be easily moved from one location to another. For mobile applications (e.g., those in a vehicle) mobile technology is the only option.

The most important aspect of GSM technology is that it enables M2M business entry now. Advanced solutions may be created today based on the existing technology, and these solutions and services will create an easy evolution path to third generation business.

The Nokia Offering

Customers in the M2M market are not a homogeneous group. M2M solutions differ from each other by size and complexity, and the needs of the customers vary from case to case. The Nokia product family for the M2M market offers several approaches to M2M solution development and operation. The Nokia offering also takes into consideration the importance of support and training activities.

Nokia M2M Platform

The Nokia M2M Platform is a complete solution for developing and operating M2M solutions. It consists of Nokia GSM Connectivity Terminals and Nokia M2M Gateway software. It is not specified for any particular M2M application segment; instead, with its compatible features it provides a standard software platform that will serve both the current and the future variety of M2M applications. The Nokia M2M Platform can be utilized in M2M solution creation by developing applications on top of the platform.

The Nokia solution offers end-to-end connectivity between the remote, embedded end (e.g., the application in an elevator) and the control and management server with user interface, i.e. a mobile device or computer with an Internet connection. Nokia GSM Connectivity Terminals connect the M2M applications to the GSM network. The Nokia M2M Gateway in turn bridges the GSM network and the Internet by means of mobile connection establishment and protocol translation.

Thereby, Nokia M2M platform covers the complete business case from the remote device up to the server application, as presented in the following figure. The number of remote devices connected can be in the thousands. When utilizing the Nokia M2M Platform, integration to different backend systems (e.g., databases or different corporate level information systems) is easy. Furthermore, with the Nokia M2M Platform, companies have the possibility to maintain several M2M applications without changing the communication solution.

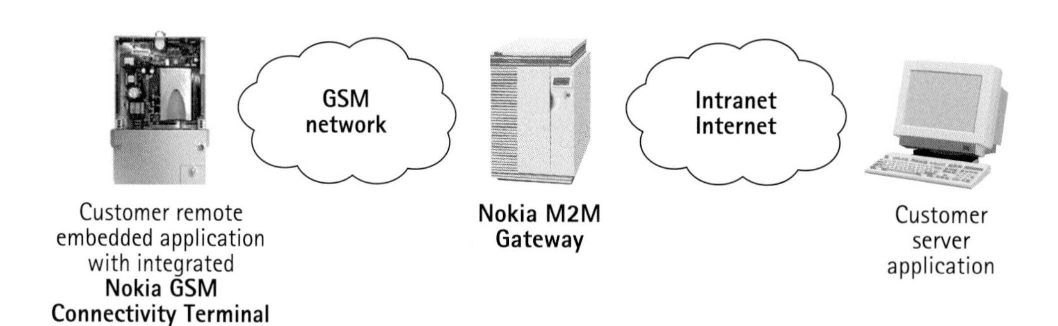

Nokia M2M Platform

As a committed promoter of open standards, Nokia provides the market with a full-featured platform for M2M communication; The Nokia M2M Platform is based on widely accepted, open industry standards (i.e., GSM, Common Object Request Broker Architecture (CORBA)).

In addition to openness and the utilization of standard mobile network technology, the Nokia M2M Platform offers several other benefits that center on the development and the operation of distributed M2M applications. Tackling the difficulty of M2M application development, the Nokia solution eases the development work by hiding the networking complexity - application software developers see normal method calls between the remote applications and the customer server application. Furthermore, the M2M Platform provides the necessary data transfer protocol layers, which allows the software developers to concentrate on the application itself. As mobile communication technology is hidden from the developers, a wider base of competent companies and developers can develop M2M applications by using any language, on any operating system.

The Nokia M2M Platform offers a good basis for meeting the requirements. The backward compatibility of the Nokia solution enables easy upgrading for M2M solutions; Nokia GSM Connectivity Terminals will support the same hardware and software interfaces in the future; therefore, replacing the device with a new model is easy and involves no need to change the application itself.

The M2M Platform supports all major mobile bearers: HSCSD, GPRS, SMS and Unstructured Supplementary Service Data (USSD). By this extensive mobile bearer choice, costs for application communications can be optimized. Rapid application development and easy management of M2M solutions enabled by the Nokia M2M Platform further provide cost savings during the whole life cycle of the M2M solution, thus making the solution affordable.

Nokia M2M Gateway Product Family

As the core of the Nokia M2M Platform, the Nokia M2M Gateway bridges the GSM network and the Internet. The Nokia M2M Gateway provides wirelessCORBA access and interoperability to the Internet as well as optimization for the wireless bearers. The Nokia M2M Gateway supports several wireless bearers, allowing data traffic optimization. The Nokia M2M Gateway software is especially designed for easy management and expandability of the M2M solutions; yet it offers security for the development of advanced wireless applications.

In order to respond to the needs of different types of businesses and usage in the M2M market, three editions of the Nokia M2M Gateway are available:

- Nokia M2M Gateway Corporate Edition
  - Corporate owned and managed gateway
- Nokia M2M Gateway Service Provider Edition
  - Service provider owned and managed gateway with support for multiple customer applications
- Nokia M2M Gateway Trial Version
  - For application development and for testing and trialing the platform technology

The Nokia M2M Gateway Corporate Edition is intended for companies wishing to own and manage the gateway along with the server applications. Mobile connectivity services (e.g., SMS Center access), can be rented from a carrier, or the company can operate its own modem pool to provide access to the remote applications. For the companies utilizing M2M solutions, owning the gateway provides independence and more control over service quality.

The Gateway Service Provider Edition is to be owned and managed by carriers or other parties providing gateway service. This gateway edition is a distributed solution for hosting and maintaining applications for many customers in the manner presented in the following figure. The Service Provider Edition offers additional support for managing and controlling access between remote devices and server applications belonging to different customers. A separate Gateway Access software is provided for the customers. This software is used to tunnel and encrypt data between the customer and the service provider's gateway; tunneling eases firewall configuration between the customers and the service provider.

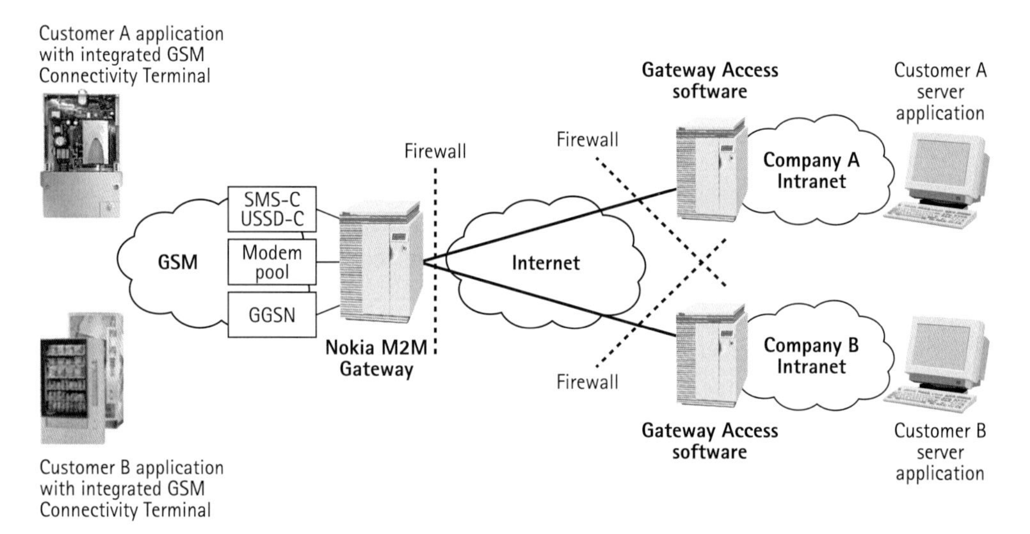

Nokia M2M Gateway Service Provider Edition architecture

For the customers, the service provider business model offers the ability to concentrate on the core business and still gain all the benefits offered by the Nokia M2M Platform. This approach eases the entry to the utilization of M2M solutions by reducing the needed capital investments. Without actual ownership of the gateway, the utilization of gateway services is still secure. The Nokia M2M Gateway has been designed for terminal and server authentication. Only the customer can access the terminals, and customer server applications are contacted only by the devices of that specific customer.

The approach to the M2M solutions enabled by the Service Provider Edition allows the emergence of a new business model. For example, System integrators can offer gateway hosting services for developed applications, thus generating new and stable revenues.

Finally, the Nokia M2M Gateway Trial Version is intended for trying out the Nokia M2M Platform technology and for testing purposes in the software development phase. The Trial Version supports the Short Message Service (SMS) and Circuit Switched Data (CSD) through a GSM terminal attached to the gateway host machine. Due to the limited connectivity services offered, the Trial Version is mainly targeted for the application developers in the M2M market.

Nokia GSM Connectivity Terminals

The Nokia product family for M2M includes GSM Connectivity Terminals optimized for M2M communications. The devices are the Nokia 30 GSM Connectivity Terminal (i.e., dual band EGSM 900/GSM 1800) and the Nokia 31 GSM Connectivity Terminal (i.e., dual band GSM 850/1900). As security and reliability are important in M2M solutions, Nokia devices have a number of features to meet these requirements (e.g., the Auto Personal Identification Number (PIN).

Beside their application segment, M2M solutions may differ from each other in size and complexity. Consequently, customer needs will vary widely. Therefore, various different operation modes are offered by which the Nokia GSM Connectivity Terminals can be used: M2M system mode, AT command mode and User control mode.

The M2M system mode can make full use of all the services that Nokia GSM Connectivity Terminals offer. The M2M system mode offers many useful features, including wireless bearer selection, ready-made protocol stacks, separation of data transfer from the application, and the possibility of introducing new technologies without changing the M2M application itself. In the M2M system mode, the reliability and security of an M2M solution can be enhanced even further with authentication and system monitoring.

In addition to being a part of the Nokia M2M Platform, GSM Connectivity Terminals can also be used in the AT command mode and in the User command mode without the Nokia M2M Gateway. The AT command mode is most suitable for point-to-point communications. The User control mode is specifically designed with man-to-machine and machine-to-man communications in mind. With the User control mode, one can control simple applications (e.g., door locking systems), easily by using the services of the Nokia GSM Connectivity Terminals with a mobile device.

Support and Training

As indicated above, application development support is most certainly needed in the M2M market. The Nokia M2M solution includes support elements that M2M application developers can utilize. Developer community access, application development tools, and other M2M related services are available in Forum Nokia. The Nokia M2M developer offering includes the Nokia M2M Platform Application Development Kit, which contains useful tools and examples that make application development easier and faster on the Nokia M2M Platform. Furthermore, special training is organized for application developers and service providers.

Several Business Opportunities

The overall business trend of networking, partnering and focusing on core competencies applies also to the M2M business. Networks of companies are needed in M2M solution creation; the Nokia M2M Platform can be seen as the core on which each M2M solution is to be created by these business networks. Specific knowledge of the business environment, communication technologies, software development, total system integration, customer care and billing is required when creating a successful M2M solution. Therefore, such solutions are always produced as a joint effort of experts in several different fields. The variety of activities needed in creating and operating an M2M solution is illustrated in the following figure.

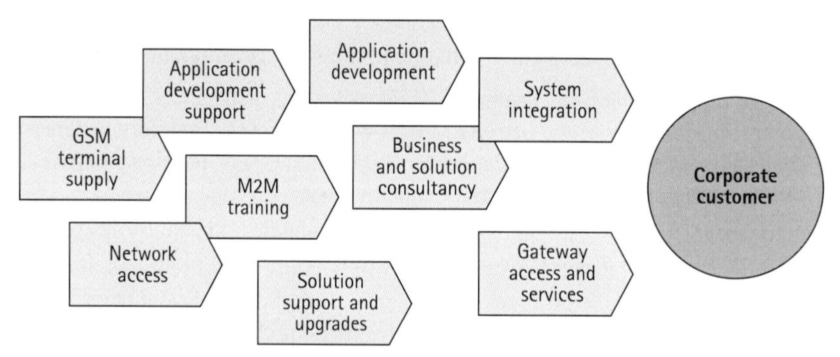

Activities needed when creating an M2M solution

The solution requirements and the optimal division of the roles between the parties within the value chain differ accordingly. Some roles (e.g., those of service providers), are simply irrelevant in some cases. Furthermore, one company may adopt several roles within the network if the required competencies are in place. The optimum division of activities and roles must be defined individually for each M2M solution.

One of the greatest challenges of the M2M business seems to be that of mastering the complexity of the value chain which provides total solutions. Customers do not want to purchase the solution piece by piece from different companies, and instead of reliable components they want end-to-end solution reliability. Therefore, the winners of the M2M game will be those companies that succeed in establishing and managing partner networks with a top competence portfolio for creating end-to-end solutions.

Corporate Customers

The obvious beneficiaries of M2M applications are corporate customers. Companies are constantly looking for new ways to increase efficiency, cut costs, and improve customer service in order to gain a competitive edge in their core business. The possibilities raised by M2M solutions are already widely recognized in several industries. By means of M2M solutions, companies can more easily analyze their current business and processes, which enhances the continuous improvement in the company. Furthermore, when competition in the traditional business area is getting more intense and eating into profits, expanding the business with the help of an M2M solution may be a way to maintain profitability.

An M2M solution integrates all assets of a company in one complete system, including those in the field and even in various locations around the world. Operation costs can be minimized when needless site visits for service, maintenance, device updates and so on can be avoided thanks to online connections with all machines. Manpower can thus be used more productively. The amount of downtime can be minimized or even eliminated, and the opportunities for fraud can be reduced or eliminated by eliminating cash as a payment method. Sometimes, M2M solutions can also help meet requirements set by legislation.

Carriers and Service Providers

With the voice market becoming saturated and competition in the mobile business tightening up, carriers are looking for new revenue streams. M2M solutions provide a new, appealing opportunity to strengthen a carrier's position in the profitable corporate sector and to expand its business scope toward providing total solutions.

From the carrier's point of view, the M2M business scenario is ideal in many ways. Traffic can often be concentrated in the off-peak hours to balance capacity utilization, and much of the traffic flow is predictable. With M2M solutions it is possible to expand the customer base to new market sectors and win all mobile traffic of the customers by bundling traditional telecom services with company-specific solutions. M2M solutions make it possible to generate significant additional revenues with a minimum initial investment. Furthermore, M2M applications offer good means for the content creation, which is especially necessary in the third generation networks.

The Nokia approach enables the emergence of a new business model into the M2M market. Some companies, including carriers, can adopt the role of offering gateway services to several different companies. M2M service providers play a critical role in developing and expanding the M2M business, and their significance will only increase along with the growing demand for M2M solutions.

Basically, offering gateway services means managing and hosting the data link between customers' remote and server applications. However, the business scope of M2M service providers may vary considerably. Probably the best known business model is that of an Application Service Provider (ASP), which manages and hosts software on the basis of renting or leasing it to companies wishing to minimize the cost of their IT resources and equipment. In addition, M2M service provision may include application development, system integration, mobile virtual network operator activity, content provision, or a combination of any of these.

As the demand for M2M services increases, there is a need for a broader spectrum of service providers. M2M service provision is an outstanding business opportunity for existing ASPs that may use M2M services in expanding their portfolio for existing customers or to penetrate new business areas. Also, companies currently acting in completely different fields, such as manufacturing, may find M2M service provision gives them a way to expand their business scope and fully capitalize on their business understanding. It could raise their profitability to a whole new level.

M2M Solution Providers

In the creation of M2M solutions, a value chain consisting of several companies is needed. The customer is owned by the whole value chain. It is rather evident that the customer typically wants to deal with a specific company instead of the whole value chain when acquiring an M2M solution. These specific companies can be defined as M2M solution providers that actually offer the total M2M solutions to the customers. Thereby, they are in the central role when interacting with the customers.

M2M solution providers will typically have competence in some particular aspect of M2M solution creation (e.g., in system integration or application software development). However, it is most likely that they need partners for their solution creation efforts. Therefore, successful orchestration of the M2M business is of central importance, particularly from the solution providers' perspective.

Because many corporate customers will find that M2M provides the way to make their operations more profitable than before, there are plenty of untapped business opportunities for companies that understand these needs and are able to adopt the role of an M2M solution provider. By noticing and utilizing these business opportunities in the corporate sector, current and future solution providers can expand their business and increase their revenue streams. Also, carriers can choose to take the role of a solution provider. M2M solutions complement a carriers' existing service portfolio well.

IV TOOLS

PART 4.1

Introduction

- Mobile Services Development Process
- Mobile Device Software Development
- Forum Nokia
- Nokia OK Process

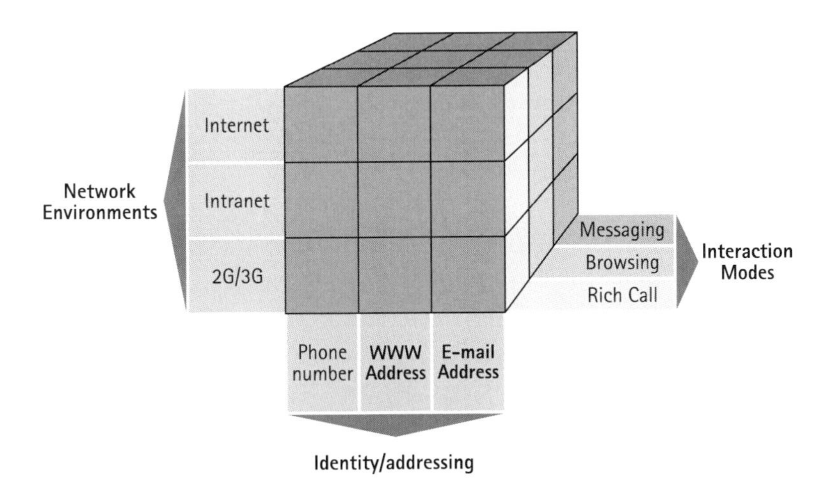

Mobile Services Development Process

In their service development activities, mobile software developers typically go through a process that begins from initializing the development project and ends in completing the software/ application sales. The different stages of the process require different roles, competencies, and experts within the company. The process may be short and straightforward or long and more complex, depending on the nature of the service being developed, as well as the company's background, core strategies, existing business relationships and partnerships, and existing competencies.

The following figure illustrates and simplifies the steps taken in a typical mobile service development process. It also highlights the different roles within the company and key questions developers face in each stage.

This process could also be called the *Mobile Internet Process*.

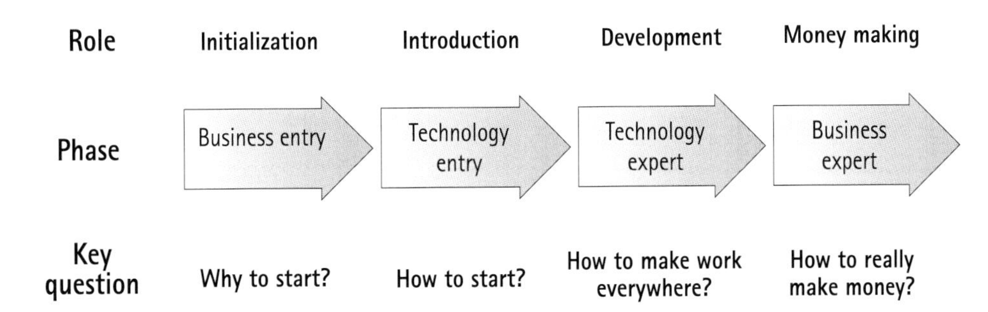

The following sections explain each stage in the process, highlighting the key activities that developers need to be aware of and undertake in order to advance in the service development project.

Initialization

The initial question, why enter a mobile service development project, is perhaps the most important one a company has to answer. This is a business level decision, and it requires support and active participation from the management.

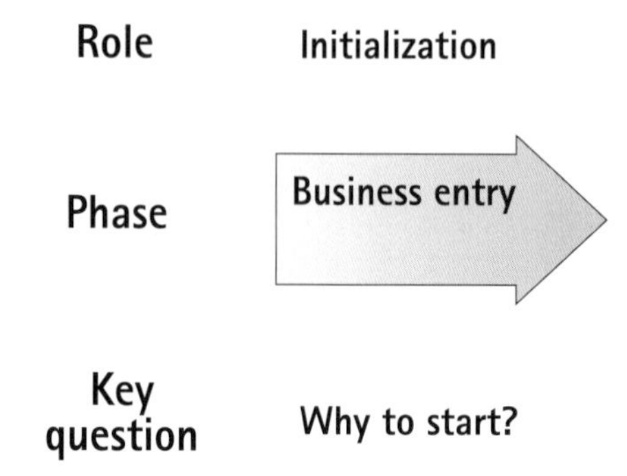

At this stage, the developer typically seeks to answer a simple question: *How to make profit.*

There is no point in making investments without reasonable guarantees of there being a pull or demand for the selected type of service, or that the given market exists and will perhaps grow considerably, that the market is accessible to the developer, or that the market is not saturated with the same or similar types of services. In short, the developer must see a business opportunity and the service development resulting in profit and positive cash flow within the desired period of time.

The developer needs to understand and have access to the following information:

What is the business case?

> Is the aim to develop a service and obtain cash inflow from service users (e.g., consumer markets)
>
> or
>
> is the aim to enhance, e.g., existing corporate processes, and to seek benefits from enhanced efficiency and cost savings in the company's own activities?
>
> Without a quantifiable business case and measurable targets, there is no point in entering or investing in mobile service development projects.

What is the size of the accessible market, when will it penetrate, and how will it grow?

> When developing a highly futuristic service that relies on future technologies, it can take a considerably long time before the market exists and penetrates. For example, it took the Short Message Service (SMS) several years before the technology penetrated to the extent (i.e., 25% of the population) that it became widely accepted and used.

What is the target group and what do they expect and desire?

> In order to have any use, it is crucial to understand the service's target segment, the barriers in their service adoption, the usability and level of support they expect, the types of devices they carry, and so on.
>
> There is no point in developing a business-like service for consumers who do not need such a service in their mobile lifestyle, and who carry the types of mobile devices that do not contain features required for accessing the service. On the other hand, it might

make a lot of sense to develop such a service for corporate users, and to learn which types of mobile devices, features and UI this segment uses.

Who are the partners needed for entering the business?

The developer needs to understand the different roles in the value chain, as well as the underlying earning logics. Depending on the market, there could be several players with a strong position in the value chain, which cannot be passed and must be worked with. Such players include carriers owning the telecom infrastructure, and content aggregators and wholesalers with service provisioning infrastructures.

Typically, these players have established rules on how to play the mobile services game on their playground. Business models could be predefined, and the negotiation cycles related to entering the value chain could take a long time.

Where is the competition?

It should also be noted that mobile services pose an interesting business opportunity for many companies. An innovation must be protected; yet, not disclosing it to the required business partners could cause delays in entering the market.

Where does the developer get support?

It is also important to identify companies that can provide assistance in different stages of the development process; companies that have experience in the process and which can advise the developers on the most obvious and typically faced difficulties. In addition, such companies might also have access to the necessary partners, which could significantly shorten the commercialization of the developed service.

Introduction

Once the developer has a unique idea and has calculated the business opportunity and made the final decision to start the mobile service development, there are various technical alternatives for developing the service. At this stage, system architects or similar experts are needed for evaluating the alternatives (e.g., technologies, standards, products, and tools), which are available for development purposes.

Introduction

How to start?

At this stage, one of the key questions involves the openness of technologies: whether to use open standards, which typically give the developer the benefit of several existing tools, a wider potential market, and interoperability between devices, or to adopt proprietary technologies/standards that limit the accessible market to certain devices, platforms or vendors/partners, but may provide some additional benefits in terms of functionality or vendor-specific support.

In principle, open technologies are always a safe bet because they typically have a guaranteed roadmap and some level of backward compatibility, and if backed up by large vendors, penetrate a significant share of the accessible and future markets. Examples of open technologies include Wireless Application Protocol (WAP)/Extensible Markup Language (XHTML) endorsed by the WAP Forum and World Wide Web Consortium (W3C), Java™ endorsed by Java Community Process (JCP) and Multimedia Messaging Service (MMS) endorsed by Third Generation Partnership Project (3GPP).

Also at this stage, the developer needs to look at the required infrastructure, and in case of proprietary technologies, at the players with the necessary infrastructure elements in place for delivering the service. An outcome of the evaluation might be that the developer continues using the infrastructure already in place, but needs connectivity to a certain carrier network element to deliver the service. Alternatively, the outcome might be that the developer needs to add certain network elements to their own infrastructure in order to have full control of service delivery and subscriptions in a secure manner.

Another critical item in the technology selection is the mobile devices at which the services are targeted. Moreover, the developer has to consider which technologies the targeted devices support, and which types of User Interfaces (UI) they contain.

In addition, it is important to evaluate the available tools and Software Development Kits (SDKs), support organizations, and available documentation and literature. They can either make the job easier or, if they are not available, significantly harder with respect to overcoming technical difficulties that might emerge. It is also important to notice that support and utilities are not always free of charge, which may have an impact on R&D costs in the project.

Typically, a service can be implemented by using several alternative methods or technologies. The best technology is not always the best choice. The developer also needs to consider the enabled market.

Development

Once the development environment, supported technologies and tools have been selected, the actual development work begins. Now, it is the system engineer's task to create the application utilizing the best available development tools, support services and literature.

At least by this stage, it is wise to register into one or more developer community programs typically managed by the selected technology vendors. Tools are often downloadable free of charge, and the hosts of developer programs have plenty of documentation available to support development activities. The most advanced programs often provide technical assistance, discussion boards, developer training and knowledge databases. Furthermore, it is possible to

Development

How to make work everywhere?

sign up for updates of related software, utilities and tools, and thereby stay up to date with respect to the application development infrastructure. The developer may also be allowed to use hosted test beds for end-to-end testing purposes, and qualification services for ensuring that the service complies with the selected technology or particular product.

Active developer communities are often able to resolve commonly recognized problems in the related technology.

One of the key dilemmas typically faced by developers at this stage is the underlying fact that there are many different types of mobile devices in the markets. One size does not fit all, and even if a service works with one particular mobile device, it does not mean that the user experience is the same or even close with another type of device. The developer needs to solve the problem of how to scale the application to support all targeted devices and potentially emerging devices.

In addition, the mobile devices are not the only things requiring interoperability. It is also required for different types of networks and network elements. The developer needs to design the application's functional logic in such a way that it is easy to adjust to support different types of devices and user interfaces, as well as different types of network servers.

For instance, carriers may have different types of protocol interfaces available for connecting to their service provisioning infrastructure, and different mobile device manufacturers follow different types of principles on how content is rendered in the device UI. The developer needs to test the product against all relevant components to ensure consumer satisfaction.

Profit Making

Mobile services are relatively easy to develop, but not necessarily easy to sell. A well-planned business case usually helps advance sales and consumer acceptance, but major effort and investment in sales are often needed as well. At this stage, it is the role of business development managers or sales/marketing staff to deliver the service to the target consumers. This process should result in reaching the goals initially set for the development project.

At this stage, the developer needs to establish relationships with the necessary partners in order to obtain a delivery channel for the service. Developer community programs that provide the technology often also provide sales channels or even business models for delivering services.

Money making

How to really make money?

However, establishing a delivery channel usually requires also the developer's own sales efforts.

One of the core decisions at this stage is to decide whether the company is capable of selling the product directly to the target consumers, whether to use partners to complete the sales, or to establish an independent infrastructure for hosting and provisioning the mobile service. The partner strategy is often suitable for companies that do not have their own sales capacity. The natural downside in using partners as re-sellers of services is that they also want their share of service revenues. Further, partners may need to have 24/7 support for the service or regional/ global system integration services.

As mentioned earlier, business models are often predefined and specific to a certain region, country or carrier. For services delivered via carrier networks, revenue sharing is a quite common business model. This type of model does not simply reward the developer for creating the service, but requires the adoption and use of the service before generating a cash flow to the developer.

Since business models vary considerably, the developer should always negotiate with the relevant parties in order to understand completely the underlying business models and earning logics.

Mobile Device Software Development

This chapter describes development tools and environments for software and content development. Examples of the environments are mainly based on the current Forum Nokia tool offerings.

Tools, Software Development Kits and Emulators

The key things a developer needs are a robust environment and process for software and content development, which offer basic functionality needed in serious application and content development.

In the case of the Mobile domain, there are several types of applications that can be executed on a mobile device or server, as well as end-to-end applications, in which a server and a mobile device application communicate with each other.

From the development point of view, this sets requirements for development tools on the mobile device and server side. If we take a closer look at these requirements, we are able to define a necessary basic set of tools. We can divide the tools as follows: general tools and software development kits (SDKs) used for server-side development, and tools, extensions and SDKs (including device-specific emulators) intended for the mobile device domain.

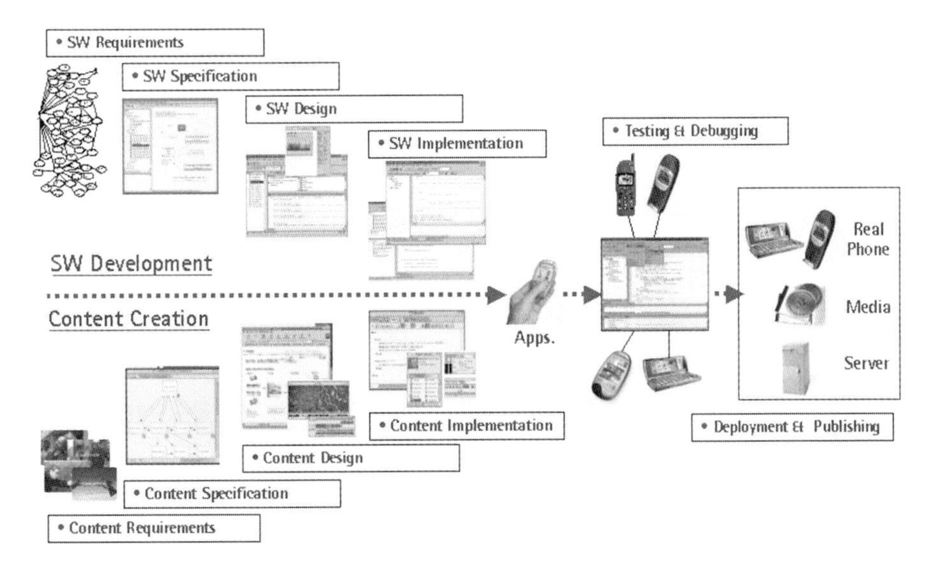

Complete software and content development processes

From the development process point of view, all development steps presented in the above figure are in use on server-side applications and there are many effective tools available for the requirements definition, product specification and design phases.

Mobile device application development is more focused on the implementation, testing and deployment phases, because of the nature of the applications. In many cases, the mobile device applications are quite small, and the logic of the application does not need a great deal of effort in the requirements, specification and design phases.

The end-to-end application development environment is a combination of server-side tools and mobile device-specific tools, and the business logic can be divided between the mobile device and server(s).

Commercial Development Environments

In the development market, these needs and requirements for general tools are called the Integrated Development Environment (IDE) functionality. IDEs are mainly used in server-side application development and they are often integrated with application servers (e.g., Borland, Sun, IBM, BEA and other tool and server vendors). Some of the leading IDE vendors (e.g., Borland, Sun and IBM) already support mobile device application development (e.g., Symbian and Java 2 Platform, Micro Edition (J2ME)) in their development environments.

There are many developers who use tools (e.g., emacs) for writing code and command line tools for compiling and composing the final applications or content, but most developers still use an IDE to develop applications or create content.

IDE tools offer hundreds of different types of functionality, but most developers only employ a fraction of them. This is quite natural, since IDE tools have been designed to suit all developers.

An IDE should offer many key features familiar to the developer. The mobile device-specific tools and extensions should be offered for the developers' own IDE, as if they were a part of it, and mobile device toolsets should use the same IDE as server tools.

SDKs and Emulators

A mobile device SDK is typically a collection of development time Application Programming Interfaces (APIs), documentation on how to develop and debug applications and how to use APIs and the emulator runtime environment with applications. After the development phase, the emulator is used for testing the application in a runtime environment. Mobile device-based emulators offer runtime implementation of development time APIs, well-defined interfaces for communicating with outside world (e.g., wrapper code for integration and a debug proxy for debugging), and behavior very close to the actual mobile device. An SDK may also include device-specific development tools (e.g., the preverifier of the Mobile Information Device Profile (MIDP) SDK) or additional tools for creating the final application package even for standalone use (e.g., Symbian SDK).

Nokia has several mobile device platforms and nearly all of them are supported by the SDKs and emulators. There are two types of SDKs: technology-specific SDKs that implement only one technology (e.g., MIDP Java) or the Multimedia Messaging Service (MMS) and SDKs that offer a collection of supported development languages and technologies (e.g., the Series 60 and Series 80 SDKs). These SDKs and emulators are based on the mobile device, i.e., the mobile device features and behavior correspond to the actual device.

There are also mobile device SDKs and emulators that are not based on any specific mobile device. These emulators only look like the actual mobile device(s) and with them, the developer can only get an idea of what the application looks like.

Nokia also offers development environments for all key mobile technology areas, (e.g., Java (MIDP and PersonalJava), native, messaging and browsing). Development environments are combinations of commercial development environments and SDKs or standalone SDKs. In the future, there will be more SDKs available for server-side application development, and technologies that provide developers with end-to-end development environments.

The special SDKs also support special technologies (e.g., Bluetooth, connectivity, SyncML and testing tools).

Challenges in Mobile Application Development

The problem in mobile application and content development is that mobile devices are embedded systems and their behavior and capacity to run code or content is not the same as that of desktop environments. Today, mobile device development solutions are typically based on one mobile device domain. Typically, the developer loads a special software package (SDK) and integrates it with the developer's selected IDE, or the developer only runs the SDK as a standalone version and develops applications or content for this specific domain. Adaptation (e.g., mobile extension) between the IDE and SDK is needed for completing a final full-featured mobile development environment.

The combination of an IDE with mobile extension and a mobile device SDK is the most commonly used environment today. The IDE offers basic functionality, while the mobile extension integrates the IDE with the mobile device SDK and offers special functionality for the mobile domain (e.g., debugging, user interface designing, code generation, application packaging), and other special tools (e.g., application deployment) in the target mobile device.

The following figure illustrates typical stages in the mobile development domain.

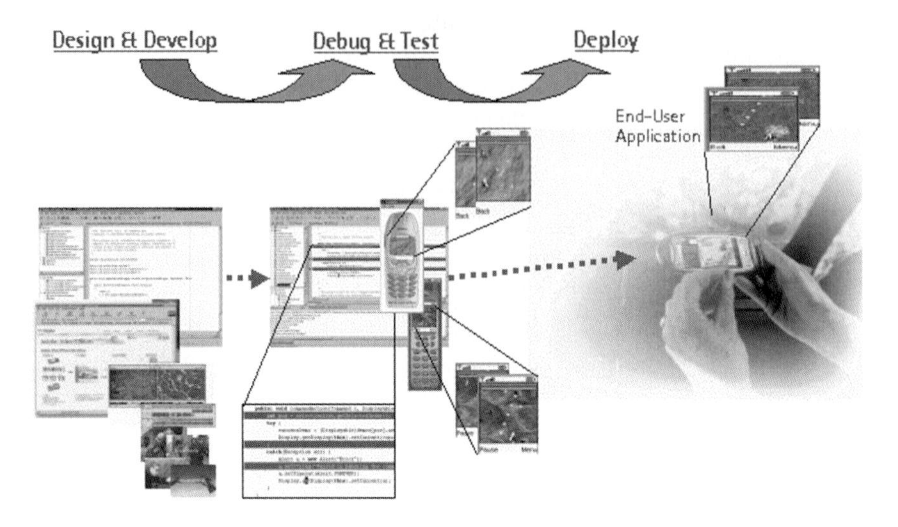

Key stages of the mobile domain development process

Java™ Development

In Java development, and especially in development in mobile device environments, the default assumption is that with its limited functionality, the Java environment works well because the running engine (i.e., Java Virtual Machine (JVM)) is the same or should function in the same way as on the Web domain. However, this is only the beginning, since mobile device environments set special requirements for developers. Usually, the display and runtime environment need customization, and this sets specific requirements for the development environment and used tools.

From Nokia's perspective, there are two Java implementations in the Mobile domain: J2ME™/ MIDP and PersonalJava. Both platforms are supported by the development environments and SDKs.

In end-to-end applications, the Java 2 Platform, Enterprise Edition (J2EE) environment has a very important role. Once vendors of J2EE application servers implement Mobile Java APIs in their application platforms, mobile devices and the capabilities of mobile networks become accessible to J2EE developers. In addition, Mobile Java APIs must be easy to integrate with the developer's environment (e.g., IDE).

Native Development

Symbian platforms use native language. The APIs in the development environment are implemented in C++. Currently, the main development environment for native development is Microsoft Visual C++®, and it is integrated with Symbian-based SDKs.

PC-side development and debugging is done with the WINS (single-process Windows platform) emulator and Microsoft Visual C++ that builds x86 binaries. For special targets, the developer must rebuild the application in ARM binaries by using a GNU C++ compiler implementation supplied with the SDK.

Nokia offers Symbian-based SDKs that integrate with the native Microsoft IDE, or alternatively SDKs can be used as standalone applications.

Content Development

The Multimedia Messaging Service (MMS) content development environment is supported by the integration of Nokia mobile extension (i.e., MMS plug-in for the Series 60 SDK) with content IDEs (e.g., Adobe® GoLive®) and on the other hand with Series 60 SDK based on Symbian OS. In the future, there will be MMS content development environments for other Nokia mobile device platforms.

The server-side MMS application development is supported by the server emulator and development libraries.

Development Environment Examples

Forum Nokia offers SDKs and mobile extensions integrated with commercial development tools (i.e., IDEs) for Nokia mobile devices as follows:

Series 30 Platform

- MIDP SDKs integrated with Borland JBuilder™, Sun Forte™ for Java, Sun Wireless Toolkit and Nokia Developer's Suite

Series 60 Platform

- MIDP SDK integrated with Borland JBuilder, Sun Forte for Java, Sun Wireless Toolkit and Nokia Developer's Suite
- Native SDK integrated with Microsoft Visual C++
- Nokia Developer's Suite for MMS including MMS extension for SDK, integrated with Adobe GoLive content IDE

Series 80 Platform

- MIDP Software for the Nokia 9200 Communicator Series and deployment functionality integrated with Borland JBuilder, Sun Forte for Java and Nokia Developer's Suite
- Nokia Developer's Suite for PersonalJava integrated with Borland JBuilder and Sun Forte for Java

- Native SDK integrated with Microsoft Visual C++
- Testing environment (Nokia Testing Suite) for Series 80 applications, integrates with Borland JBuilder and Sun Forte for Java

The following examples of development environments are snapshots of Forum Nokia's development tool offering. All of these tools are downloadable from the Forum Nokia Web site, excluding commercial development environments.

Nokia Developer's Suite for J2ME

Combining an IDE, Borland JBuilder or Sun Forte for Java with Nokia Developer's Suite for the Java 2, Micro Edition (which includes the Nokia 6310i MIDP SDK) creates a full J2ME MIDP development environment. The emulator provides an interface to, e.g., the Sun J2ME Wireless Toolkit. This solution guides the developer through the different phases of application development, testing processes and application deployment for the actual mobile device.

Nokia Developer's Suite for J2ME takes advantage of JBuilder's IDE services (e.g., project management and compiling). In addition, Nokia Developer's Suite has been built in such a way that the new feature enablers in future mobile devices can be easily integrated as mobile technologies mature.

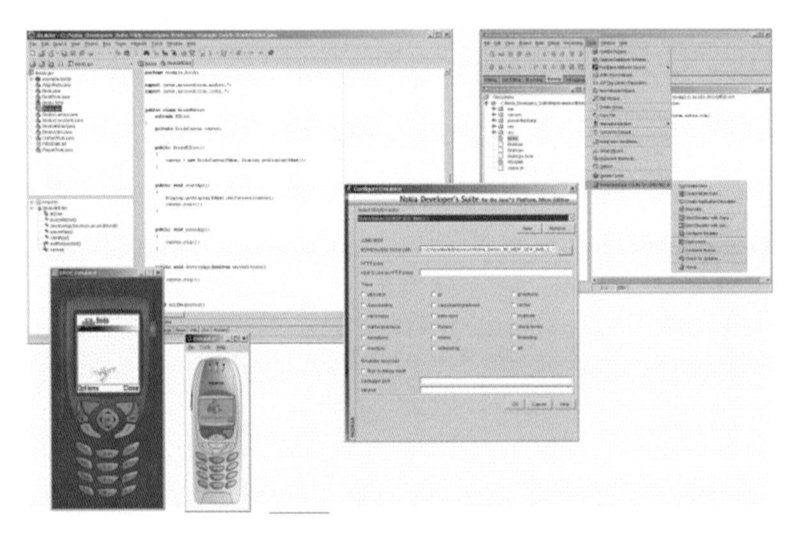

Different elements of the J2ME MIDP development environment

The J2ME development environment offers the following features:

1. Integration with

   - o Borland JBuilder 5 and 6
   - o Sun Forte for Java 3

2. Non-integrated use (standalone)
3. Automated Wizards

   - o the developer can create useful code skeletons, e.g., user-defined methods
   - o an application packaging based on standard specifications

4. Interfacing with Nokia SDKs and emulators

   - o application deployment for the following Nokia mobile device emulators:
     - Nokia 6310i MIDP SDK
     - Nokia Series 60 MIDP SDK
   - o J2ME Wireless Toolkit 1.0.3 interface in an IDE integration supported

5. Deployment to Nokia mobile devices

   - o For Nokia 6310i:
     - Microsoft Windows NT users: Nokia 6310i compatible cable
     - Microsoft Windows 2000 users: Nokia 6310i compatible cable, IrDA

6. Additional features

   - o Command Runner; a tool for creating, saving, modifying and executing command line scripts
   - o Check for Updates; a tool for checking and updating a development environment, and for finding marketing and sales channels for applications

Product Availability

- **www.forum.nokia.com**: Download Nokia Developer's Suite for J2ME and the supported Nokia SDKs
- **www.borland.com/jbuilder**: Download or CD-ROM ordering information, Borland JBuilder
- **www.sun.com/forte/ffj**: Download or order CD-ROM, Sun Forte for Java

Nokia Developer's Suite for the PersonalJava

The combination of an IDE, Borland JBuilder or Sun Forte for Java, Nokia Developer's Suite for the PersonalJava Application Environment (PJAE), and the Nokia 9200 Communicator Series SDK for Symbian OS creates a full PersonalJava development environment. This is an integrated solution that guides the developer through the different phases from application development to runtime emulation. It provides an easy-to-use and consistent graphical user interface for packaging, emulating and deploying mobile device applications.

Nokia Developer's Suite for PJAE takes advantage of JBuilder's IDE services (e.g., project management and compiling). While operating seamlessly together with JBuilder, it contains no overlapping functionality with the parent environment. The Nokia 9200 Communicator Series SDK for Symbian OS provides the development environment with the necessary emulator and tools. In addition, Nokia Developer's Suite for PJAE has been built in such a way that new mobile technologies can be easily added into the development environment.

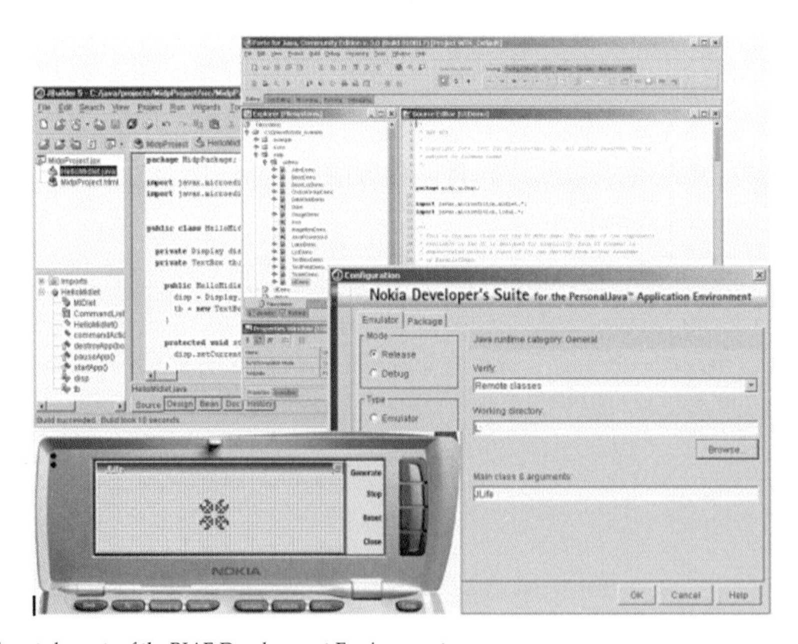

Different elements of the PJAE Development Environment

The PersonalJava development environment offers the following features:

- Integration with
  - Borland JBuilder 5 and 6
  - Forte for Java 3.0
- Non-integrated use (standalone)
- Integration with the services and tools of the Nokia 9200 Communicator Series SDK for Symbian OS
- Application packaging based on standard specifications
- Emulator integration for testing runtime behavior of applications
- Mobile device deployment tool integration

Product Availability

- **www.forum.nokia.com**: Download Nokia Developer's Suite for PJAE, CD-ROM ordering form, the Nokia 9200 Communicator Series SDK for Symbian OS
- **www.borland.com/jbuilder**: Download or CD-ROM ordering information, Borland JBuilder
- **www.sun.com/forte/ffj**: Download or CD-ROM ordering information, Sun Forte for Java
- **Local dealers**: Nokia 9200 Communicator Series device (including PC Suite software for application installation)

Nokia Developer's Suite for MMS

The environment allows developers to create and edit a Synchronized Multimedia Integration Language (SMIL)-based presentation and to convert it easily into MMS format. Nokia Series 60 SDKs provide a preview feature for the created messages. The External Application Interface (EAIF) emulator of the Nokia Multimedia Messaging Service Center (MMSC) allows developers to see MMS messages in the MMSC server EAIF.

Nokia Developer's Suite for MMS, the Nokia Series 60 MMS SDK and the Nokia MMSC EAIF emulator can be downloaded free of charge. The Nokia Series 60 SDK can be ordered from the Forum Nokia Web site. GoLive can be downloaded or ordered from Adobe's Web site.

Nokia Developer's Suite for MMS takes advantage of Adobe GoLive services (e.g., content management and authoring of text, images and audio clips). In addition, Nokia Developer's Suite has been built to allow easy integration with the new features in future mobile devices, as MMS technology matures.

Development environment for creating MMS messages

Nokia Developer's Suite for MMS integrates all tools required to enable MMS message creation. It provides the following key features:

- Integration with Adobe GoLive
- MMS encapsulation
- Emulator integration
  - MMS mobile device emulator
  - MMSC EAIF emulator
- Deployment of created MMS messages to emulators

Product Availability

- **www.forum.nokia.com**:

  Download, Nokia Developer's Suite for MMS, Nokia Series 60 MMS SDK for Symbian OS, Nokia MMSC EAIF emulator

  CD-ROM ordering form, Nokia Series 60 SDK for Symbian OS

- **www.adobe.com/products/golive**:

  Download or order CD-ROM, Adobe GoLive

Nokia MMSC EAIF Emulator

As a MMS server-side developer, you will need to interface with the MMSC. This will most likely happen over an interface designated in the Third Generation Partnership Project (3GPP) specifications as MM7. The Nokia Artuse MMS Center provides an EAIF, which developers can use to communicate with the Nokia MMSC.

The EAIF supports three types of applications: originating, terminating and filtering. Additionally, terminating and filtering applications can be synchronous or asynchronous. Synchronous applications always handle one request at a time, and respond to that request before accepting new ones. Asynchronous applications can accept new requests while still handling previous ones, and then respond to each request as their processing is completed.

Nokia offers an EAIF Emulator, which imitates the interface between the MMSC and the third-party developer. It allows you to test the functionality of your applications without having to access a full MMSC.

The EAIF Emulator provides the following functionality:

Support for Originating Applications

The emulator is able to receive multimedia messages sent by an originating application. The emulator verifies that the message is sent according to EAIF specifications, validates the format of the received message, and finally returns a response to the request.

Support for Terminating Applications

The emulator is able to submit an MMS message to a terminating application. The emulator contains ready-made MMS messages, with different contents, which can be sent to applications according to the EAIF specification. After the message is sent to the application, the emulator is able to receive and display the response that the application sent.

Support for Filtering Applications

The emulator is able to submit an MMS message to a filtering application. The same ready-made MMS messages used for testing terminating applications can be submitted to a filtering application. The emulator can also send headers, without the message body, to the filtering application. After processing the message, the emulator is able to receive the response and the modified message from the filtering application.

Delivery Reporting

The emulator allows an originating application to request a delivery report. The delivery report can be submitted via the emulator's Graphical User Interface (GUI) to a terminating application if the originating application requested a delivery report in the message.

Support for Synchronous and Asynchronous Applications

The emulator is able to receive messages from an originating application and the responses from terminating and filtering applications synchronously. From terminating and filtering applications, the emulator is also able to receive responses in an asynchronous manner.

Data Logging/Status Reporting

The emulator keeps track of message- and system-related events as well as error information. All events and error information can be stored in log files for later analysis. The data logging / status reporting functionality allows the developer to view the structure of messages and to identify reasons for reported errors.

Templates for Creating Multimedia Messages

The emulator provides several ready-made templates and sample messages. The sample messages contain combinations of different media and they can be easily submitted to external applications.

Addition of New Templates and Example Messages

The emulator allows developers to add new templates and sample messages to be used in testing. Developers can add their own messages to the emulator with different contents to better meet the requirements of the tested application.

Nokia Testing Suite

Nokia provides an environment for testing the behavior of, e.g., C++ and Java applications in the Nokia 9200 Communicator Series or an emulator. The environment thereby enables developers to take into account the runtime requirements of applications.

The testing suite also encourages developers to become acquainted with the Nokia OK process, a testing and evaluation process for third-party products running on Nokia mobile devices.

The Nokia Testing Suite consists of PC software and client software in a Nokia 9200 Communicator Series device or in the Nokia 9200 Communicator Series SDK emulator. An additional GSM mobile device can be used to test the phone functions in the Nokia Testing Suite client. Mobile devices are connected to the PC via serial port or IrDA. When an emulator is used for testing, a serial cable must be connected between two serial ports (i.e., null modem cable). When testing Java applications, the Nokia Testing Suite can be launched from Borland JBuilder or Sun Forte for Java. The Nokia 9210 Communicator PC Suite is required for file transfer. It is included in the sales package of the mobile device.

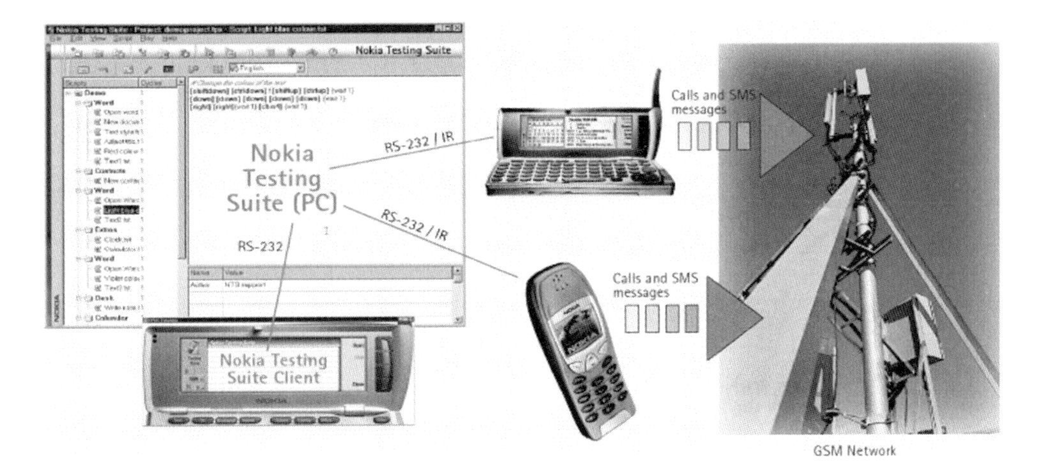

Nokia Testing Suite environment

The Nokia Testing Suite provides the following key features:

- Testing applications in the Nokia 9200 Communicator Series and Symbian emulator
- Run automated commands on the Nokia 9200 Communicator Series devices
  - Easy-to-use script language
  - Advanced visual script editing
  - Sample scripts
  - XML-based script format
  - Multiple scripts in one project
  - Adjustable play speed
  - Testing transactions with GSM networks (e.g., calls and SMS)
- Multilanguage support for the 9200 Communicator Series
- Non-integrated use
- Integration with
  - Borland JBuilder 5 and 6
  - Forte for Java 3.0

Product Availability

- **www.forum.nokia.com**:

  Download, Nokia Testing Suite

  Order CD-ROM, Nokia 9200 Communicator Series SDK for Symbian OS

- **www.borland.com/jbuilder:**

  Download or order CD-ROM, Borland JBuilder

- **www.sun.com/forte/ffj:**

  Download or order CD-ROM, Sun Forte for Java

- **Local dealers:**

  Nokia 9200 Communicator Series device (including PC Suite software for application installation)

Forum Nokia

Open technologies and industry initiatives are together supporting the transformation of mobile devices from voice-only devices into multipurpose data devices that will bring a myriad of new usage contexts, balanced efficiency and increased personal choice to consumers across the globe. Nokia has a long tradition of emphasizing openness and interoperability. A support for open standards and platforms enables independent software developers to participate in the development work together with Nokia.

Nokia offers these software developers a wide range of tools and support via Forum Nokia. Nokia believes that the expertise acquired from the emerging fields of software development, together with the global Nokia mobile device base and an understanding of mobile device usage patterns in Nokia, will produce the most useful and attractive services and applications for consumers.

Forum Nokia was established in 1995 and today boasts more than 500,000 memberships. Free registration enables software developers across the world to design applications and services for Nokia's broad base of mobile devices. Today, Forum Nokia supports all major mobile technologies, both on the mobile device and server side. Moreover, since all of Nokia's products are based on widely adopted standards, the fruits of the development work can be easily modified to benefit the entire industry. A good example of this is the Nokia 9210 Communicator, a multi-task mobile device targeted to meet the varying needs of mobile professionals and corporate users. The latest communicator, which operates on Symbian OS and is equipped with a color-display, is an excellent platform for software developers to design add-on functions and applications easily and effectively.

Even if the technologies are standardized, User Interface (UI) characteristics (e.g., display size and input methods) still vary. The aim of Forum Nokia is to be a centralized source for programming guides, but perhaps even more importantly, to deliver information on how to optimize applications and services for Nokia platforms and UIs. Delivering the optimization information before the actual products are in the market helps us in reaching the goal: the add-on applications and services are available to consumers at the same time as the products become commercially available.

Access

Nearly all content in Forum Nokia can be accessed without any registration. However, access to certain areas (e.g., tool download sections) requires a simple registration.

The actual development work is done independently - Nokia does not control the projects.

Process

The slogan frequently used to describe Forum Nokia is Build-test-sell, and it also illustrates the process, which often begins from obtaining the tools.

Various tools and development kits are available for developing software and content. Most of the tools are provided free of charge, but there is a fee for development kits that include hardware (e.g., the M2M Application Development Kit). Software development kits (SDKs) can often be downloaded, but larger files are more conveniently installed from CD-ROM and this is why selected SDKs are delivered on CD-ROM after a request form has been filled out on the Forum Nokia Web site.

Nokia develops the tools independently, but also cooperates with the world's leading development tool providers in order to be able to offer professional Integrated Development Environments (IDEs). Such professional IDEs include advanced debugging, wizards, compilers and similar features that speed up the programming, testing and deployment of applications. Cooperation with leading IDE providers allows the option of selecting familiar programming tools, but also extends the development possibilities beyond the preferred programming language, when a compiler is used for, e.g., translating a software application programmed with Basic into a C++ application.

To facilitate software and application development carried out with the tools provided by Nokia and its partners, Forum Nokia also offers developers an extensive selection of documentation. The material includes white papers, programmer's and developer's guides, data sheets, specifications, as well as installation and user guides for toolkits. FAQs address technologies but also Nokia implementation, and for that purpose, Nokia frequently produces UI style guides for various phone models. The documentation covers all the latest technologies supported in Nokia's mobile devices.

The developer newsletters address hot development issues and they are regionally flavored to include industry news on the latest products, events, standardization and other development in the Mobile domain. Technical tips and code samples demonstrate the type of content that brings additional value to programmers.

During the development process, there is often a need for information that is unavailable at the time. In the Forum Nokia discussion areas, developers can search for solutions and present their problem descriptions to be read not only by Nokia experts but also active co-developers. A dedicated group of experts provides developers with technical help on a daily basis through a support service subject to a charge. The cases build up a knowledge base, which is often recommended as the first place to search for a solution to a particular problem.

The development tools are not abandoned even when the application is complete. Emulators are an integral part of the development tools and they are needed in the testing phase. Terminal emulators are used in testing how the service is rendered in a mobile device display and if the functionality works as planned. The advantage is that developers do not need to obtain every mobile device model that Nokia brings to the market, considering the fact that Nokia alone introduces about 20 new models each year. Nokia has published four UI categories, easing the task of optimizing software for every UI and mobile device model. On the server side, emulators test the functionality of gateways and servers in mobile networks, which eliminates the need for a connection to a real server or gateway.

The developed applications can be tested in the Nokia OK program. Customers, including consumers as well as carriers and service providers, prefer applications and services that are tested to function correctly when installed or accessed. In the Nokia OK process, the application is tested, not the content. The testing is carried out by external, independent testing houses based in several locations around the world. The software used in the testing is the Nokia Testing Suite, which can be obtained from Forum Nokia. The Nokia OK PreTest Set is a bundled package of documentation and special scripts that can be used to test applications with the Nokia Testing Suite before entering the Nokia OK process. Successful Nokia OK pre-testing shortens the formal Nokia OK testing period.

Even if the application development ends once the program code is completed and tested, the life cycle of the application has only begun at that point. Nokia provides marketing services and distribution channels for applications, and applications tested in the Nokia OK process gain visibility on Nokia Web sites. The Nokia OK logo can be used in marketing successfully tested applications and the logo can be printed on application brochures and packaging. The target market can be reached through Nokia's distribution channels. Nokia Tradepoint is a business-to-business e-marketplace for mobile applications and content. The customers, carriers and service providers, can visit the site whenever they want to extend the offering in their portals. The sales agreement is made directly between the customer and the developer, and Nokia's role is only to provide the marketplace for this matchmaking. Nokia Software Market is another distribution channel and it is targeted directly at consumers who wish to extend the capabilities of the mobile devices. Entering an application into Nokia's sales channels does not prevent developers from using additional channels for reaching their target markets.

Handpicked applications may end up in Club Nokia, or they can be integrated into products or included in the Nokia product sales packages. Club Nokia is Nokia's customer loyalty program and for many the place to familiarize themselves with add-on mobile applications. An increasing number of consumer-targeted utility applications are delivered together with the product. These applications can be delivered on CD-ROM in the sales package or as pre-installed, and services can be bookmarked in the browser's list of bookmarks when the product is taken out of the sales package for the first time.

Conclusions

Open platforms and standards form a strong base for supporting the transformation of mobile devices from voice-only devices into multipurpose data terminals. Open interfaces and platforms offer tremendous opportunities, but no company alone can design all applications of the Mobile domain. Nokia believes that it's support of third-party developers and successful cooperation with them will produce the most useful and attractive services for consumers.

Nokia OK Process

The Nokia OK process is a testing and evaluation process for applications and products created by third-party developers. Once an application or product has been tested successfully, the Nokia OK logo can be used in marketing the application or product. Currently, the Nokia OK process includes four different categories:

- Terminal Software Applications
  - Nokia Symbian mobile devices
  - Nokia J2ME enabled mobile devices
- Server Software Applications
  - Nokia browsing products
  - Nokia MMS platform
- Hardware Products
  - Various accessories for Nokia products
- Covers
  - Color covers for Nokia mobile devices

In all of the categories, the Nokia OK approval is given to an application or product. However, the Nokia OK Covers category audits the cover painter and their production methods, sells the covers that the painter produces, but does not test each individual cover.

The entire Nokia OK concept is introduced to developers on the Forum Nokia Web site (www.forum.nokia.com/ok). These Web pages provide information on the Nokia OK concept in general, and specifically on all four categories. All information sharing towards developers is managed from these Web pages.

From the main page, the four categories have separate Web pages that are not related to each other. In fact, the four categories differ from each other considerably. Their processes are generally the same, but due to the differences in technologies and hardware versus software, the testing criteria are different. However, each set of pages offers a general introduction, documents to assist the developer, and an application form for the Nokia OK process.

Process Overview

The Nokia OK process contains three main elements, which are shown in following figure.

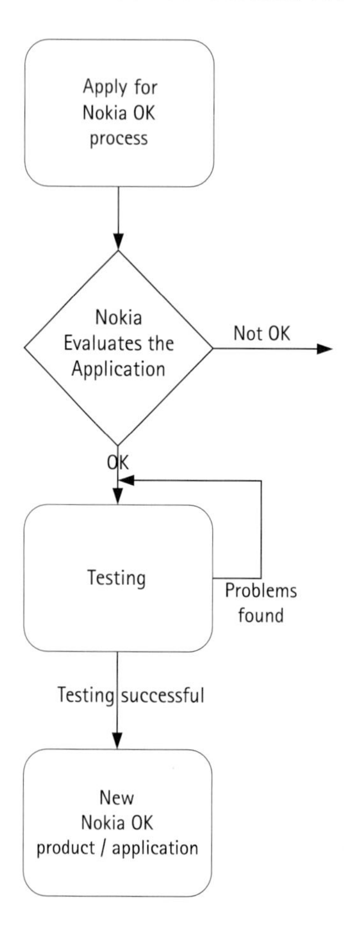

Nokia OK process

The first task for the developer is to apply for the Nokia OK process. Nokia evaluates the application according to the category standards. If the application is considered suitable for the Nokia OK process, the developer is informed about the details on how to proceed to the product or application testing phase. If the evaluation results in the rejection of the application, the developer is notified and provided with an explanation. After a successful testing, the developer has to sign a Nokia OK License Agreement, which grants the developer a right to use the Nokia OK logo. The agreement is a standard and global document. When the legal procedure has been finalized, a new Nokia OK application or product is launched and the developer can enjoy the advantages produced by the Nokia OK process.

To be accepted into the Nokia OK process, the developer needs to meet a set of criteria. The main idea, however, is that the developer's product or application works in the Nokia device or platform. Additionally, there are criteria related to each category (e.g., a Nokia OK Cover painter is audited, and a new application for the Nokia 9210 Communicator is verified to comply with the humanistic values required of software applications).

Nokia OK Testing

Each Nokia OK category has its own requirements. Nokia OK Covers have strict environmental requirements, Nokia OK Hardware Products require a Consumer Electronics (CE) label on the product, and Nokia OK Software applications are required to pass all the user interface and technical testing procedures. Since developers cover the testing costs, it is very important that the developer become familiar with all the requirements. It would be a waste of money from the developer to submit a beta version to Nokia OK testing. However, some testers may offer pre-testing possibilities to developers. Also Nokia offers pre-testing documentation and tools.

All testing of the developer's applications or products is conducted using real Nokia products or platforms. It is important to get a view of the functionality of the application or product in real situations, typically in situations that the consumer is likely to encounter.

All testing is conducted by outside companies, which invoice the developer directly. These companies carry out the testing as their own business. However, Nokia always issues the testing requirements and in many cases offers the products and the possibly required infrastructure to the developer. Thus, all parties know that the testing is always conducted in a similar environment.

The testing house delivers the test results to Nokia, where the persons responsible for the case determine possible issues that the developer has to do to finalize the testing. The developer also has a chance to go through the testing requirements before applying for the Nokia OK process. This reduces the amount of detected defects in the products.

Nokia OK License

If the developer is issued the Nokia OK logo, a Nokia OK License Agreement must be signed. Usually the agreement is signed for three years at a time for each Nokia OK product. The agreement outlines the use of the logo, liability issues and the way in which both parties are involved in the use of the Nokia OK logo. Only selected Nokia representatives are entitled to sign the agreement and two signatures are required from Nokia, as well as the original copy of the agreement.

Advantages of the Nokia OK Process

The Nokia OK logo is the most visible advantage for a Nokia OK application. The Nokia OK logo is illustrated in the following figure.

Nokia OK logo

The Nokia OK logo makes it easier for customers to identify reliable third party applications and products (i.e., they meet Nokia's testing criteria). These associated applications and products allow consumers to get more out of their Nokia products.

Nokia's own sales channels also provide added visibility for Nokia OK products.

PART 4.2

Java

- Java MIDP Application Development

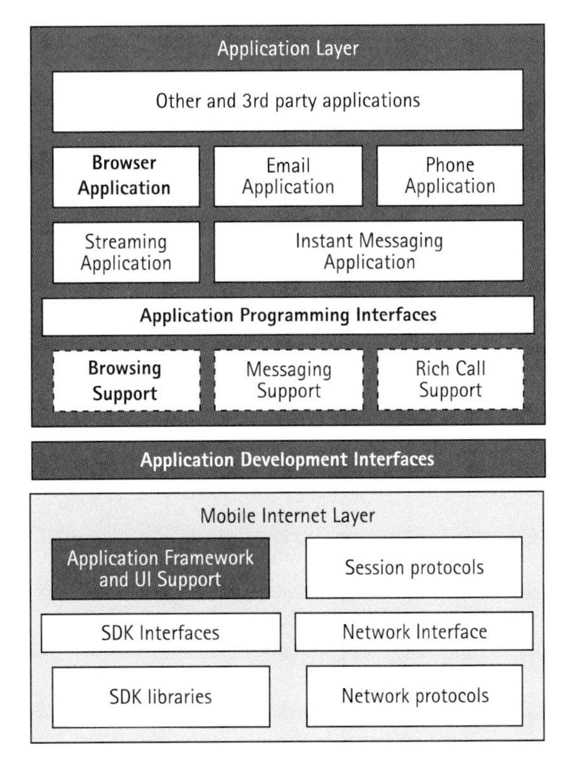

Java™ MIDP Application Development

This section describes the Java™ MIDP from a developer's point of view. It gives many valuable ideas and guidelines on how to produce MIDP applications of good quality for Nokia devices. Only basic information on the Java technology itself is covered.

The Java™ 2 Platform, Micro Edition (J2ME™) is the edition of the Java 2 platform targeted at consumer electronics and embedded devices. The J2ME technology consists of a virtual machine and a set of APIs. The J2ME technology has two primary kinds of components: configurations and profiles.

The Mobile Information Device Profile (MIDP) is a set of Java APIs, which, together with the Connected Limited Device Configuration (CLDC), provides a complete J2ME application runtime environment. It allows new applications and services to be dynamically deployed on mobile devices.

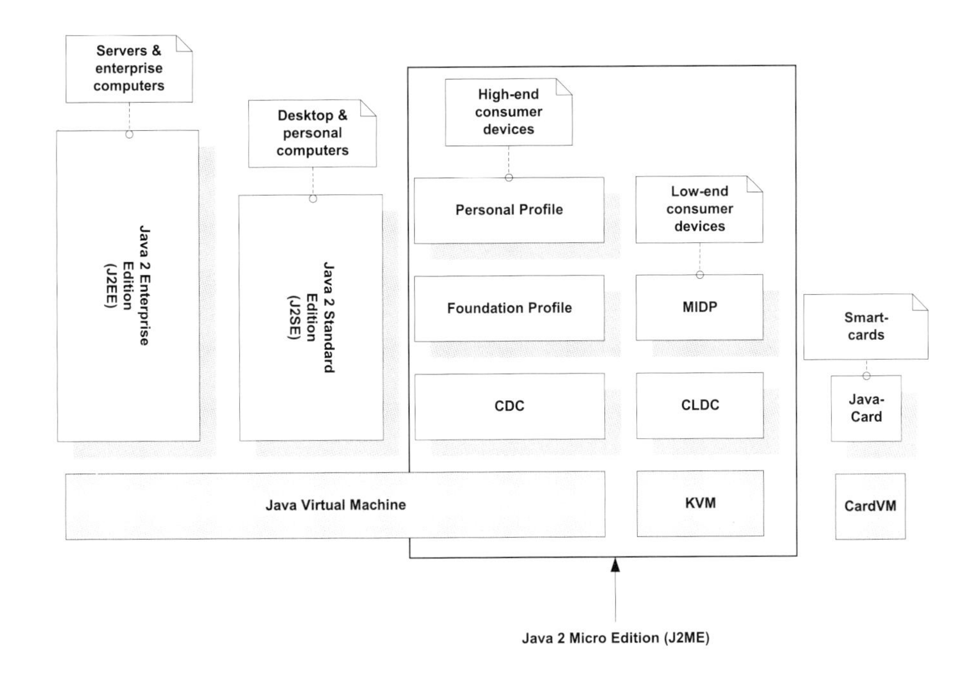

Java 2 Platform, Micro Edition architecture

Configurations

A configuration defines J2ME functionality targeted at particular device ranges: virtual machine operations, secure code download and installation, and a set of core APIs. The CLDC-based limited Java Virtual Machine (JVM) defines the features of the Java language and virtual machine that are used.

- Java language and VM features (java.lang)
- Input/output features and handling of data streams (java.io)
- Calendar, date, random number (java.util)
- Basic networking features (javax.microedition.io)

Profiles

A profile is built on top of a configuration necessary to provide a complete runtime environment for a specific kind of device. Profiles specify both APIs and the configuration.

Profiles have the following benefits:

- A profile provides a complete toolkit for implementing applications for a particular kind of device (e.g., a mobile device).
- A profile may also be created to support a coherent group of applications that might be hosted on several categories of devices.

MIDP has the following APIs:

- User Interface – Defines User Interface APIs (javax.microedition.lcdui)
- HTTP implementation – Defines HTTP network connections (javax.microedition.io.HttpConnection)
- Persistent storage – Defines a record oriented database (javax.microedition.rms)
- Application life cycle – Defines the application model (javax.microedition.midlet)
- Timers – Defines the timers (java.util.Timer and java.util.TimerTas)
- One new exception case (java.lang.IllegalStateException)

Developing Applications

A MIDlet is an application written for the MIDP. In designing MIDP applications for mobile device use, there are several items that developers should keep in mind:

- The applications should be useful to consumers who are not necessarily experts in other technology areas and with devices other than the mobile device they are currently using.
- The MIDP applications should be useful in many different kind of situations (e.g., where people are not capable of concentrating fully on the application).
- There are different kinds of MIDP devices that developers must be aware of (e.g., different sizes of display, different keyboards and different *look and feel* in the devices).
- Developers should also think about cases of interruption (e.g., when a phone call or SMS comes during the execution of a MIDlet). The MIDlet goes to background automatically, but it should also recover from that situation smoothly. Another example is a situation where a device suddenly loses the network connection when the MIDlet is running. So, various test cases are needed, and it is crucial that they be considered in testing in order to ensure development of high-quality applications for Nokia devices.

Levels of the MIDP User Interface

There are two different User Interface (UI) levels in the MIDP:

- High-level API
- Low-level API

High-Level API

The high-level API does not take the whole screen for its own use but instead leaves space also for the battery and other icons. It is always recommended to use high-level API components where possible. There is no direct access to native device features (e.g., no direct access to soft buttons). The high-level user interface API is designed for applications whose client components run on mobile devices. The high-level API has the following properties:

- System software writes content to the display. Applications do not define the visual appearance (e.g., colors or fonts) of the components.
- The device performs navigation, scrolling and other simple interactions with the UI components, not the applications.
- Applications cannot access concrete input mechanisms (e.g., individual keys).

Low-Level API

Low-level APIs are mainly used for various kinds of games and other applications that require the full screen for showing graphics. Full-screen applications for Nokia devices always leave some specific icons and indicators visible on the screen. However, it is possible to bring even the reserved area of the screen into use with the FullCanvas class of the Nokia UI API.

There are two classes that are meant to be implemented at the low-level user interface level: Graphics and Canvas. The Graphics class provides methods to paint lines, rectangles, arcs, text and images to a Canvas or an Image. The low-level API gives developers access to key press events.

Examples of user interface APIs:

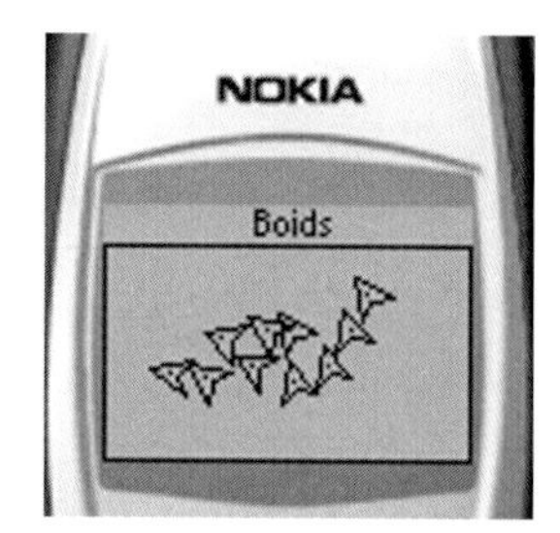

Examples of high-level (left) and low-level (right) APIs in a MIDlet

Command Class

The Command class is a primary mechanism for use in user interaction (e.g., changes of view between Displayables). The Command class is an abstract entity for a UI element that invokes an action. Every Screen and Canvas can have an arbitrary number of Commands. Commands are mapped to the real UI elements (e.g., soft keys, menu items, buttons, and button widgets) with the MIDP implementation.

The Command object has three parameters:

```
ExitCommand = new Command(Label, type, priority);
```

1) The Label is shown to the consumer when the command is rendered on the display. It describes the function to the consumer.
2) The type of the command can be one of the following: BACK, EXIT, STOP, HELP, ITEM, OK, CANCEL or SCREEN. For example, the BACK command type causes the application to go back to a previous state.
3) The priority allows the implementation to make high-priority commands more accessible.

Commands have an application-defined abstract type and priority that are used to map commands to concrete UI elements. Commands have labels that are shown to the consumer. If the Label is missing, the default label is shown. Default labels are based on the type of the commands. After the right type for each command is resolved, the priorities are chosen. The actual label for the command should be short but descriptive.

- o BACK - returns to the previous display.
- o OK/CANCEL - pair should be used when creating a confirmation dialog for the consumer.
- o EXIT - close the current application. The EXIT Command should call the MIDlet's notifyDestroyed() method, after doing the needed resource clean-up and state saving operations.
- o HELP - provides help about the current Displayable or an application. Help should be presented as a Form.
- o STOP - stops some ongoing action (e.g., aborts the network query).
- o ITEM - should be used for tasks that relate to the focused/selected content of the Displayable.
- o SCREEN affects the whole content of the Screen or the whole application.

The application-level handling of commands is based on a listener function. Each Displayable object has a single CommandListener. When the user invokes a Command on a Displayable, its listener is called. A listener object must implement the interface CommandListener and its method, commandAction.

MIDlet Commands, their probable functions, Nokia's default placements and their Nokia default Command labels

MIDP Command type (constant value)	Intent of Command (probable function)	Nokia default placement	Nokia default Command label
SCREEN (1)	MIDlet-defined command relevant to the current display	Left Soft Key	Select
BACK (2)	Navigation command which probably returns the user to the logically previous display.	Right Soft Key	Back
CANCEL (3)	Standard negative response to a dialog on the current display.	Right Soft Key	Cancel
OK (4)	Standard positive response to a dialog on the current display.	Left Soft Key	OK
HELP (5)	Request for MIDlet help information.	Left Soft Key	Help
STOP (6)	Stop a currently running process or operation.	Right Soft Key	Stop
EXIT (7)	Exit the MIDlet.	Right Soft Key	Close
ITEM (8)	MIDlet-defined command relevant to a specific item on the display. Context-sensitive.	Left Soft Key	Select

Important design notes about Commands:

- Avoid using a large number of Commands. The presence of many commands in the options menu makes the user interface inconvenient to use because the consumer has to scroll through the whole list when selecting a command that is near the end of the menu.
- In the design phase, break the application into views and design interaction between each view. Screens and Commands are then used to realize the actual tasks in views.
- Think about the order of Commands in the menu carefully. The basic principle is that the most commonly used functionality would be the first item in the list. Logically, EXIT would always be the final item in the menu. Always provide an Exit option to consumers so that they can smoothly exit the application.
- Limit the length of Command labels; try to describe the title as clearly and as concisely as possible. Remember to put the most important thing at the beginning and think about different cropping options during the implementation phase.
- It is also important to notice that in Nokia devices there are certain behavioral rules that are already very familiar to the consumers. For example, normally if there are two soft keys in the device, the right one provides Way back or Exit functionality to the consumer. Developers should respect these conventions when designing easy-to-use applications for Nokia devices. In MIDP implementations, this is handled by Command mapping; negative backward actions are always mapped to the right soft key and positive actions to the left soft key.

Command Mapping

On most Nokia mobile devices, Commands are mapped to the soft keys, but in Series-80 types of devices, Commands are mapped to the buttons and menus. This is the case for Screen class displays and normal Canvas class displays but not for FullCanvas displays. Soft keys are not shown in the FullCanvas Displayables.

Events and Actions in the Low-Level UI

Commands make user interaction possible on the high-level UI API side, but in the low-level UI API user interaction methods are called events and actions.

When the application needs to handle key Canvas events, it must override the Canvas methods keyPressed, keyReleased and keyRepeated. When a key is pressed, the keyPressed method is called with the key code. When that key is released, the keyReleased method is called. Also, in all MIDP devices there must be support for the telephone keys. Key codes are defined in the Canvas class for the digits 0 trough 9, * and #.

The Canvas class also has methods for handling action events from the low-level user interface. The API defines actions as follows: UP, DOWN, LEFT, RIGHT, FIRE, GAME_A, GAME_B, GAME_C and GAME_D. The device maps the action events to suitable key codes on the device with the Canvas.getKeyCode method.

Displayable Class

A Displayable object is an element that can be placed on the display. A Displayable object may have Commands and associated Command Listeners with it. Only one Displayable is active and displayed to the consumer at a time. The contents displayed and their interaction with the consumer is defined by subclasses.

The Displayable class has two direct subclasses:

- o Canvas and
- o Screen

An application developer may use both Canvases and Screens in the same application; for doing so, there is a special *setCurrent* method which displays the required component.

The next figure describes the major classes in the MIDP user-interface class hierarchy:

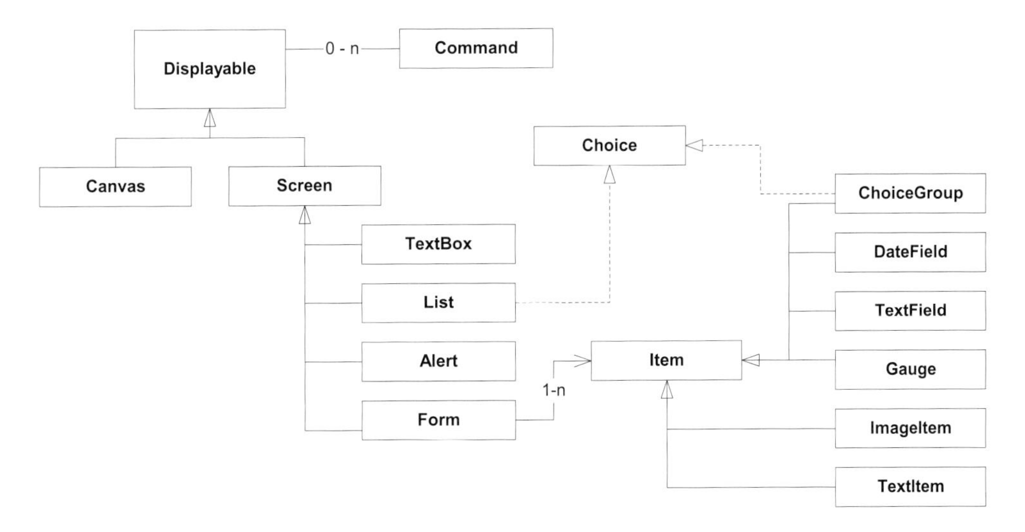

MIDP UI class hierarchy

Canvas Class

The Canvas class (javax.microedition.lcdui.Canvas) is a base class for writing applications that need to handle low-level events and to issue graphics calls for writing to the display. Game applications will likely make heavy use of the Canvas class. Canvas is a low-level component that the application defines itself. It provides a low-level graphics interface for applications. Graphics operations are similar to those in J2SE™ and Personal Java™ (java.awt.Graphics). The Canvas provides methods to handle game actions and key events. Methods are also provided to identify the device's capabilities and keyboard mapping.

Screen Class

The Screen is a common super-class for all high-level user interface classes. Every Screen provides presentation and layout itself. MIDP applications do not define presentation or layout in Screen, just the content. Typically, classes derived from the Screen class will map directly to native UI controls with the same behavior.

Screen consists of high-level UI components as follows:

- Alert
- Form
- List
- Textbox
- Ticker

MIDP User Interface Elements

The following sections serve to describe UI elements in MIDP.

Command

Commands are used for achieving user interaction. Their mapping (e.g., to the soft keys or menu buttons) depends on the type of device.

Alert

Alert is a screen that shows various kinds of messages to the consumer, mainly error messages. There may be an application-specific icon in it. The developer should consider the amount, tone and actual text of the message carefully because consumers do not want to get similar notes all the time. Try to clarify all the possibilities during the design phase.

Form

The Form class is suitable in cases where a screen with a single function is not enough. The Form class can contain other user interface elements. Developers should, however, keep in mind that it is not suitable to have many different components in one display, as the size of the display is very limited. A simple and understandable display with a minimum number of components is much more sophisticated and usable than displays consisting of several components.

The items that can be placed inside a form are as follows:

- **Choice group** is used for single and multiple selections.
- **Date field** is used to display times and dates.
- **Gauge** is used to display a value graphically.
- **Image** item is used for displaying images.
- **String** item is used for text and strings.
- **Textfield** is used for textual input, with constraints.

List

The List class is a Screen containing a list of choices. When a list is present on the display, the user can interact with it indefinitely. These operations do not cause events which are visible to the application.

There can be three different kinds of list, which are as follows:

- IMPLICIT where selection causes immediate notification of the application if there is a CommandListener registered. The element that has the focus will be selected before any CommandListener for this List is called.
- EXCLUSIVE where the selection operation changes the selected element in the list. The application is not notified.
- MULTIPLE where the selection operation toggles the selected state of the element with the focus. The application is not notified.

TextBox

The TextBox class is a Screen that allows the user to enter and edit text. A TextBox has a maximum size of the maximum number of characters that can be stored in the object at any time. TextBox can support normal text, Predictive text input text (T9) or encoded text (e.g., for passwords where the letters are represent as asterisks (**)).

Nokia User Interface Categories

This chapter looks at MIDP issues in regard to four different Nokia user interface categories. Current range of Nokia MIDP devices consists of:

- **Series-30**, the first product is Nokia 6310i
- **Series-40**, the first product is Nokia 7210
- **Series-60**, the first product is Nokia 7650
- **Series-80**, the first product is Nokia 9210 Communicator

Series-30

The Series-30 is a UI concept with a monochrome display whose resolution is 96 x 65 pixels. The Series-30 UI is based on a two soft key concept. The basic idea is that there are left/right soft keys, a Send key, End key and scroll keys. The principle in Series-30 navigation is that the left side (left soft key, Send key) is used for positive actions (e.g., acceptance and selection). The right side (right soft key, End key) is used for negative actions (e.g., clearing and moving backwards).

Standard Hardware Keys

- Down and Up scroll keys
- Left and Right soft keys
- Send and End keys
- Numeric keys (0-9, *, #)
- Power key
- Volume up/down keys

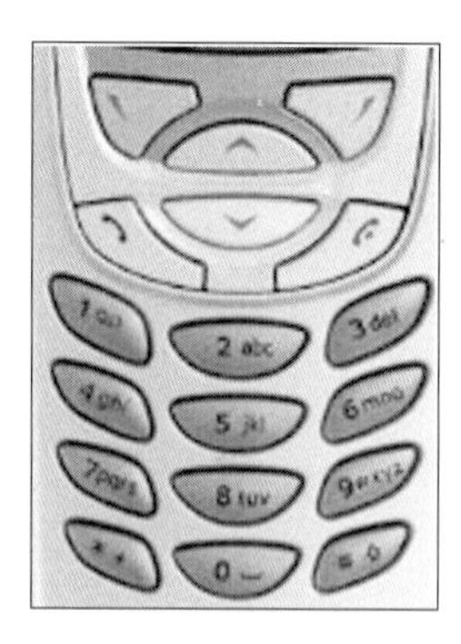

Standard keys in Series-30

Scroll Keys

The scroll keys provide the necessary functions for effective navigation in the menu tree.

Soft Keys

The left soft key is in essence used as a yes/positive key. It is associated with options that execute commands and go deeper into the menu structure: Select, OK, Options and similar. The right soft key functions as a no/negative key. Its options cancel commands, delete text and go backwards in the menu structure: Back, Exit, Clear and so forth. The consumer should be able to use the device as much as possible through only the scroll keys and the left soft key. When a soft key provides a function, it must be labeled. The same function cannot be available from both soft keys at the same time.

Send and End Keys

The Send key is mainly used for answering an incoming call and initiating an outgoing call but can also be used as a select button in various cases. The End key is mainly used for terminating an ongoing call, for rejecting an incoming call, and as a global exit key which closes the active applications and brings the phone to idle state.

Display Components

Series-30 supports 96 (horizontal) x 65 (vertical) pixel displays.

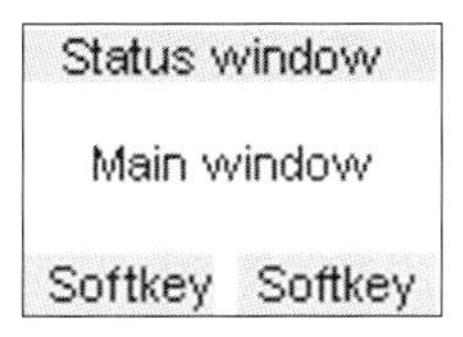

The Series-30 UI display is split into the following main areas

- The Status window is for displaying status indicators (e.g., battery charge level). The status window also includes the header text.
- The Main window is for displaying menu lists and application-specific data.
- The soft key window is for displaying soft key functions.

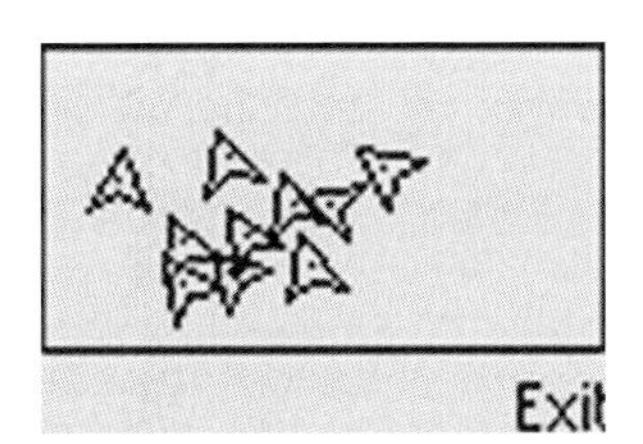

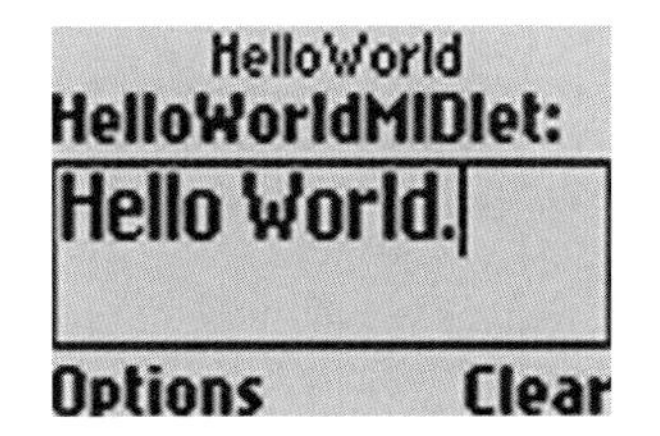

Examples of a Series-30 UI, with a 96 x 95 display

Button Mappings and Basic Navigation

Navigating the MIDP high-level UI elements is done with the Up and Down keys.

The Send key (green phone receiver key) can be used as Select. Commands get mapped to the two soft keys below the screen. Soft key labels are visible only when using high-level LCDUI elements. The following table maps device keys to game actions.

Game action mapping

2 key and Up arrow key	UP
8 key and Down arrow key	DOWN
4 key	LEFT
6 key	RIGHT
5 key and Send key	FIRE
* key	GAME_A
0 key	GAME_B
# key	GAME_C
9 key	GAME_D

Key constants not defined in MIDP specification

Up arrow key	-1
Down arrow key	-2
Send key	-3

Series-40

The Series-40 is a size- and cost-driven UI platform for the mass market. It has a high-resolution color display and supports four-way scrolling. The screen size is 128 x 128 pixels, and 4096 colors are supported. The Nokia Series 40 UI is a smooth evolution of the Nokia two soft key UI, and it hence inherits the proven great usability of previous Nokia mobile devices. The color display is used to improve key applications (e.g., MMS, picture viewing, MIDP Java, Browser and Calendar) in addition to personalization. In fact, it increases the usability of all applications.

Standard Hardware Keys

- Left Soft Key (LSK)
- Right Soft Key (RSK)
- Up and Down scroll keys
- Left and Right scroll keys (optional but strongly recommended)
- Send key
- End key
- Numeric keys (0 - 9, *, #)
- Power key
- Volume up and down keys (optional but strongly recommended)

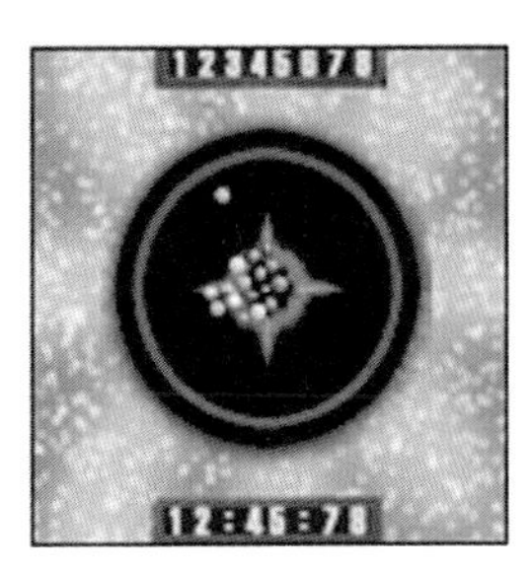

Example pictures of a Series-40 UI, with 128 x 128 display and color support

Series-60

Series-60 is a UI style for imaging phones. It is one-hand operated, Symbian OS feature platform. Series-60 has a large color display, which is well-suited to various kinds of applications. Display size is 176 x 206 pixels. The first product using the Series-60 UI style is the Nokia 7650.

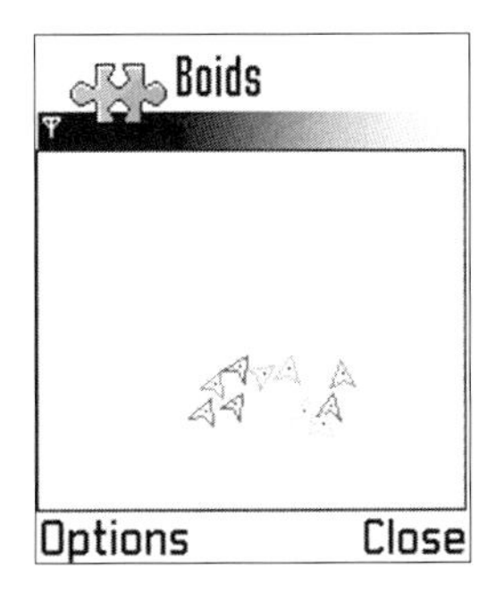

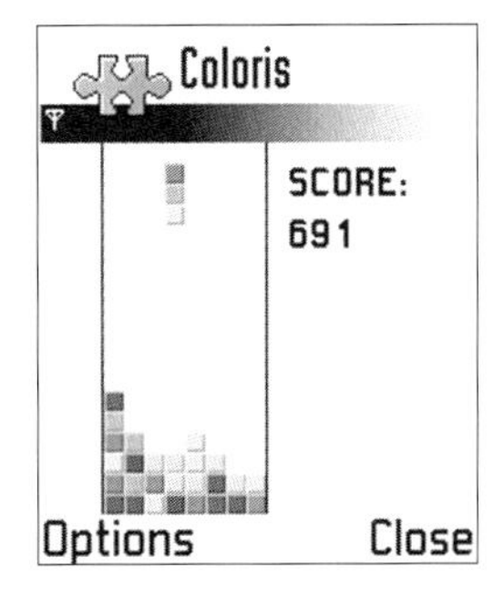

Example pictures of a Series-60 UI, with 176 x 208 display and color support

Standard Hardware Keys

- Two soft keys
- Five-function Select key (Up, Down, Left, Right, and Select)
- Applications keys (Send and End)
- Clear
- Shift (ABC)
- Numeric keypad (0-9, *, #)
- Voice key (dialing, recording)
- Power key

Select Key Concept

- o Movements in four directions and selection. The principal navigating device.
- o Twisting up/down:
  - Move focus
  - Browse lists
  - In editor: move cursor
- o Clicking:
  - Open next lower level of current item
  - When opening is impossible, offer Roller Options menu

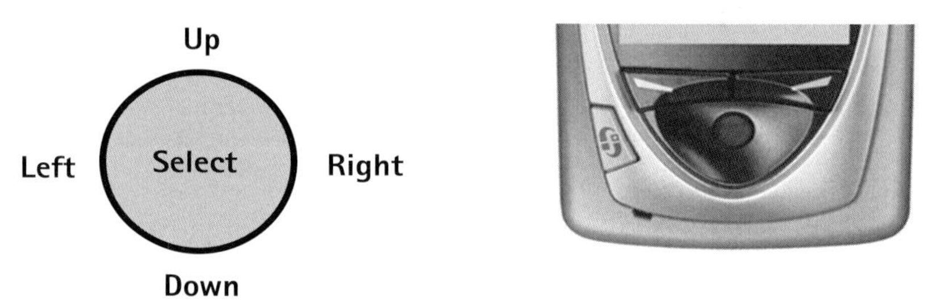

Principle of Select key - component and its implementation in Nokia 7650

Command Mapping

The implementation will add an Exit command to the Options menu if one is not provided by the application. For this reason, it is sometimes possible to see two Exit commands in the Options menu. This happens if the application uses Command types incorrectly (i.e., has not used the proper Command).

Form

The commands "Copy text" and "Find in page" are automatically added to the displayable.

Button Mappings and Basic Navigation

Navigating the MIDP high-level UI elements is done with the navigation keys. Pressing OK can function as Select. Commands are mapped to the two soft keys below the screen.

Game action mapping

2 key Up key	UP
8 key and Down key	DOWN
4 key and Left key	LEFT
6 key and Right key	RIGHT
5 key and OK key	FIRE
7 key	GAME_A
9 key	GAME_B
* key	GAME_C
# key	GAME_D

Series-80

Series-80 is a two hand operated feature concept platform. There is a color screen and plenty of space for different types of applications.

The Main Interaction Elements

- o Four command buttons on the right side of the display
  - The Command Button Area (CBA) consists of four command buttons.
  - The basic functionality of the device should be managed by the command buttons.
  - The width of the command button area is dynamic but view-dependent; it is as wide as the longest command text string that could appear on the application screen in question.
  - The first word of a command text starts with a capital letter. Use of abbreviations is not recommended. Command texts are aligned to the right. Use clear, concise commands and remember to prioritize the commands so that only the most important functionality is available via the command buttons.
- o Menu
  - The menu button activates and deactivates the Menu.
- o Keyboard residing below the display

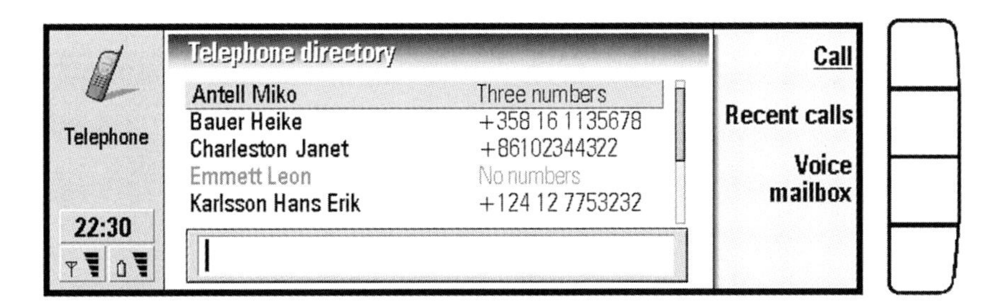

Example of the Series-80 UI

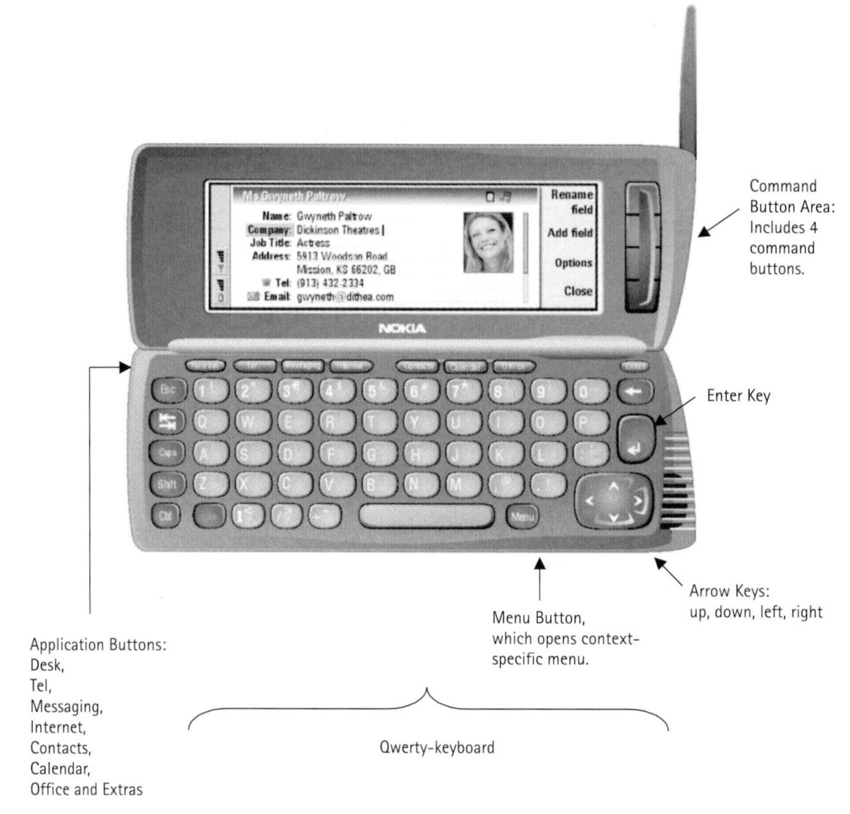

The Series-80 keyboard

MIDP UI Design

MIDP Applications in Different Products

The main goal and promise of Java is portability; the *Write once; run everywhere* principle. In practice, there are many challenging aspects to portability work because devices are different. Here are a couple of examples of Nokia user interfaces in different products:

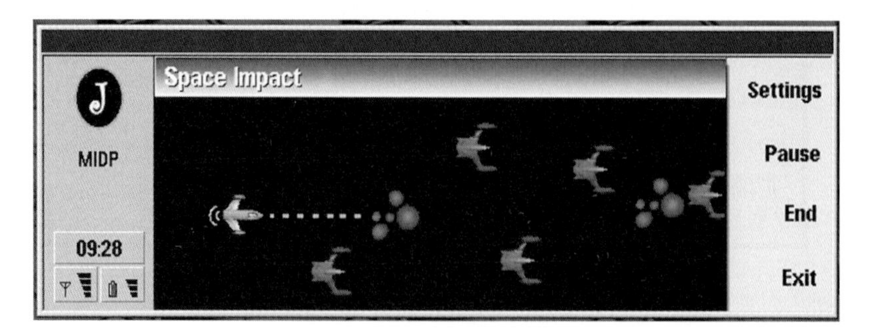

Space Impact game on a Nokia Series-80 UI

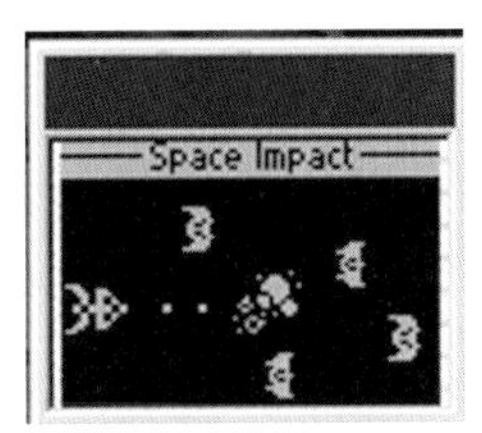

Space Impact game on a Nokia Series-30 UI

Ways of Designing User Interfaces

In designing user interfaces for mobile devices, a new set of issues should be considered by developers.

1) Target group. Designers should have a clear vision of the application's target audience and the target devices before actual design and implementation starts.
2) Place early focus on consumers. Designers should have direct contact with intended or actual consumers to make sure that developers are answering their requirements. Applications should be simple and easy to use. They should feel comfortable.
3) Early and continual user testing. Test enough, to discover any usability problems or misleading aspects of the application in as early phase as possible.
4) Integrated design. All aspects of usability (e.g., user interface, help system, documentation) should evolve in parallel rather that sequentially.

When the developers know the consumers well enough, it is time to start producing the actual applications. Here are a couple practical design tips:

1) Use a screen map or some other modeling techniques to visualize the design. Split the application into states and clarify transitions between states (starting and end points). In this phase, think also about navigation through the whole application, and make sure that consumers can always go back.

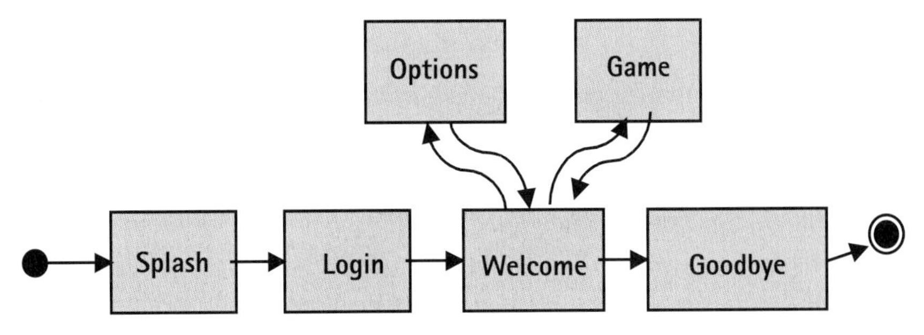

Example of the screen map technique

2) Then progress to a more detailed level; think about the different messages that will be given to the consumer in various situations. Also consider all possible error situations - those are also good input for the testing of the application.

3) Remember that the MIDlet could be used on very different kinds of Nokia devices, and the screens, shapes and sizes of these can vary. Test as much as possible with different Nokia MIDP devices.

4) Take advantage of the MIDP high-level user interface where possible so that the MIDlet behaves like the device's native applications.

5) Remember to define and implement comprehensive Instructions or Help as part of the application so that the consumers can immediately find answers to their questions without calling any help desks.

Also, developers should take into careful consideration the different methods of navigation and input mechanisms of different devices.

MIDP Application Localization

Developers are encouraged to consider different cultural issues when making global software for devices; consumers use the same Nokia devices and the same applications in many different countries.

In Java there is the possibility to localize a MIDP application by putting specific strings in the JAD file. As there can be different JAD files for the same MIDP program, the developer can, for example, supply English and Finnish versions of the JAD file for the MIDlet. These two JAD files would include strings for the different languages, but both files still refer to the same JAR file. Then, when the MIDlet is active, it retrieves the correct text strings from the JAD file and displays them.

MIDP Usability Issues

Usability means that a consumer of the product or application can accomplish the intended tasks quickly and easily:

1. Usability means focusing on consumers.
2. Consumers use products to be productive.
3. Consumers are busy and trying to accomplish tasks.
4. Consumers decide when the product is easy to use.

The following questions can be used for determining the general usability of an application:

1. Is it easy to learn?
2. Is it efficient to use?

3. Can the consumer recover quickly from errors?
4. Is it easy to remember?

MIDP Application Design Checklist

There are certain things to consider about user interfaces:

- Great variation in display sizes and shapes.
- Color and monochrome displays.
- Different input mechanism in different devices and different *look and feel* of the devices.
- Images behavior in different sizes of displays.
- The importance of testing the code.
- Pictures, tables and color behavior.
- The need to take care of backward navigation.
- Use of titles and labels.
- Performing a usability test.

Nokia Java APIs

MIDP 1.0 was designed for maximum portability and concentrated only on features implementable by all candidate devices, which vary greatly in capabilities. Hence, MIDP 1.0 excluded sound features and advanced graphics features, making it more portable for a wide range of devices.

A major use of Java in mobile devices is entertainment (e.g., games). Games often need low-level access to device hardware. MIDP was designed to be hardware-independent, so there is no support for this kind of low-level access.

The NOKIA UI API extensions enhance the developer's capability of delivering good Java applications for Nokia devices supporting the Mobile Information Device Profile.

Currently, the Nokia UI API has two packages, both of which contain an interface and classes for providing features for playing simple sounds and displaying more advanced graphics; com.nokia.mid.ui and com.nokia.mid.sound.

com.nokia.mid.ui

The com.nokia.mid.ui package contains some graphics-related extensions for MIDP low-level UI APIs (e.g., Graphics and Canvas). The DirectGraphics interface contains some graphics extensions for MIDP Graphics, with which polygons and triangles can be drawn and filled, images rotated or flipped, alpha channel color supported, and raw pixel data directly obtained from the graphics context or written to it.

com.nokia.mid.sound

The com.nokia.mid.sound package provides an API for simple audio capabilities. SoundListener interface is used by applications that need to receive events that indicate changes in the playback state of the Sound objects.

User Interface Extensions

The Nokia UI API adds to MIDP the following features:

- Full-screen Canvas extending the normal screen area
- Drawing and filling triangles and polygons
- Drawing images reflected or rotated
- Transparency support
- Extra ways to create mutable images
- Low-level access to image pixel data

Full-Screen Canvas

The screen shot in the next figure shows the difference in screen sizes. The picture on the right side shows the usage of the Nokia UI API's FullCanvas class, which extends the original Canvas to the whole screen for graphics. Unfortunately, Commands cannot be added because there is no space onscreen for soft commands.

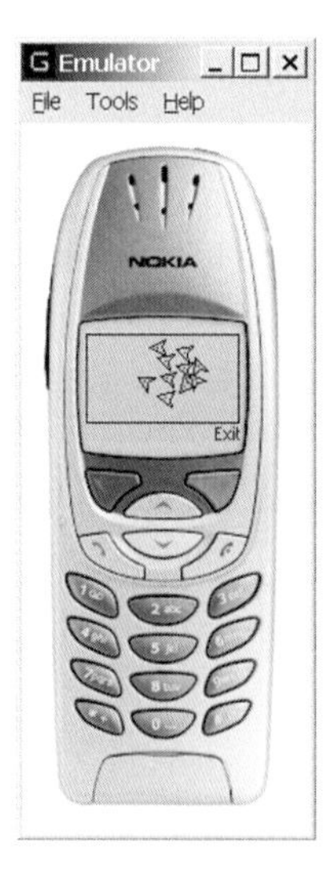

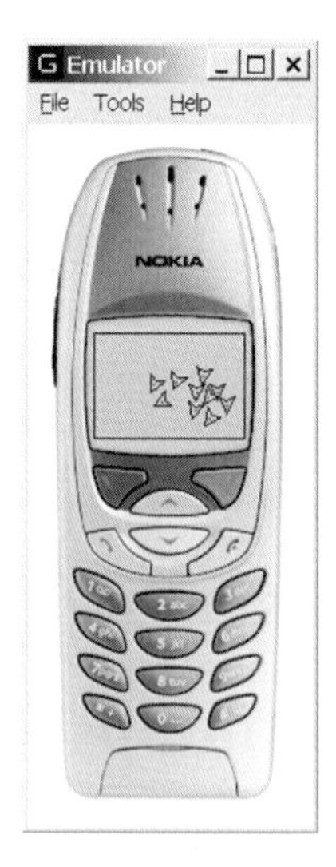

The difference when using FullCanvas

Drawing and Filling Triangles and Polygons

```
public void fillPolygon(int[] xPoints, int xOffset,
                        int[] yPoints, int yOffset,
                        int nPoints, int argbColor)
```

Fills a closed polygon defined by the arrays of the x and y coordinates. This method draws the polygon defined by nPoint line segments. The figure is automatically closed by drawing a line connecting the final point to the first point if those points are different.

Drawing Images Reflected or Rotated

```
public void drawImage(javax.microedition.lcdui.Image img,
                        int x, int y,
                        int anchor, int manipulation)
```

Draws an image to the graphics context. Does common image manipulations during the drawing of an image. Manipulation can be 0 if no manipulation is done. Draws the specified image by using the anchor point - the anchor point is applied after the manipulation. Anchor values are defined in Graphics. The image can be drawn in different positions relative to the anchor point by passing the appropriate position constants. Manipulation is flipping or rotating values or a combination of them.

Transparency Support

```
public void setARGBColor(int argbColor)
```

Sets the current color to the specified ARGB value. All subsequent rendering operations will use this specified color. This changes the color value of Graphics.

The high-order byte specifies opacity; that is, 0x00RRGGBB specifies a fully transparent pixel and 0xFFRRGGBB specifies a fully opaque pixel. Implementations must treat any pixel with a nonzero top byte as being non-transparent. Most implementations treat a nonzero top byte as fully opaque; i.e., alpha blending is not implemented.

Additional Ways to Create Mutable Images

```
public static Image createImage(byte[] imageData, int imageOffset,
                                  int imageLength)
```

Creates a mutable image that is decoded from the data stored in the specified byte array at the specified offset and length. The data must be in a self-identifying image file format supported by the implementation (e.g., PNG).

Low-Level Access to Image Pixel Data

```
public void getPixels(int[] pixels, int offset, int scanlength, int x,
                        int y, int width, int height, int format)
```

Copies the pixel values of the graphics context from a specific location to an array of int values. The pixels will be passed in the format defined by the `format` parameter. If an implementation does not support the format, an IllegalArgumentException is thrown. Note that it is possible that only the native format is supported via the appropriate version of the getPixels method. This method returns only int-based formats. Requesting all other formats will result in an IllegalArgumentException.

Throws an ArrayIndexOutOfBoundsException if array size is too small for image pixels.

The getPixels methods stores the pixel data to the pixels array in the following fashion:

```
pixels[offset + (x1 - x) + (y1 - y) * scanlength] = P(x1, y1),
for each P(x1, y1),
where (x <= x1 < x + width) and (y <= y1 < y + height).
```

getPixels

```
public void getPixels(byte[] pixels, byte[] transparencyMask,
                        int offset, int scanlength,int x, int y,
                        int width, int height, int format)
```

Copies the pixel values of the graphics context from a specific location to an array of byte values. The pixels will be passed in the format defined by the `format` parameter. If an implementation does not support the format, an IllegalArgumentException is thrown.

Note that it is highly possible that only the TYPE_BYTE_1_GRAY and TYPE_BYTE_1_GRAY_VERTICAL formats are supported with this method.

This method returns only byte-based formats. Requesting all other formats will result in an IllegalArgumentException.

Throws an ArrayIndexOutOfBoundsException if array size is too small for image pixels or transparency mask. The argument transparencyMask can be null if the caller is not interested in getting the mask.

Note that the `scanlength` and `offset` parameters indicate the `scanlength` and `offset` in number of pixels. This is not necessarily the same as array indices since multiple pixels may be stored in a byte.

Sound Extensions

The Nokia UI API adds to MIDP the ability to play sound. There are two types of sound supported:

- Single notes, specified by frequency and duration
- Simple tunes, specified using the Nokia Smart Messaging ringing tone library format.

Playing a Single Note

```
Sound s = new Sound(440, 1000);     //frequency and time in ms.
s.play(1);                          //loop
```

Playing a Simple Tune

```
byte[] tune =
    {
        (byte)0x02, (byte)0x4A, (byte)0x3A, (byte)0x80,..

    };
Sound s = new Sound(tune, Sound.FORMAT.TONE)
s.play(1)
```

Sound State Model and soundListener

Registers a listener for playback state notifications. It is very helpful in checking state before playing a new tone (e.g., has the previous tone stopped).

Vibration and Light Control Extension

The Nokia UI API adds to MIDP the ability to control the device's vibration feature and screen backlight. Vibration might be used in a game to signal a collision or explosion. Flashing the backlight might be used for emphasis when the consumer completes a level.

Controlling Vibration

```
void vibrate()
    {
        try
        {
            // Vibrate at 100% for 200 msec.
            DeviceControl.startVibra(100, 200);
        }
        catch(Exception e)
        {
            // An IllegalStateException is thrown if the
            // device doesn't have vibration support.
            // Nothing can be done, so let's just
            // ignore it.
        }
}
```

Controlling Screen Backlight

```
void flashLights()
{
    DeviceControl.flashLights(250);   // 250 msec
}
```

Game MIDlets

Usually games differ from other applications in their intense use of graphics, but to offer the right application the implementer must take care to also:

- Offer all basic functionalities
- Offer immediate feedback

The basic functionalities common to every game are:

1. Start a new session of the game
2. Save/pause a session
3. Retrieve the saved/paused session
4. Exit the current session
5. Show and keep track of highest scores
6. Customized settings
7. Instructions

Feedback is essential to the consumer during game interaction because it helps in achieving his/her goals. Unlike in other applications the text format is often not enough during game interaction. A more immediate form of feedback is often necessary. Consequently, the MIDlet should include the use of:

- Sounds
- Vibra functionality
- Colors
- Images
- Use of backlight
- Text showing the total score achieved

Sounds and Vibra features are not always appropriate (e.g., sounds when the consumer wants to play in a silent environment). Therefore, the settings functionality should enable the consumer to switch them on/off.

It is also important not to overdo feedback and also to maintain its consistency across the application.

Provisioning

Many companies and individuals will be creating Java applications for mobile devices. Typical use might involve downloading the applications to the Java enabled device over a WAP connection. Thus, carriers will be in a key role, making sure that their subscribers have easy access to downloadable applications by providing WAP bookmarks for Java application portals.

For example, Club Nokia will offer downloadable Java applications to Nokia mobile devices. All of the Nokia mobile devices supporting J2ME also support downloading of Java applications. Many devices also support the downloading of Java applications via the PC Suite. Consumers with the PC Suite support can browse the Internet to find Java applications that they can install on their devices or can e-mail applications to friends who have devices with the PC Suite.

The MIDP API specification does not specify the means for the discovery and installation of MIDP applications on a device. There are several ways to do this: applications can be pre-installed at the factory, downloaded over a serial cable from a PC, or downloaded Over The Air (OTA). In the future, OTA downloading is expected to be the most important means for downloading new MIDlet applications to devices.

Over-the-Air Downloading

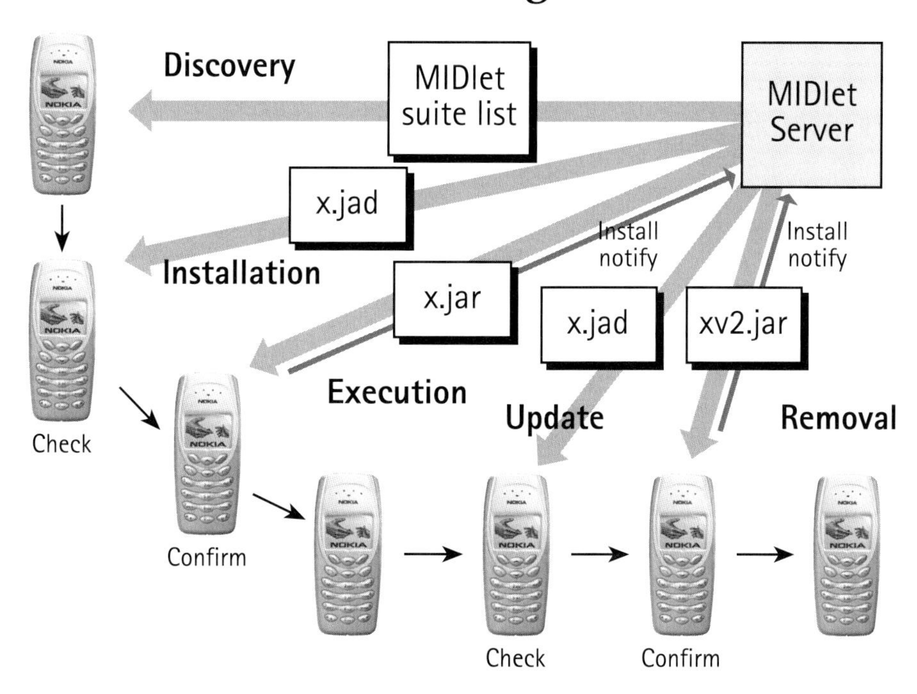

MIDlet deployment and life cycle.

For OTA downloads, the deployment and life cycle of the MIDlet is described roughly as follows.

Discovery

A consumer uses a browser on his/her mobile device to browse Web pages on a remote server, where the consumer finds a Web page containing a link to an interesting MIDP application. Actually the link points at a Java Application Descriptor (JAD). JAD file contains the core attributes of the application.

Installation

When the consumer selects the JAD file, the browser downloads the descriptor and provides it to the Application Management Software (AMS).

The AMS uses the attributes in the descriptor to check whether the device is able to run the application and if there are other factors that would prevent downloading. If application downloading can be performed, the AMS uses the Uniform Resource Locator given in the descriptor to locate and download the Java Archive file from a MIDlet server.

Next, the consumer is asked for permission to install the application. After it is provided, the AMS can install the MIDlet on the terminal. At this point, the AMS may also send a confirmation notification to the server. The server uses this confirmation for billing and customer care purposes.

Execution

After successful installation, the application is runnable and can be used.

References

http://java.sun.com/

http://www.forum.nokia.com/

PART 4.3

MMS

- MMS Service Development
- External MMS Applications

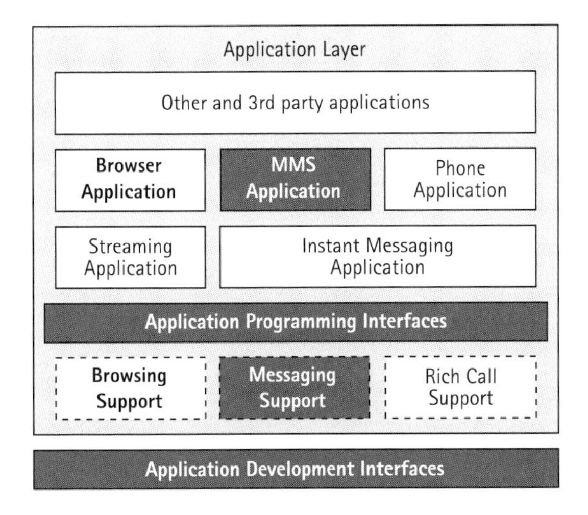

MMS Service Development

Nokia is fully committed to making MMS successful. Among other things, Nokia is implementing MMS in all User Interface (UI) categories, across the board. Nokia also supports developers in the creation of new MMS services.

We would like to provide you with a good starting point for understanding the basics of MMS before you go into the specifications, and then try to give you an idea of how to continue from there.

Here are a few quick scenarios to give you an idea of what types of services might be worth developing:

- A woman subscribes to a news service - every morning she receives an MMS message with the top stories of the day as well as the related images.
- A young boy subscribes to a music service - when one of his favorite bands is releasing a new album, he receives an MMS message with a sound clip from the title track.
- A frequent flyer receives an MMS message with the following month's offers, including enticing images of far-away lands.

Understanding Specifications

The amount of information available on MMS can be both over- and underwhelming. At first sight, any sort of relevant information may seem impossible to locate. This section describes the main specifications related to MMS, gives a brief synopsis of what each one is about, and then tries to make sense of it all.

MMS Standards

Third Generation Partnership Project (3GPP) has published the following MMS-related specifications:

- TS 22.140 Service Aspects [TS 22.140]
- TS 23.140 Functional Description [TS 23.140]

Service Aspects is a short specification describing system requirements at a general level.

Functional Description is more detailed than the Service Aspects specification. It describes the various architectural elements that are part of a multimedia messaging system, and specifies where the different interfaces between these elements are. The specification also lays out a set of media types and formats that are seen as minimum support requirements for MMS mobile devices, to ensure compatibility between MMS-enabled mobile devices.

In addition to 3GPP specifications the WAP Forum has created the following specifications:

- WAP-205 MMS Architecture Overview [WAP-205]
- WAP-206 MMS Client Transactions [WAP-206]
- WAP-209 MMS Encapsulation Protocol [WAP-209]
- WAP-203 Wireless Session Protocol Specification [WAP-203]
- WAP-230 Wireless Session Protocol Specification [WAP-230]

WAP-205, the architecture overview is a starting point for MMS. It is a very brief introduction to MMS, while WAP-206 and WAP-209 examine the actual implementation in more detail.

WAP-206 provides a detailed description of client transactions.

WAP-209 explains exactly which bytes should go where.

WAP-203 and WAP-230 describe the Wireless Session Protocol (WSP), and while they are not directly related to MMS, they strongly support WAP-205, WAP-206 and WAP-209. Note that for WSP-related issues in WAP-205 or WAP-206, you should consult WAP-230, but for the same issues in WAP-209, consult WAP-203.

Naturally, each of these specifications refers to a number of other specifications. However, the ones described above should provide a very good starting point.

MMS Conformance Document

The MMS Conformance Document [MMSCD] was written jointly by the MMS Interoperability Group. It lays out a guideline, which states the media types and formats to be supported by MMS mobile devices. The idea behind the document was to provide better interoperability, and to give application and service developers a clearer idea of what types of MMS messages mobile devices will support.

Making Sense of it All

It appears that most vendors are going to combine the functionality of the MMS Proxy-Relay and the MMS Server in the Multimedia Messaging Center (MMSC). Nokia also follows the approach, and for the rest of this document, we will be referring to the MMSC.

In attempting to tackle the big picture, we are first going to look at a very simplified view of MMS, then go deeper into what sort of messages are exchanged, and where exactly they are processed.

Basic Service

Most people are familiar with at least the basics of sending a Short Message Service (SMS) message. The following figure describes how an SMS message is delivered. There are several bits missing, but the basic concept is as follows:

- The message originator addresses the short message to the receiver.

- o The mobile device contains information about the SMSC and the message is sent there.
- o The SMSC attempts to forward the message to the receiver.

If the receiver cannot be reached for some reason, the SMSC stores the message for a time, and if possible, delivers the message later. If the message cannot be delivered within a certain period of time, it is eventually discarded.

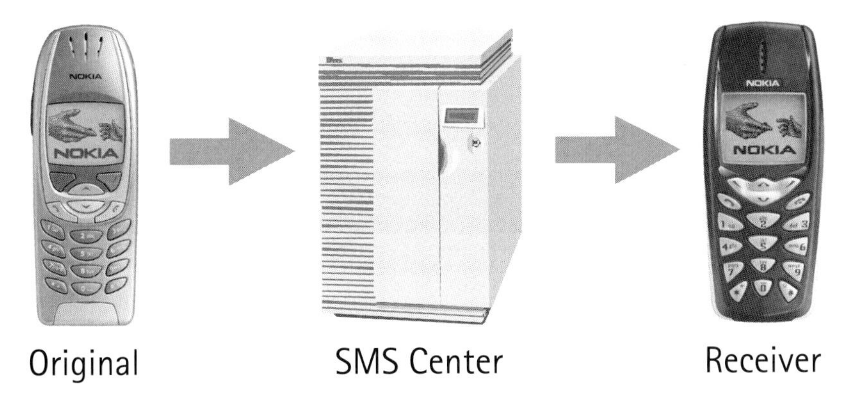

Sending an SMS message

The basic concept of sending an MMS message is exactly the same:

- o The message originator addresses the multimedia message to the receiver.
- o The mobile device contains information about the MMSC and the message is sent there.
- o The MMSC attempts to forward the message to the receiver.

If the receiver cannot be reached for some reason, the MMSC stores the message for a time, and if possible, delivers the message later. If the message cannot be delivered within a certain period, it is eventually discarded.

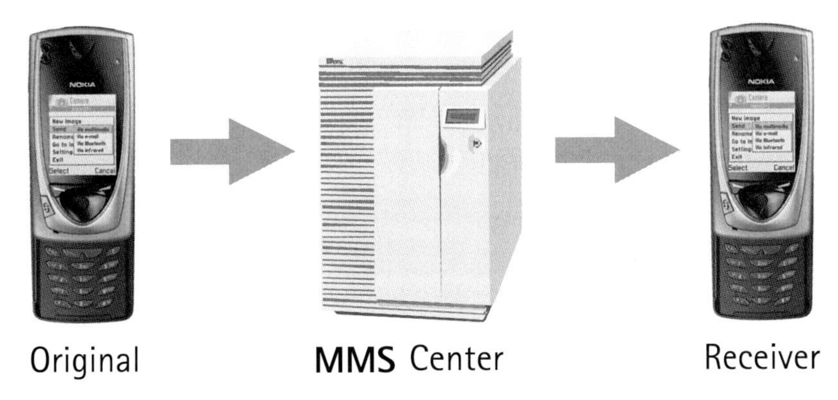

Sending an MMS message

MMS Service in Detail

The MMSC does not actually try to send the MMS message directly to the receiver, but instead sends a notification to the receiver about a message. Depending on the mobile device settings, the receiver's mobile device tries to fetch the message immediately, postpones retrieval as long as the consumer wants, or simply discards the notification altogether. Note that in the immediate retrieval, the consumer is not notified of an incoming message until it has in fact been delivered. The mobile device itself handles the retrieval, and only then informs the consumer about a received message.

The following table provides a more detailed description of MMS sending, which is divided into four main steps. The process is also illustrated in the following figure.

A: Originator sends message
1. The message originator addresses it to the receiver.
2. The mobile device contains information about the MMSC, initiates a WAP connection (CSD/GPRS), and sends the message as the content of a WSP POST.
3. The MMSC accepts the message, and responds to the originator over the same WAP connection. The originator's mobile device displays "message sent".
B: MMSC informs receiver
4. The MMSC uses WAP PUSH to attempt to send a notification message to the receiver.
C: Receiver fetches message
5. Presuming that the receiver's mobile device is set to accept MMS messages, it initiates a WAP connection (CSD/GPRS), and uses WSP GET to retrieve the MMS message from the MMSC.
6. The MMS message is sent to the receiver as the content of a WSP GET RESPONSE over same WAP connection. The receiver's mobile device displays "message received".
7. The receiver's mobile device acknowledges receipt with a WSP POST message, still over same WAP connection.
D: MMSC informs originator of delivery
8. The MMSC uses WAP PUSH to inform the originator that the message was delivered. The originator's mobile device displays "message delivered".

Steps in sending an MMS message

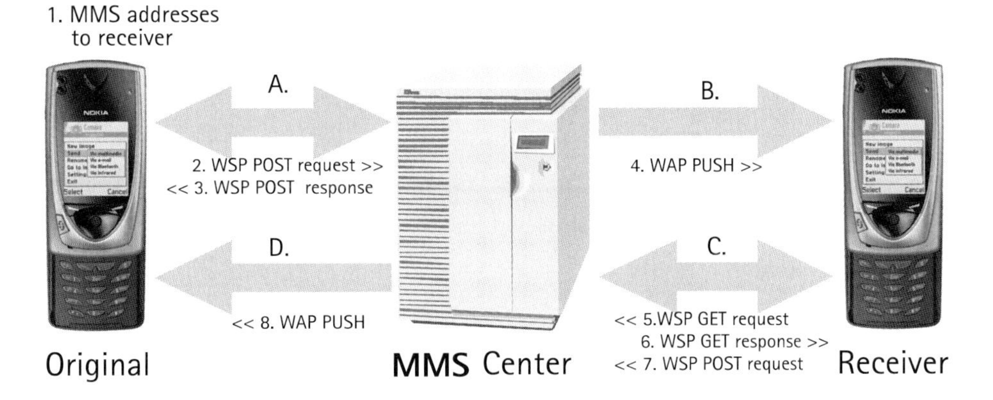

Sending an MMS message in detail

MMS Network Elements

Here is a closer look at basic MMS message delivery, this time including the mobile network and a few other key network elements.

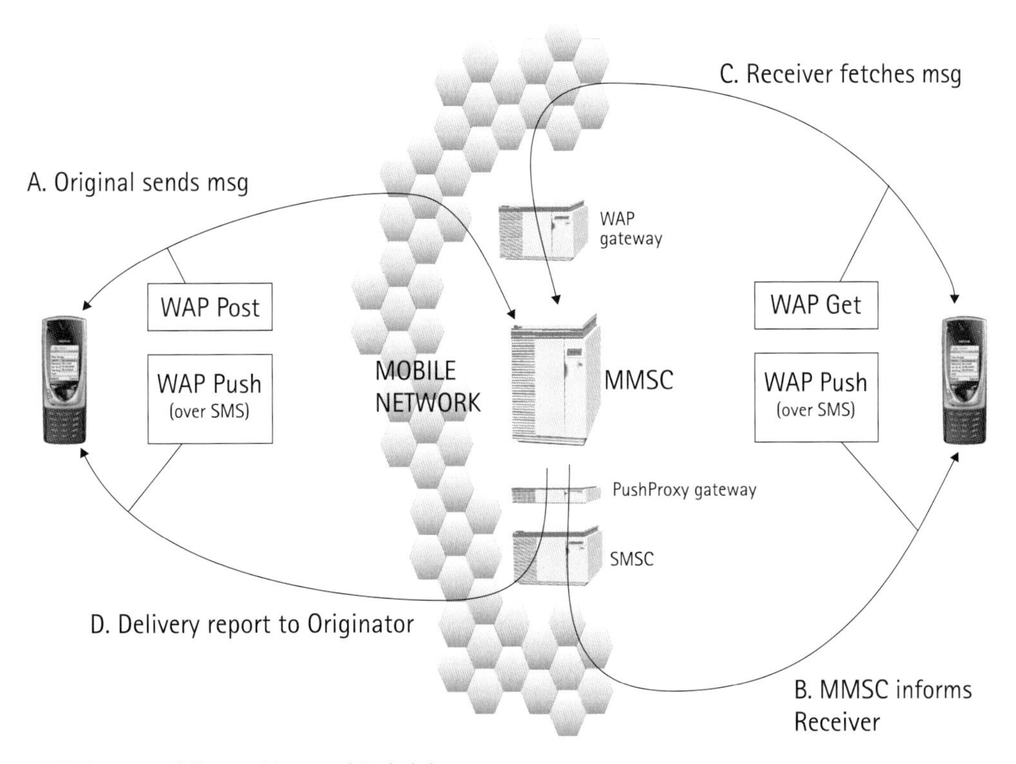

MMS message delivery with network included

The above figure can be extended with additional service elements as illustrated in the following figure. Together these elements produce an end-to-end MMS solution, which third party developers can further extend with their services.

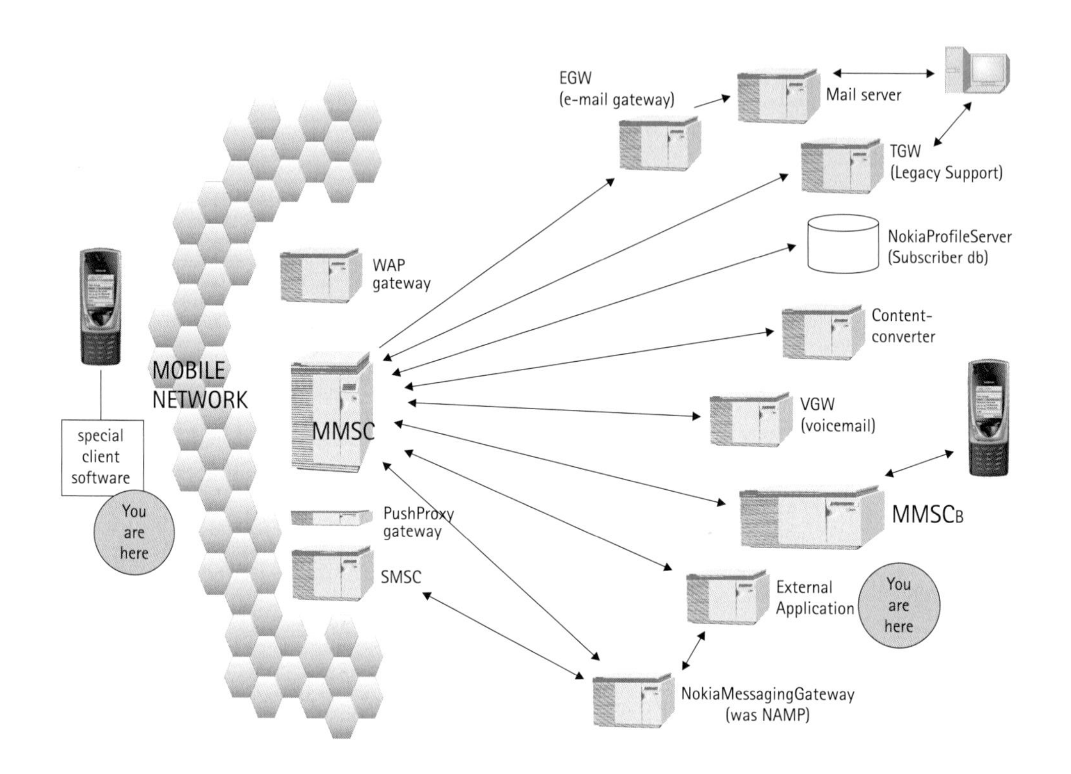

Possible elements in a Multimedia Messaging System

E-Mail Server/Gateway

The delivery of MMS messages to e-mail addresses requires that the MMSC have some way of communicating with existing mail servers. This most likely occurs by using the SMTP protocol. Consumers access their e-mail by using their normal e-mail client. The Nokia solution is the Nokia Multimedia E-mail Gateway (EGW), which is placed between the MMSC and the e-mail server.

Legacy Support

In order to support the delivery of MMS messages to legacy terminals, there must be some sort of legacy messaging server. The Nokia Multimedia Terminal Gateway (TGW) provides this type of service by storing MMS message content in its own local storage. It then sends an SMS message to the receiver, notifying the consumer about a Web address where the content can be viewed with a Web browser. The TGW also provides consumers with a shoebox for storing images. These images can be accessed over the Internet and used to create new MMS messages, which can be sent through the TGW.

Subscriber Database

A database of subscriber profiles can help the MMSC decide what type of content to deliver. The Nokia implementation of the subscriber database concept is called the Nokia Profile Server. It allows subscribers to set up various forwarding and carbon copy options (e.g., all incoming MMS messages are copied to a mailbox). It also allows for personal barring settings (e.g., if person X tries to send me an MMS message, block it).

Content Converter

In another situation, A could have sent B an image in a format, which is not supported by B's mobile device. The MMSC determines this using the subscriber database from above, then routes the message to a content-converting application. After conversion, the new message is sent forward.

Voicemail

The Nokia Multimedia Voice Gateway interfaces between the MMSC and a voicemail application. Instead of receiving a text message indicating that there is a voice message waiting, the voice message can be encapsulated as an MMS message and sent directly to the device.

Foreign MMSC

When A and B do not belong to the same carrier network. The MMSC of A's network forwards the MMS message to the MMSC of B's network. B's MMSC then takes care of notifying B of an incoming message. If a delivery report is to be sent to A, it is first sent from B's MMSC to A's MMSC.

Other

The Nokia Messaging Gateway will soon be able to interact with an MMSC, allowing it to be used also for multimedia content fetching. In this case, the consumer sends an SMS message to request an image. The request is routed to the Messaging Gateway, which retrieves the image and delivers it via the MMSC as an MMS message.

Where the Developer Fits

From the MMS Service perspective, the mail server, the TGW, the user database and content-converter are all examples of external applications. Some developers will most likely provide extensions to this service and some developers may utilize client MMS handlers in order to send and receive MMS messages from and to their specialized applications.

Envisioned Applications

Most of the material presented so far has focused on user-to-user MMS transactions. The following figures should help visualize some other alternatives.

Mobile Originated Transactions

In Mobile Originated (MO) transactions, the sender is a mobile device.

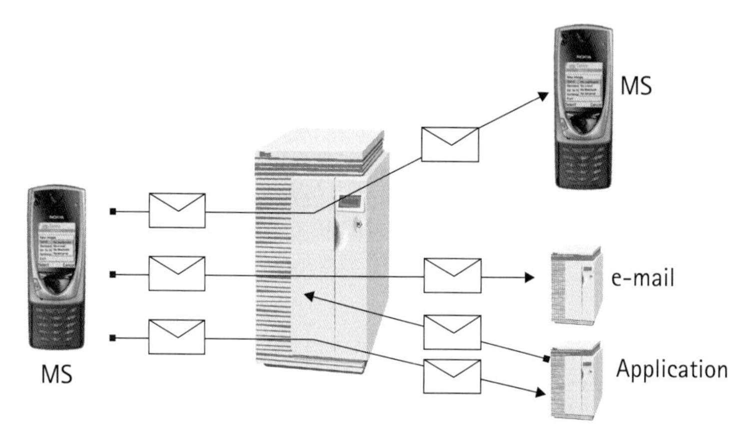

A message can terminate directly in another mobile device, or possibly in an e-mail address. If an image has to be converted into another format (e.g., JPEG to GIF), it can be sent to an application that handles the conversion. After the conversion, the message is sent to its destination.

Mobile Terminated Transactions

In Mobile Terminated (MT) transactions, the message is sent to a mobile device.

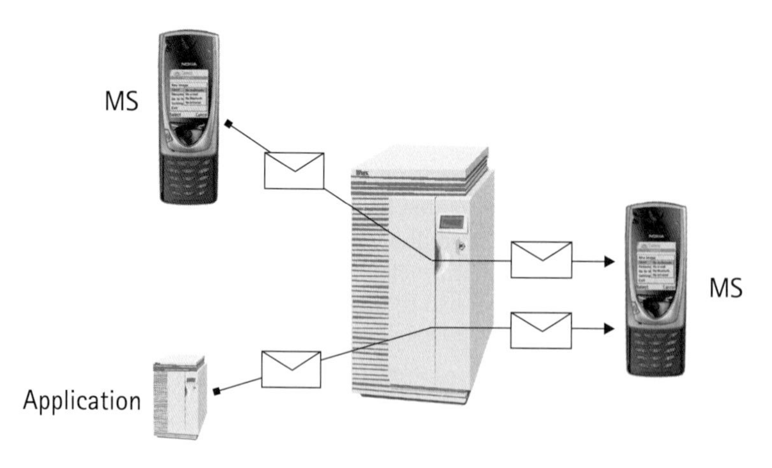

The originator of the message can be another mobile device or an application (e.g., a Web-based image service application).

Application Originated Transactions

In Application Originated (AO) transactions, the sender is an application.

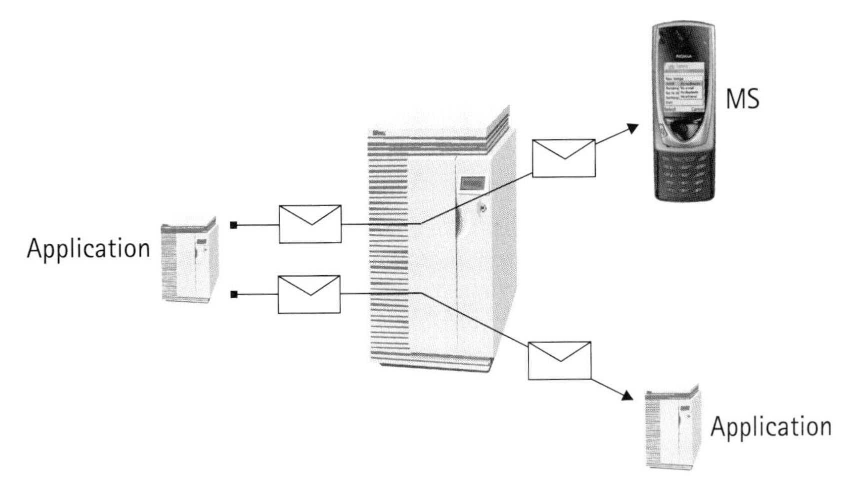

A message can terminate directly in a mobile device or in another application. The message can be processed in one or more applications before it is sent to the receiving mobile device. In inter-MMSC messages, both MMSCs have an IMMSC application, which is seen as an external application. The receiving MMSC sees the message as an AO message.

Application Terminated Transactions

In Application Terminated (AT) transactions, the message receiver is an application.

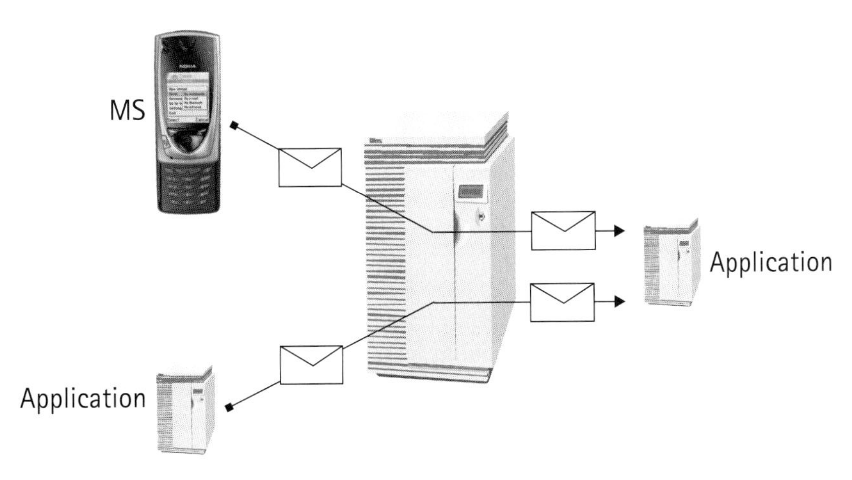

The message originator can be a mobile device or another application, e.g., if a message was sent to JPEG-to-GIF conversion before being sent to the shoebox storage of the TGW.

Application Types and Examples

Consider the following three types of applications from the MMSC point of view: originating, terminating and processing.

An originating application takes the initiative and sends an M-Send.req to the MMSC. From the MMSC's perspective, this is very much the same as if it had received the MMS message from a mobile device. An example of an originating application could be a Web-based MMS creation service, in which consumers can create MMS messages online, and then send them to a friend who has an MMS-enabled mobile device. When the consumer sends the message, the MMSC sees it as an application-originating message.

A terminating application is the receiver of our earlier illustrations, but rather than sending the application an M-Notification.ind over WAP PUSH, the MMSC simply forwards the M-Send.req to the application, to let it determine how to deal with the message. An example of a terminating application is again the shoebox/photo album storage facility. The consumer has taken a photo, or perhaps received a great image and wants to save it, and therefore sends it to the photo storage application. The image reaches the MMSC addressed to a number assigned to the application inside the MMSC, and is forwarded from there.

A processing application is both the sender and the receiver, although usually in the opposite order. It first receives an MMS message, performs some sort of processing or conversion on it, and then sends the new MMS message via the MMSC to its final destination. An example of a processing application could be a service sponsored by a beverage company, in which consumers are allowed to send MMS messages for a discount rate. The catch is that these messages are all routed through a processing application, which tacks a small logo of the beverage company onto the end/beginning of the message.

Some of the categories in which MMS messaging services could be seen to emerge:

- Information services - local content, traffic, finance, weather, e-mail delivery
- Entertainment and personalization services - animated wallpaper images, collector cards, games, music and video samples
- Communication - MMS chat, dating service
- MMS as medium - sending various media over MMS

Conformance

The content of this section is largely based on the MMS Conformance Document, and explains what MMS mobile devices should at least be able to support. Any of these solutions can be implemented, but by creating content that complies with the Conformance Document, developers ensure that the widest possible audience is able to see the content in the intended manner.

The minimum supported message size is 30 kB. From a content provider's point of view, this means that the maximum message size for which interoperability is guaranteed is 30 kB.

Synchronized Multimedia Integration Language Support

The early MMS-enabled mobile devices will offer limited Synchronized Multimedia Integration Language (SMIL) [SMIL] support.

The first MMS messages should be thought of as slide shows. Each slide has one or two regions, one for text, and the other for an image. The layout and ordering of the slides is specified by using a layout language called Synchronized Multimedia Integration Language (SMIL). The actual text and images are packaged as separate message elements, but within the same message body. The SMIL presentation simply defines when and where different message elements are displayed. See the example below.

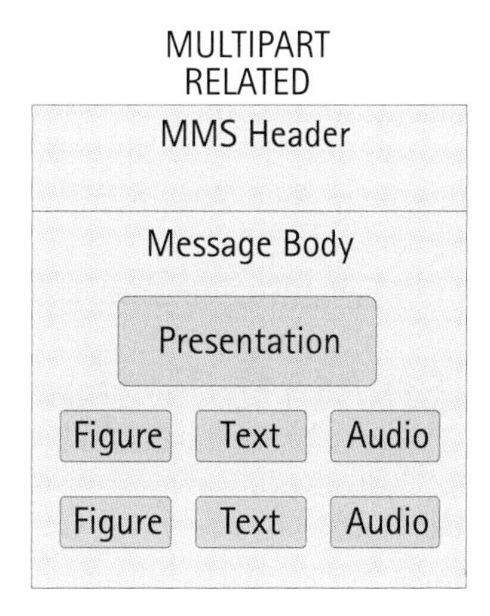

Bundling message elements

High-end MMS enabled mobile devices will support the reception of MMS messages that contain multiple slides, each containing up to one image and one text part. Not all mobile devices will support speech or audio, or the sending of MMS messages.

The first SMIL enabled mobile devices can support a very limited number of SMIL features. As a result, under the early MMS implementations of SMIL, a client may override certain attributes of the presentation (e.g., a client may replace durations with a button push, which the consumer can manually use to move to the next slide).

The MMS Interoperability Group has drafted the MMS Conformance Document, which discusses what exactly is to be supported in more detail about.

Note that while in normal SMIL the names of layout regions can be anything, in the MMS implementation, the image region must be named `Image`, and it must contain an image element. Correspondingly, the text region must is named `Text`, and it must contain a text element.

SMIL timing mechanisms include two time containers, <par> and <seq>. Anything inside a <par> </par> tag pair is considered as happening in parallel. Elements inside a <seq> </seq>

tag pair take place in sequence. The <body> element is defined as a sequence time container. Each slide is a parallel time container - the elements are shown/played at the same time, and each slide is displayed in sequence, one after another. Please note that unlike in normal SMIL, the nesting of <par> and <seq> time containers is not allowed. Multiple images within a single slide are also not allowed.

Supported Media Types and Formats

The different message elements, which contain one media type or another, must be encoded in a supported format. For the first generation of MMS messages, the media formats guaranteed to be supported across clients are limited.

The supported image formats are baseline Joint Photographic Experts Group (JPEG) with JFIF exchange format, Graphics Interchange Format versions 87a and 89a (i.e., GIF87a and GIF89a), and Wireless BitMap (WBMP). The image size that should be supported by all mobile devices is 160 x 120 pixels. Not all mobile devices actually have displays of that size, but they have some way of displaying images of this size, and mobile device vendors have therefore agreed to this size in the MMS Conformance Document. For text, the supported formats are US-ASCII, Universal Transport Format 8 (i.e., UTF-8), and UTF-16 with explicit Byte Order Mark. For speech, the supported format is Adaptive Multi-Rate (AMR). For Personal Information Management (PIM), the supported formats are vCalendar version 1.0, and vCard version 2.1, with the condition that if the mobile device has a calendar, then it must support vCalendar.

The Nokia 7650 MMS Features

Supported Formats

When receiving messages, the Nokia 7650 can handle the following formats directly with its MMS Viewer:

- Basics from Conformance Document
- Animated GIF89a
- Progressive JPEG, also including EXIF exchange format
- Portable Network Graphics (PNG)
- Adaptive Multi-Rate (AMR)
- Windows Audio File (WAV) - including encoding Adaptive Differential Pulse Code Modulation (ADPCM), Pulse Code Modulation (PCM), aLaw, μLaw, GSM 6.10
- Plain text - encoding from Conformance Document (US-ASCII, UTF-8, UTF-16 with explicit Byte Order Mark)

In addition, any content that is supported by the Nokia 7650 and which has a Multi-purpose Internet Mail Extensions (MIME) [RFC2387, RFC2557] type associated with it in the mobile device can be received by using a separate Objects view. The supported formats include:

- Nokia ringing tone
- vCard
- vCalendar
- Symbian OS application installation package
- Java application installation package
- Wireless Markup Language (WML) content
- File formats supported by third-party applications

Note that to enable support for a third-party application, the application should be implemented with the Series 60 SDK. The application must announce its mimetype and provide a recognizer to map a file to a particular mimetype. A good recognizer is based on both the file extension and the actual file contents - usually a file can be identified quite reliably from the first few bytes.

For MMS message creation, the following formats are supported:

- JPEG
- GIF
- WBMP
- PNG - converted to JPEG before sending
- AMR
- Plain text - UTF-16 with explicit Byte Order Mark

Other Features

- **Integrated Camera** - the integrated camera of the Nokia 7650 could not make MMS message creation any easier. Point and click, and you instantly have an image to add to your MMS message. There is memory reserved for storing photos as well.
- **Recorder** - the user can record sound clips and include them in MMS messages.
- **MMS addressing** - MMS messages can be addressed to multiple recipients, including e-mail addresses.
- **Image sending** - when including images in MMS messages, the consumer can choose to include a small (max 160 x 120 pixels) or large (max 640 x 480 pixels) image size.

- **Object viewing** - if an MMS message contains an element not native to MMS messages, the Nokia 7650 can still separate the extra objects, and open any format that the mobile device supports.
- **Wallpaper** - an image can be placed as the background image of the idle mode of the Nokia 7650.
- **Screen saver** - the Nokia 7650 screen saver is a colored bar that moves around on the screen and displays either the date and time or a user-specified text.
- **Screen size** - the available area is 174 x 142 pixels, but for MMS, there are certain issues that need to be taken into account. The screen is divided horizontally into 17-pixel-high bands. Images are placed on the edge of a band. Eight such bands fit in the height of 142 pixels, with six pixels remaining left over in the margins. The result is that the maximum image size for messaging is 174 x 136, or for simultaneously displayed picture and associated text, 174 x 119 pixels. Note that larger images are supported, but when received in an MMS message, they are initially scaled down to fit into the screen. These larger images can be viewed in full size by using a separate function.

Nokia MMS Java Library

Nokia has created a Java library for handling MMS messages. It can be used to construct an MMS message out of various bits and pieces, and to encapsulate the created message. The library can then add HyperText Transfer Protocol (HTTP) headers to the message so that it is ready to be sent to the External Application Interface (EAIF) or EAIF Emulator. Received MMS messages can be decapsulated and broken up into parts.

The Nokia MMS Java Library provides examples of the following functionality:

Message Creation and Encoding

The Nokia MMS Java Library provides an example of how to create and encode a multimedia message from different content types. The library illustrates how messages are created and encoded according to WAP-209. The message creation functionality example can be used when designing originating or filtering applications.

Message Decoding

The Nokia MMS Java Library provides an example of how to decode a received multimedia message, encoded according to WAP-209, and how to extract the multimedia content obtained from the message body. The decoding functionality example can be used when designing terminating or filtering applications.

Message Sending to MMSC

The HTTP 1.1 protocol and EAIF should be used for sending a multimedia message from the application to the Nokia MMSC. The Nokia MMS Java Library provides an example of how this can be done.

The Java library package includes three sample applications, source code for the classes and the related documentation.

References

[TS 22.140] Service Aspects
www.3gpp.org/ftp/specs/2001-12/R1999/22_series/22140-310.zip

[TS 23.140] Functional Description
www.3gpp.org/ftp/specs/2001-12/R1999/23_series/23140-301.zip

[WAP-205] MMS Architecture Overview
www1.wapforum.org/tech/terms.asp?doc=WAP-205-MMSArchOverview-20010425-a.pdf

[WAP-206] MMS Client Transactions
www1.wapforum.org/tech/terms.asp?doc=WAP-206-MMSCTR-20020115-a.pdf

[WAP-209] MMS Encapsulation Protocol
www1.wapforum.org/tech/terms.asp?doc=WAP-209-MMSEncapsulation-20020105-a.pdf

[WAP-203] Wireless Session Protocol Specification
www1.wapforum.org/tech/terms.asp?doc=WAP-203_001-WSP-20000620-a.pdf

[WAP-230] Wireless Session Protocol Specification
www1.wapforum.org/tech/terms.asp?doc=WAP-230-WSP-20010705-a.pdf

[MMSCD] MMS Conformance Document
forum.nokia.com/files/disclaimer/1,1167,2032,00.html

[SMIL]
www.w3.org/AudioVideo/

[RFC2387] The MIME Multipart/Related Content-type
www.ietf.org/rfc/rfc2387.txt

[RFC2557] MIME Encapsulation of Aggregate Documents
www.ietf.org/rfc/rfc2557.txt

External MMS Applications

This chapter reviews the External Application Interface (EAIF) of the MMS Center with respect to the following concepts:

- Application types
- Synchronous and asynchronous applications

Depending on the configuration, an external application acts in a role similar to a Web client (originating application) or a Web server (terminating application). The MMS Center acts in a role similar to a Web client (terminating application) or a Web server (originating application). The roles are illustrated in the following figure.

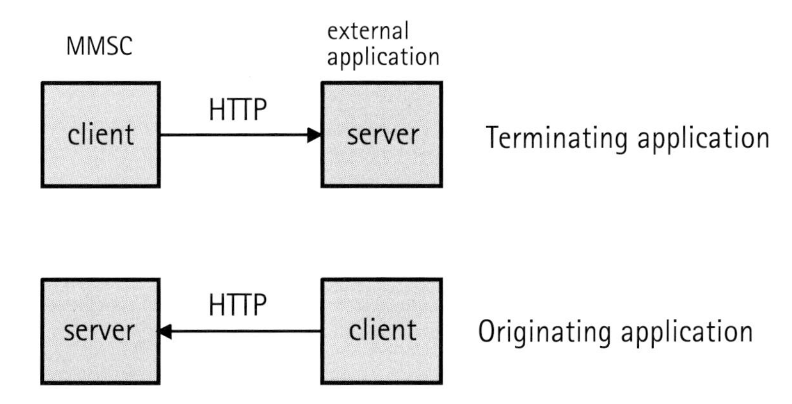

Clients and servers in different roles

Application Types

Applications may be configured as: originating, terminating or filtering. Application types are shown in the figure below.

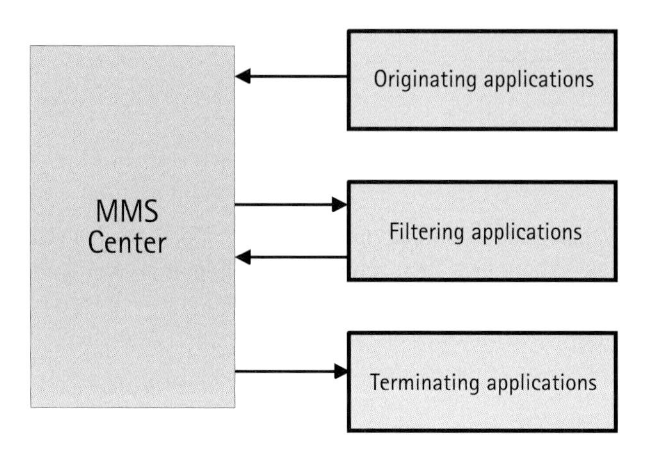

Application types in relation to the MMS Center

Type of application	Description
Originating application	These applications are the originating sources of messages. They send application-originated (AO) messages. An example of an originating application is a news service that provides information such as a weather advisory.
Terminating application	These are the applications in which messages are terminated. They receive application terminated (AT) messages. An example of a terminating application is the email gateway transmitter. In this example, the multimedia message originates in a mobile device and is destined for termination in an email device. Terminating applications can be either synchronous or asynchronous.
Filtering application	Filtering applications receive a message from the MMS Center, process the message, and then send the message (or status) back to the MMS Center for further processing. Filtering applications may • modify the message (for example, content conversion) • process the message in some other way Filtering applications can be either synchronous or asynchronous.

Application types

Synchronous and Asynchronous Applications

Synchronous applications are able to handle one message at a time. Essentially, such an application receives a message, processes it, and returns the message status before accepting another message for processing as illustrated in the next figure.

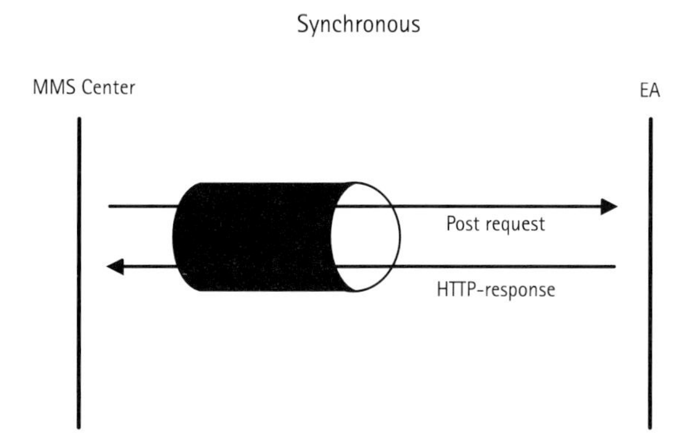

Requests and responses from synchronous applications

Asynchronous external applications are able to receive a message, check whether the message can be processed, and send an interim status report to the EAIF. Such applications are able to handle several messages at the same time. Subsequent messages can also be received for processing before the first or previous message is returned. After the external application has processed the message, it sends a modified message or a final status report to the EAIF. Asynchronous communication is illustrated in the next figure.

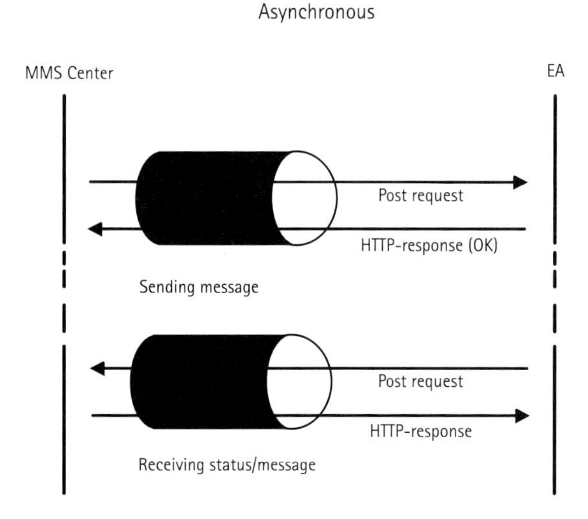

Requests and responses from asynchronous applications

EAIF Concepts

Persistent Connections

The EAIF is designed to be used with HTTP 1.1 and persistent connection mechanisms. Using a persistent connection mechanism means that once the HTTP connection between the EAIF and the external application has been opened, several request/responses can be sent by using the same connection. This is not the default case with HTTP 1.0, in which the connection has to be opened and closed separately for each request/response. This slows down the traffic and causes unwanted processing overhead.

Message Format

HTTP messages consist of two parts: HTTP headers and the message body. The MMS Center uses standard HTTP headers as well as some HTTP extension headers specific to the Nokia MMS Center. The HTTP headers may be in any order but they must precede the message body. Multimedia messages are sent in the HTTP message body as shown in the following figure.

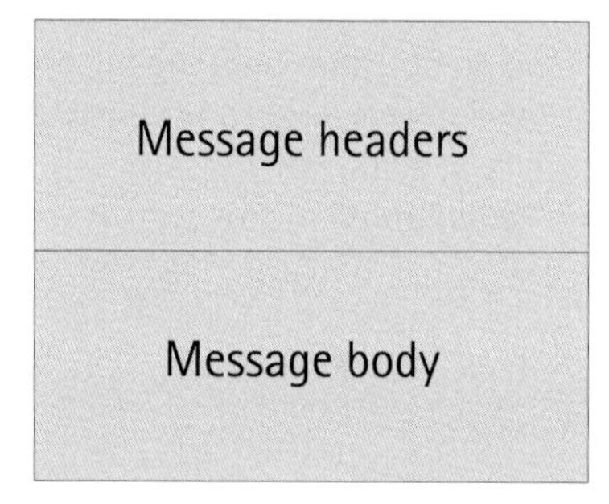

HTTP message format

Message Headers

The mandatory HTTP headers that are used in the MMS Center are the following: Host, Content-Type and Content-Length.

The next table collects the HTTP extensions that MMSC supports.

Header	Description	Example
X-NOKIA-MMSC-Message-Id	This header identifies the message in the MMS Center. Any character including numbers may be used. The message ID is case-sensitive.	`x-nokia-mmsc-message-id: O71grawVc3cA@AI5AAAAAQAAAAMAAAAA`
X-NOKIA-MMSC-Status	This header is used for passing the processing status, a three-digit number, of the message from asynchronous applications to MMS Center. These are based on standard HTTP status codes (e.g. 200 signifies OK).	`x-nokia-mmsc-status: 200`
X-NOKIA-MMSC-Charging	This header is used for passing charging information from applications to MMS Center. Charging information is expressed as a tariff class number (integer).	`x-nokia-mmsc-charging: 5`
X-NOKIA-MMSC-To	This field identifies the intended recipient.	`x-nokia-mmsc-to: +123455555555/TYPE=PLMN` and `x-nokia-mmsc-to:recipient@external.application.com`
X-NOKIA-MMSC-From	This field identifies the sender.	`x-nokia-mmsc-from: +123444444444/TYPE=PLMN` and `x-nokia-mmsc-from:sender@external.application.com`
X-NOKIA-MMSC-Message-Type	This field identifies the message type. The message type is case-sensitive. Values: • MultiMediaMessage • DeliveryReport	`x-nokia-mmsc-message-type:MultiMediaMessage`
X-NOKIA-MMSC-Version	This field identifies the version of the EAIF. Values: • 1.0= MC1 • 1.1 = MC1 CD1	`x-nokia-mmsc-version: 2.0`

MMSC Center's HTTP extension headers for MMSC

Message Body

The multimedia message format is based on WAP Forum standards. See WAP-209 MMS encapsulation.

The EAIF recognizes two MMS Protocol Data Units specified in WAP-209 MMS encapsulation:

- m-send-req (multimedia message)
- m-delivery-ind (delivery report)

The message body contains a binary encoded MMS PDU.

Charging Information

The external application may send charging information to the MMS Center. The charging information is sent as a tariff class. The tariff class is an integer whose allowed value range is specified by the carrier. If the message is successfully delivered to its destination, a CDR containing the tariff class is generated. The billing system will use the tariff class to generate actual billing information.

The carrier specifies whether the external application is allowed to send charging information and which tariff classes the external application is allowed to send. The MMS Center discards any unsolicited charging information sent by an external application.

Delivery Reporting

To find out whether the message has been successfully delivered to its destination, an originating external application may request a delivery report (mdelivery-ind).

When the message has been delivered to the recipient or the MMS Center has detected that the message cannot be delivered for some reason, the MMS Center generates and sends a delivery report to the terminating application specified in the MMS Center routing rules. Typically, the MMSC routing rules use the sender address as routing criteria, but other options may also be available.

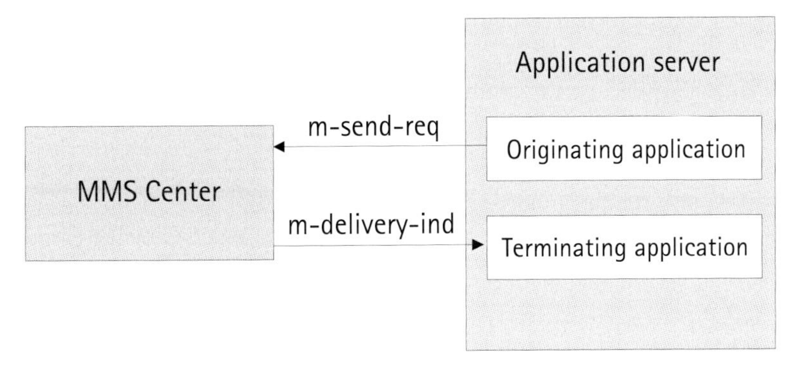

Delivery reporting between the MMSC and an application server.

The carrier may disable delivery reporting by:

- rejecting messages requesting a delivery report
- accepting the messages but disabling the delivery report request

Security

The Secure Sockets Layer (SSL) is an optional MMS Center feature that can be added to enhance security between the EAIF and external applications. The carrier may require external applications to use SSL. The security parameters are configurable.

Configuration

The interface between the MMS Center and the external application has some configurable parameters. Application developers and the carrier have to agree on suitable parameter values. The following parameters can be set:

- Application type
- Connection parameters

Different application types behave in different ways and consequently have different configuration parameters:

- Application type (e.g., originating, terminating, filtering)
- Operation mode (e.g., synchronous, asynchronous)

For filtering applications, the following parameters must be specified:

- What the MMS Center sends to the external application
- What the external application sends to the MMS Center

Applications may send charging information to the MMS Center, if this has been specified by the carrier. The allowed values for tariff classes are also specified by the carrier.

The following are the key connection parameters:

- Host address
- Port number
- Timeout values (configurable by the carrier in the MMS Center) for HTTP operations such as the following:
  - Opening a connection
  - Sending a request
  - Receiving a request

Status Codes

The following table contains the status codes relative to numeric values:

Error code	Description
200 OK	The EA sends this when the processing was OK and the EA sends back m-send-req in the message body.
204 No Content	The EA sends this when the processing was OK. The EA sends back only the status and any necessary headers, but the message body is empty.
400–499	The MMS Center considers these as permanent errors. The EA sends this when the MMS Center is not to resend the message.
500–599	This is a temporary error. The EA sends this when the message processing failed, but the MMS Center is to resend the message at a later time.

EA to EAIF status codes

The following table contains the status codes relative to numeric values:

Error code	Description
204 No Content	The MMS Center has received the message successfully.
400 <reason phrase>	The MMS Center has rejected the message. Check the reason phrase for a more specific error cause.
400 Erroneous Message ID	An asynchronous EA has sent a message to MMS Center, but the MMS Center rejects the message because the routing information for the message shows that the application has either already handled the message or is not specified in the routing information.
405 Method Not Allowed	EAIF only supports POST-method.
413 Request Entity Too Large	The size of the HTTP message exceeds the maximum configured allowed size.
498 Message Not Found	An asynchronous EA has sent a message to MMS Center, but MMS Center rejects it because it cannot find the message in the DB. Either the message id was erroneous or the message has already been removed from MMS Center.
499 Sender Barred	The MMS Center has barred incoming traffic from this sender address.
499 Address Hiding	The operator has configured the MMS Center to reject messages that request address hiding.
499 Rejected	MMS Center rejects the message.
499 Desired Delivery Time	MMS Center rejects the message because the desired delivery time has been set too far in the future.
503 Service Unavailable	MMS Center could not process the message.

EAIF to EA status codes

Error code	Description
504 Gateway Timeout	The message from the EA was successfully validated and EAIF tried to send the message to MMS Center kernel, but kernel failed to respond within the allotted time. The status of the message is unknown, the message may or may not have been received by kernel and delivered to the recipient.
596 Duplicate Id	An originating application has sent a message but MMS Center rejects it because there already is a message with the same message id in the DB.
597 Barred	The MMS Center has barred incoming traffic from this application id.
599 CCR Error	MMS Center rejects the message because the number of incoming messages exceeds the capacity licensed by the carrier.
599 Kernel Overloaded	MMS Center rejects the message because the MMS Center kernel is overloaded and cannot handle all incoming messages.
599 DB Error	MMS Center rejects the message because the message could not be stored into the DB.

EAIF to EA status codes

References

1. RFC 822, Standard for the format of ARPA Internet text messages, The Internet Society 1982
2. RFC 2616, Hypertext Transfer Protocol HTTP/1.1, The Internet Society 1999
3. WAP 209, Message Encapsulation, WAP Forum 2001
4. SSL 3.0 Specification. Available on the Internet at: http://www.netscape.com/eng/ssl3/draft302.txt
5. TLS 1. Available on the Internet at: http://www.ietf.org/rfc/rfc2246.txt

PART 4.4

Browsing

- Browsing Introduction
- Series 20 Browsing
- Series 40 Browsing
- Series 60 Browsing
- Nokia 9210 Communicator WAP Browsing
- Nokia 9210 Communicator Web Browsing
- Nokia Mobile Internet Toolkit

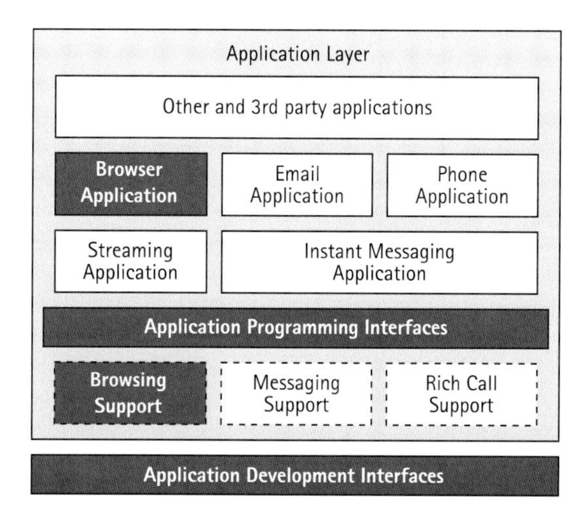

Browsing Introduction

The Wireless Application Protocol (WAP) enhances the functionality of mobile handsets through real-time interactive services. The protocol has been designed especially for small screens and low bandwidths, and it offers a wide variety of wireless services over the Internet for mobile devices. It was also designed to allow content to be delivered over any bearer service, even when delivery of the services is enabled over General Packet Radio Service (GPRS), 3G, or any other type of network. WAP over GPRS opens up new possibilities for application development, and there are also some optimizations in GPRS that can be performed by service developers.

The Nokia Mobile Internet Toolkit offers developers an environment for creating, testing, and demonstrating WAP applications. This allows service providers to evaluate the usability of wireless applications and services together with the consumers. This guide collects together a lot of what Nokia has learned that can help developers improve their services. It seems clear that good usability will increase use and satisfaction and thus increase revenues for service providers.

Mobile Browsing Architecture

The WAP is a set of protocols that allow the development of applications and services for use with mobile devices. These protocols and their related standards and specifications are maintained by the WAP Forum.

WAP Architecture

In order to apply as much leverage on the existing Internet standard as possible, the WAP stack closely follows the Internet model. This is illustrated in the next figure.

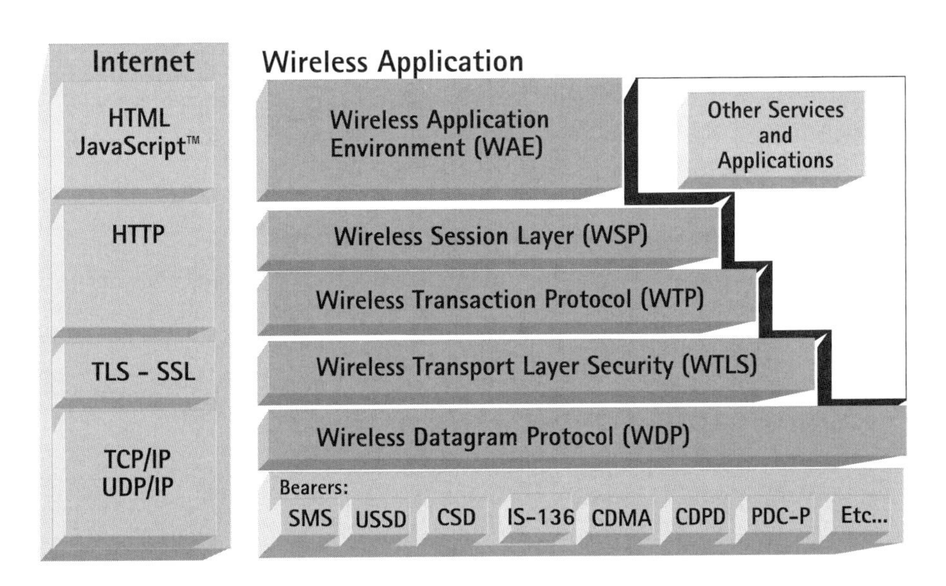

Comparison of Internet and WAP Architecture

This layered architecture allows applications to utilize the features of the WAP stack through well-defined interfaces. This close link to the Internet architecture allows developers to utilize their existing knowledge and expertise when developing applications for mobile devices.

Wireless Application Environment

The Wireless Application Environment (WAE) is a general-purpose application environment that uses a combination of Internet and mobile device technology. It provides a framework for the development of applications on a mobile device. WAE contains support for the following functionality:

- Wireless Markup Language (WML) - a lightweight presentation language, similar to HyperText Markup Language (HTML) but optimized for use with mobile devices.
- Wireless Markup Language Script (WMLS) - a lightweight scripting language, similar to JavaScript™.
- Wireless Telephony Applications / Interface (WTA / WTAI) - telephony services and programming interfaces.
- Content formats - defined data formats (e.g., vCard and vCalendar).

Wireless Session Protocol

The Wireless Session Protocol (WSP) provides the application layer of WAP with an interface for two session services. The first is a connection-oriented service that operates above the transaction layer protocol. The second is a connectionless service that operates above a secure or non-secure datagram service. The WSP is optimized for low-bandwidth bearer networks with high latency.

Wireless Transport Protocol

The Wireless Transport Protocol (WTP) runs on top of the datagram service and provides a lightweight transaction-oriented protocol, suitable for use in mobile devices. WTP operates over secure or non-secure wireless datagram networks.

Wireless Transport Layer Security

Wireless Transport Layer Security (WTLS) is based on the industry-standard Transport Layer Security (TLS) and is optimized for use over narrow-band communication channels. WTLS may be used for secure communication between terminals, and applications can selectively enable WTLS features.

Developing Applications with WAP

Application developers can use the principles of WAP to develop new services or adapt existing Internet applications for use with mobile devices. Applications are written in WML and WMLScript (WMLS) and are stored on either a normal Web server or directly on the WAP gateway. The content stored on the Web server is accessible from mobile devices via the mobile network and a WAP gateway or proxy.

The proxy server acts as a gateway between the cellular network and the Internet or intranet. The data sent between the origin server and the mobile device are binary encoded to optimize transmission over the narrow bandwidth of the mobile network. Note that the content stored on the Web server might be in either text or binary format.

When the WAP gateway fetches text content, it automatically compiles this to the encoded format to minimize network load. The next figure shows the network-related elements required for developing and offering mobile browsing services to customers.

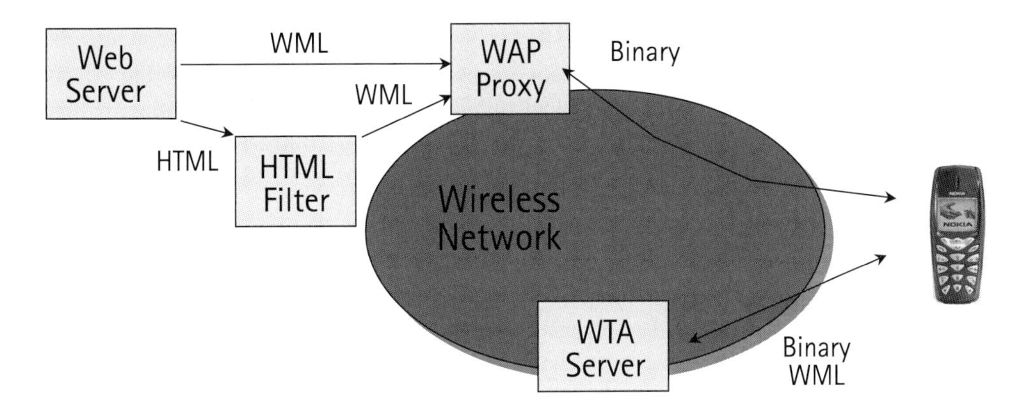

WAP architecture

Server	Description
Web server	Stores the applications written in WML. Alternatively, existing HTML applications can be used.
HTML filter	Any applications written in HTML will have to be converted to WML before they are sent to the mobile device. This HTML filter may form part of the Web server or the WAP proxy.
WAP proxy	The WAP proxy acts as the gateway between the mobile network and the Internet or intranet. It encodes the information which is to be sent to the mobile device in binary format and decodes information sent from the mobile device.
WTA server	The WTA server handles network-specific applications.

General Usability Issues

Nokia mobile devices are renowned for their simple-to-use and intuitive user interface. In order to create a service that will be perceived as usable and easy to understand, This section provides some general guidelines to help service providers develop their applications.

Mobile Browsing

When deciding what information to include in the different applications on a mobile device, think about what information might be relevant in the situations where the mobile device will be used. A mobile device is primarily used when there is no access to the Internet with a PC. Consumers of mobile applications will probably be interested primarily in brief, quickly delivered information. For example, quick access to flight schedules from the mobile device might be relevant for users. Similarly, several short news flashes are more relevant than longer news articles. Quick access to weather information may also be of use for quickly checking the temperature at a traveler's destination. However, it is less likely that consumers will surf the Internet using the application on the mobile device.

Validate the WML

There are several Extensible Markup Language (XML) validators available that validate documents against the Wireless Markup Language (WML) Document Type Definition. It is recommended that authors validate their WAP pages because invalid WML is always treated as an error and is discarded by the WAP gateway.

GPRS Usability

GPRS features efficient use of resources, instant access, fast delivery of information, and innovative charging models. Together, WAP and GPRS not only improve the user experience for existing applications but also enable new services.

GPRS enhances the consumer experience for the mobile services currently being delivered over Circuit Switched Data (CSD) networks. Since the WAP standard was designed to allow content to be delivered over any bearer service, it is not necessary for developers to make changes to their WAP-compliant services or applications, even when delivery of the services is enabled over GPRS, or any other type of network.

It is recommended to use a HyperText Transfer Protocol (HTTP) proxy to cache WML content whenever the content is accessed via the Internet. The proxy should be placed close to the WAP gateway to minimize the distance for data transfer between the two components. The home page might alternatively be kept on a local server, close to the WAP gateway. Most clients have a cache, and using it is an important way to provide speed of use for the consumer.

Round trips in a network always cause a minimum of a four second delay in response time. Therefore, the number of round trips should be minimized. For example, bitmaps cause additional round trips. Response time can also be minimized by keeping WAP decks as compact in size as possible. This is especially important for pages that require an instant response. The response time of the first deck has a strong impact on the consumer experience. Therefore, it is worthwhile to maximize infrastructure optimization.

Minimize latency between the WAP gateway and content server. Remember that each query traverses this link twice, once as a request and once as a response.

Place the WAP gateway close to the Gateway GPRS Support Node (GGSN). Close in this instance refers to both latency and probability of packet loss. Lost messages cause additional delay due to HTTP retransmission.

Site Organization

The consumer may access the WAP site over a GSM data call and pays per second. It is not recommended to use as a front page a doormat page which serves no purpose other than perhaps to greet the visitor and to display a logo. It is better if the consumer can go to the service directly. If there is a need to use a timer, it should not be longer than about 1.5 seconds. Otherwise, add a link incorporating the *Continue* text to give the consumer the possibility of exiting the card.

If one is using a modern Web site hosting environment, it is possible to detect the browser as well as the language and to supply correct content transparently without input from the consumer.

Nokia mobile devices send a user-agent field in the Wireless Session Protocol (WSP) header to the WAP gateway when they fetch content from the origin server. One can use this user-agent field to define the browser type and then build the logic on the origin server to serve suitable content. From the WAP gateway, the user-agent information is then delivered inside the HTTP header.

The size of the content is critical. If there are large decks, consider splitting them into multiple parts for faster downloading.

As for the total downloading time, some studies place an upper limit for an acceptable delay on a PC-based browser at 10 to 15 seconds, including all images. It is highly recommended to have a response time in mobile browsing of less than 10 seconds.

It is very useful to give a descriptive name for the card. It might be a good idea to start the title with the service's name and to keep the total length of the title short.

It also pays to use meaningful Uniform Resource Locator (URL) addresses since the consumer sees the URL of the currently selected link on the screen and can use it as a navigational aid, especially when images have not been loaded.

The first screen of any page is the most important one. All of the frequently used navigational links, search fields, login screens, and bulk of the information should reside there. The consumer is then able to navigate forward before the rest of the card has been loaded, and the consumer does not have to scroll through the card.

Avoid wasting the top of the page on banner advertisements or non-informative graphics. It is better to place the advertisements at the left or right edges than at the top.

When images are used, the use of absolute values is not recommended. Sizes should be specified as percentages of the total width or height.

Always use descriptive and short labels for all <do> elements. Favor local <do> elements instead of anchored links that do not fit into their surrounding context. Global <do> elements should be used only when especially needed at the end of the card. Always include a <prev> element in every card to enable backward navigation.

Pictures and Tables

Downloading images takes time, and many consumers may switch off the loading of images for more speed. Try to optimize the size of images. If there are large pictures on the site, consider using thumbnails for the image index.

Always give alternative text for images that convey information. Always use a null alternative text for images that do not convey information or are used for page layout or decorative purposes only.

If the table size exceeds the maximum width of the application screen due to the number of columns, the table size will be scaled down to fit the screen. In order to keep the cell content readable, special attention should be paid to table structuring.

Taking Care of Backward Navigation

Due to the differences between WAP and the Web with respect to the processing of the history, only the history processing described in the WML specifications is followed. This means that the service provider must be responsible for navigation as a whole.

Use of Card Titles and Element Labels

Card titles describe the content of the display, and their use is recommended. They help the consumer to navigate in the application because they function as a reminder of where the consumer is in the application. The item previously selected by the consumer should determine the header text. For instance, the card title *Bookmarks* tells the consumer that the display contains a list of bookmarks in the application and that the options item previously selected was *Bookmarks*.

Proportional fonts are used in header texts, and if the header text is too long, it is automatically truncated. Truncation is usually better than abbreviation because the consumer might be confused by unfamiliar abbreviations that can be difficult to understand.

Performing a Usability Test

It is always good to perform a usability test for new applications. People who have not been involved in the design or development of the applications tend to notice potential usability problems that are often not obvious to those who know the design by heart. Usability tests should always be performed as early as possible in the development process. Any need for changes, which become apparent in the tests, can then be implemented within the development timescale. Try to recruit testers who are representative of the consumers of the application, and try to conduct the usability test on a smaller scale, if the schedule does not allow for extensive testing.

Series 20 Browsing

This section provides information and practical examples for developers who want to optimize their existing Wireless Application Protocol services for the Series 20 user interface. The Series 20 is a UI category for Nokia screens with an 84 x 48 pixel resolution. It comprises a black and white screen with one or two soft keys. This section highlights the possibilities, limitations, and requirements of service development, and it provides a good introduction to the Nokia style of user interface design.

Series 20 User Interface

This chapter gives a short overview of each of the type of user interface found in Series 20 phones. Emphasis is on the WAP services element of the phone. The WAP browser user interface is designed to be compatible with the user interaction handling of other applications in the device.

The user interface is a combination of specific user interface hardware like keys and display; user interaction conventions, which include input and output functions and their relationships; and audio-visual user interaction conventions. This chapter concentrates on the hardware element of the Series 20 user interface.

Series 20 Devices

The Nokia browser in Series 20 phones includes a WAP browser with enhanced features and increased usability. The deck size is extended to 2.8 kbit and cache size in the device is 50 kbit or more. Other WAP features include predictive text input (T9) and a picture viewer. Three different image formats are supported; Wireless BitMap (WBMP), static Graphics Interchange Format (GIF), and animated GIF. In addition devices support push service indication, Wireless Telephony Applications Interface (WTAI) public standard, and cookies.

Nokia 5510	Nokia 5210	Nokia 3330	Nokia 3360/20	Nokia 8310/90	Nokia 8910
WAP 1.1	WAP 1.1	WAP 1.1	WAP 12.1	WAP 12.1	WAP 1.2.1
GSM900/1800	GSM900/1800	GSM900/1800	TDMA	GMS900/1800 (8310) GSM 1900 (8390)	GSM900/1800
CSD	CSD	CSD	(TDMA) CSD	CSD, GPRS	CSD, GPRS
One soft key UI	Two soft key UI	One soft key UI	Two soft key UI	Two soft key UI	Two soft key UI

Few Nokia Series 20 devices and their browsing features

Display and Keys

Two Soft Key Display

The display is a full dot matrix display with a resolution of 84 pixels (horizontal) by 48 pixels (vertical). The display consists of the application area with header text and the area used for the soft keys.

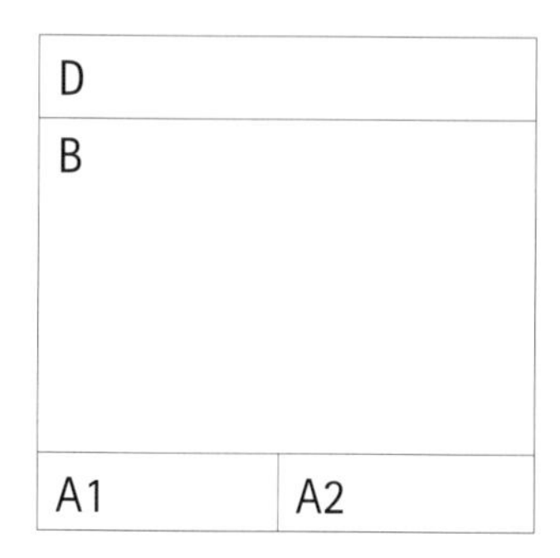

Structure of the browser screen in the Series 20 UI

The application area (B+D) is 84 pixels (horizontal) by 39 pixels (vertical). It includes three lines of main text (B) and header text (D). The main text area (B) can also be used for displaying graphics. The graphics area is a maximum of 84 pixels wide and 30 pixels high but is scrollable in both dimensions to allow even the maximum deck size to be viewed.

- The **Send/Talk key** works as a selection key.
- The **End key** exits a data call and causes the device to go into idle state when pressed twice.
- The **two soft keys**: The soft keys are assigned actions that enable the consumer to manipulate the user interface by making selections and entering, editing, and deleting text.
- The **left soft key** is used as a yes/positive key. It is associated with options that execute commands and go deeper into the menu structure (e.g., Select, OK, and Options).
- The **right soft key** is used as a no/negative key. It is associated with options that cancel commands, delete text, and go backwards in the menu structure (e.g., Back, Exit, and Clear).
- The **scroll keys (arrow keys)** allow the consumer to scroll the options or text in the current display.

One Soft Key Display

The display is a full dot matrix display with a display resolution of 84 pixels (horizontal) by 48 pixels (vertical). The display consists of the application area with header text and the area used for the Navi key™. The application area is 84 pixels (horizontal) by 39 pixels (vertical). It includes three lines of main text plus space for header text. The main text area can also be used for showing graphics. The graphics area is a maximum of 84 pixels wide and 30 pixels high but is scrollable to the maximum deck size.

The Navi key™ works as a selection key. It is assigned to an action, which enables the consumer to manipulate the user interface by making selections and entering and editing text. It is basically used as a yes/positive key. It contains options that execute commands and go deeper into the menu structure (e.g., Select, OK, Options), and similar commands.

- The **Cancel key (c)** is basically used as a no/negative key. It contains options that cancel commands, delete text, and go backwards in the menu structure (e.g., Back, Exit, and Clear). In the WAP service, it can be used for back navigation.
- **Scroll keys (arrow keys)** allow the consumer to scroll through the options or text in the current display.
- **Shortcuts**: number keys 1 and 3 function as shortcuts in selecting a link or entering a UI element in the browser.
- **Four-way scrolling**: number keys 2, 4, 6, and 8 are used for scrolling pictures both horizontally and vertically in picture view.

Display Fonts

The font size is eight pixels, with a line break of one pixel. All fonts are proportional fonts. Proportional fonts give a dynamic width for each character rather than assigning each character the same size block. They give improved readability of displayed text and generally allow more characters to be displayed per line. On the other hand, having proportional fonts means that it is difficult to tell how many characters there can be on each line.

WAP Browser Display

The WAP browser's home page can be accessed with a long press of "0". It can also be accessed by entering the *Services* menu. One can then select a home page or use bookmarks to access a service. The Home option in the list fetches information from the home page which is related to the access point used.

Navigation, Labels and Titles

The consumer should be provided with consistent card headers, element titles, and do element labels. The title of a select element is used in the header of a selection list or option groups list. The title of an optgroup element is used as an option group title and in the header of its selection list. The title of an input element is used in the editor title.

Scrolling

The consumer can move up and down in Card view when it contains elements and static text areas between them. This is done by jumping from element to element. Scrolling through long static sections is done line by line. The first element of a card is highlighted by default if it is on the first display.

Picture Viewer

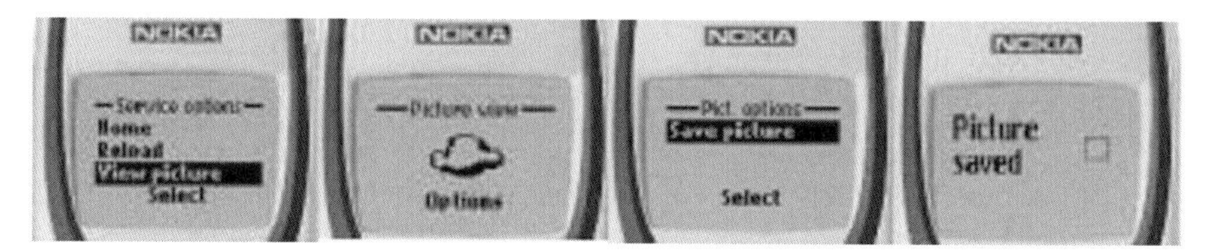

Picture viewer and saving a picture to phone memory

In Nokia WAP browsers, there is a picture viewer where pictures can be viewed and saved to the phone. Larger pictures can be scrolled both horizontally and vertically.

Viewing larger pictures in picture view

Saving Images and Screensavers

All supported images, independent of the image format, can be protected against saving to phone by using the text `Nokia` in the `alt` attribute of the image element. Protection disables the saving of images to the phone. In other words, images can be only previewed in the browser display. Any other text in the "alt" attribute leaves the image unprotected.

Example - IMG element

```
<img alt="part cldy" src="file://…/partcldy.wbmp"/>
```

Example - Protected IMG element

```
<img alt="Nokia" src="file://…/partcldy.wbmp"/>
```

Cache

The browser places viewed cards in cache. Therefore, the previously visited cards can be quickly accessed, as there is no need to reload them. The cards stay in cache until it is manually cleared by the consumer or until the memory is full.

Content Elements for the Series 20 User Interface

This section is a guide for using Wireless Markup Language 1.1 (WML) in designing services for Series 20 devices. The critical WML elements are described from the rendering point of view and according to the WML capabilities supported by the browser. All the elements introduced here are supported in Series 20 devices. However, this chapter does not include all possible WML elements and attributes. WAP service developers should especially pay attention to TABLEs and IMAGEs when optimizing their existing services.

The WML elements are briefly described and demonstrated with the use of screen shots. Note that the figures in this section are just to demonstrate the functionality and appearance of UI elements and are not from the actual device UI.

Text Formatting

The contents of a WML card are displayed in the Card view. The card is a container for text, images, tables, and input elements. The order of elements in a card is significant, as they appear on the screen in the same order.

The paragraph element, <p>, enables word wrapping and content alignment. A paragraph always starts on a new line. Normal static text information is always wrapped on a display, unless word wrapping is turned off in the browser's settings.

Insignificant white space is ignored. If more than one white space separates sections of a text, these white spaces are ignored unless the <pre> element is used.

Content inside a paragraph can be aligned to the left, center, or right; left alignment is used by default. Alignment is determined in paragraph attributes (e.g., <p align="right">). Word wrapping can be set to wrap or nowrap by using the "mode" attribute of the paragraph element.

Example - Alignment <align>

```
<p align="center">
Align &quot;center&quot;
</p>
<p align="right">
```

```
Align &quot;right&quot;
</p>
<p align="right">
<img alt="8310" src="file://…/8310.wbmp" align="top"
hspace="0" vspace="0"/>
</p>
```

New lines in text can be defined by a line break. The line break element <br> can be used inside other elements as well, as long as it belongs to a paragraph. If a line break is defined after an anchor, <a>, element, the line break is ignored. If an empty line is needed between two links, it is necessary to add two line breaks between the anchor elements.

The <fieldset> element allows the grouping of related fields and text. The basic idea of grouping is to show the grouped items on the same screenful of information if possible. If the items cannot be displayed on the same screen, the consumer is not given any notification. This element always starts a new line and ends with a line break.

The <pre> element is supported. When the pre element is used, the content shown is rendered as "pre-formatted" to the extent which is possible. This implies that white space is left intact when rendered, that the font in the cards remains the same as for plain text in a card, and that word wrapping is enabled/disabled according to how the browser is set.

TABLE

The <table> element is used together with the <tr> elements and <td> elements to create sets of rows and columns of data (e.g., text and images). It is possible to have text, images, and tables on the same card. The cells are shown in bordered rows and columns.

The size of the cells is dynamic, based on the content of the cells. The widest cells affect the width of the other cells in the same column. A minimum cell width of 10 pixels is necessary in order for the columns to remain discernible. The width of the rows will be adapted so that all can fit. Where more cells are defined than can fit on the screen, the cells are all rendered at the defined minimum width. Where the content of the cells is too large to fit inside the cell, the content is truncated and three dots are added.

A maximum of one text, image, or link element can be shown in each cell when no row in the table has been selected. But otherwise, text, image, and link elements can be shown in a cell. With a text element, if line breaks are defined, several lines can be shown at a time. When no row has been selected, the longest line in a cell defines the width of the cell if the cell can be shown in full width. Otherwise, lines of excessive length are truncated and three dots added. The full content of each cell can be viewed by scrolling.

The title of the table is shown when a row is selected. If the table has no title, the title of the card in which the table is situated is used as the title for the table.

Example - table element

```
<table align="LCC" columns="3">
      <tr>
            <td>Date</td>
            <td>F'cast</td>
            <td>T °C</td>
      </tr>
      <tr>
            <td>
            <anchor title="date">M 6/7
            <go href="#date" method="get" sendreferer="false"/>
            </anchor>
            </td>
            <td>
            <anchor>
            <img alt="rain" src="file://…/rainy.wbmp" align="bottom"/>
            <go href="#descr" method="get" sendreferer="false"/>
            </anchor>
            </td>
            <td>25°C</td>
      </tr>
      <tr>
            <td>T 6/8</td>
            <td>
            <img alt="part cldy" src="file://…/partcldy.wbmp"
            lign="bottom"/>
            </td>
            <td>27°C</td>
      </tr>
      <tr>
            <td>W 6/9</td>
            <td>
            <img alt="cloudy" src="file://…/cloudy.wbmp" align="bottom"/>
            </td>
            <td>24°C</td>
      </tr>
      <tr>
            <td>T 6/10</td>
            <td>
            <img alt="rainy" src="file://…/rainy.wbmp" align="bottom"/>
            </td>
            <td>28°C</td>
      </tr>
```

```
        <tr>
            <td>F 6/11</td>
            <td>
            <img alt="sunny" src="sunny.wbmp" align="bottom"/>
            </td>
            <td>29°C</td>
        </tr>
    </table>
```

Images

The WBMP, static GIF, and animated GIF graphics formats are supported. The static graphics area is a maximum of 84 pixels wide and 30 pixels high but is vertically and horizontally scrollable up to the maximum deck size. In contrast, the animated GIF graphics area is a maximum of 72 pixels wide and 28 pixels high. Images fitting in the graphics area are centered unless specified otherwise by the service provider. Static images that are too wide are left-aligned and truncated on the right. Images that are too long are top-aligned and can be scrolled down.

However, displaying images is optional and can be turned off in the appearance settings. Images can also be used inside a table and as links. An image that functions as a link is represented with a full-line frame around it.

Images with a maximum size of one line (i.e., 10 pixels high) may be shown with two lines of text on the same display above and/or below the image. Similarly, with an image of a maximum of 20 pixels, there can be one line of text. There cannot be text next to an image; the image will always start its own line.

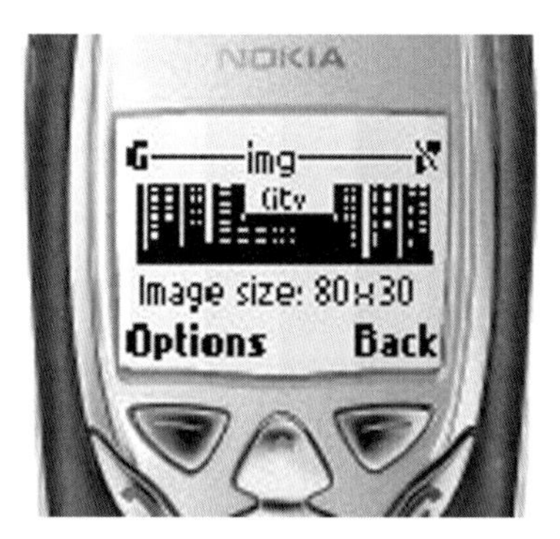

Image and one line of text

If a requested image does not exist, a small default picture will be shown. It is recommended to use an `alt` attribute value for images.

Animated GIFs

The most recent Nokia browsers support animated GIF format. The maximum number of frames allowed is 13.

The animation will start showing when the phone has been idle for a certain time. After running the animation in looping mode for 50 loops, the animation will stop. The last frame of the animation will be shown as a static GIF.

Example - IMG element

```
<img alt="part cldy" src="file://…/partcldy.wbmp"/>
```

Links

The anchored link element specifies a hotlink. Links are underlined. An active link is shown with inverse colors. When a user selects a link, an associated task is performed. When the link is active, the options list of the browser display is extended with the Select option. The user can also select a link by pressing the Send key.

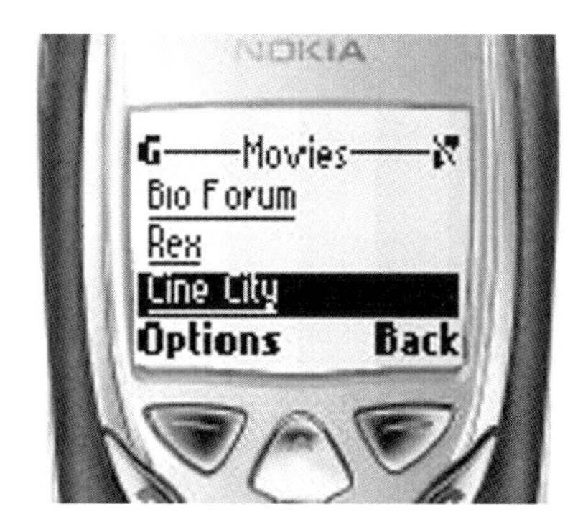

Selected link is highlighted

The <a> element is a short form of the anchor element and is bound to a go task without variables. In general, it is recommended to use the <a> element instead of anchor where possible, to allow more efficient compression.

Example - Image as a link

```
<anchor>text<go href="#card2"/>
</anchor>
<anchor>
<img alt="part cldy" src="file://…/partcldy.wbmp"/>
<go href="#card2"/>
</anchor>
```

DO Element

The do element provides a general mechanism for the consumer to act upon the current card. The <do> elements are mapped behind the browser's options list together with the preloaded options. If a <do> element contains a prev task, the right soft key is labeled "Back" and the options list is extended with Back. Use of a prev task is highly recommended for every card because it enables backward navigation. DO elements have a label that is the text of the item in the browser's options list. If the label is available, it is used as an option list item. If there is no label, a default text is displayed. However, it is highly recommended to use the label attribute.

Type	Static text
Accept	OK
Prev	Back
Help	Help
Reset	Reset
Options	Options
Delete	Erase
Unknown	Unknown

Default text of DO element label

The author of the WAP service is always responsible for the working navigation model within the given service. If there is a need for back functionality, it should be explicitly defined with the prev type <do> element. The WAP browser does not have any implicit back functionality.

The <do> element can be expressed in two ways: in card-wide scope or in deck-wide scope in a template. The <do> elements will be stored in the browser's options list together with the preloaded options.

Example - Deck-wide backward navigation, prev

```
<template>
<do type="prev" label="Back">
<prev/>
</do>
</template>
```

Example - Card-wide backward navigation

```
<do type="prev" label="Back">
<prev/>
</do>
```

Example - DO element

```
<wml>
<template>
<do name="help-button" type="options" label="Ask Help">
<go href="http://.../help.wml" method="get"/>
</do>
<do type="options" label="Contact">
<go href="http://.../contact.wml" method="get"
sendreferer="false"/>
</do>
<do type="prev" optional="false">
<prev/>
</do>
</template>
<card id="card1" title="Homepage" ordered="true">
<p align="left">
Please, register
<br/>
Username:
<input name="username" type="text" title="Username"
emptyok="false"/>
Password:
<input name="password" type="password"
title="Password" emptyok="false"/>
<do type="accept" label="Enter">
<go href="#confirm" method="get"
sendreferer="false"/>
</do>
</p>
</card>
<card id="confirm" title="Confirmation"
ordered="true" newcontext="false">
<p align="left">
$(username), thank you for registering.
</p>
</card>
</wml>
```

Input Processing

Input processing enables the consumer to input requested information to the service. There are two kinds of input element, text fields determined by an input element and selection lists determined by a select element. Option elements are used to specify a single-choice option in a select element. Option elements can be grouped by using an <optgroup> element.

The <input> element specifies a character entry object. The input element is displayed with brackets. By selecting the input element, the consumer invokes the editor. The editor is never displayed directly in Card view. The editor layout is alphanumeric data query layout. The options list of the browser display is then extended with the Edit option. The T9 option is enabled in the browser. The user can select the input element by pressing the Send key. The input element consists of a title, brackets, and a value. There can be a default value inside the brackets. The title of the element is only displayed when the editor box is displayed, which occurs after the input element has been selected. The value with the brackets is always wrapped to the next line. If the value cannot fit into one line, the content is truncated and three dots are added at the end.

The consumer can also select the input element by pressing any number key when the edit box appears, and this keystroke will already be placed in the edit box. In other words, the consumer can just start inputting characters and the edit box appears automatically.

When T9 is activated, the soft keys are "Options" and "Back" when the editor is empty. Otherwise, the soft keys are "Options" and "Clear". This also applies if T9 is deactivated. Input fields can be specified by the input element type and format attributes.

Example – Text input <input>

```
<template>
<do type="previous" label="Back" optional="false">
<prev/>
</do>
</template>
<card id="card1" title="Homepage">
<p align="left">
Please, register
<br/>
Username:
<input name="username" type="text" title="Username"/>
Password:
<input name="password" type="password" title="Password"/>
<do type="accept" label="Enter" optional="false">
<go href="#confirm" method="get" sendreferer="false"/>
</do>
</p>
</card>
<card id="confirm" title="Confirmation" ordered="true">
```

```
<p align="left">
$(username), thank you for registering.
</p>
</card>
</wml>
```

SELECT Element

Selection lists are elements that specify a list of options for the consumer to choose from. Two kinds of selection list are supported: single-choice and multiple-choice lists. The consumer can select multiple options, if the multiple attribute is set as true. The consumer can highlight and select the selection list item on a card. The options list of the browser display is extended with Select. The consumer can also select the selection list by pressing the Send key. That same item will be highlighted and displayed with a selected icon in front of it, once the consumer re-enters the list during the same browsing session.

A selection list item on a card looks similar to an input element item; it consists of a title, brackets, and a value. There is always a default value inside the brackets in a single selection list. If there are no options in the selection list, the ellipsis is displayed between the brackets. The title is not displayed in the card itself. The value with the brackets is always wrapped to the next line, which means that there will never be text and a value with brackets on the same line. If the value cannot fit onto one line, the content is truncated and three dots added at the end. The title of the selection list is the first item of the card containing the selection list. If the value is a multiple-selection value , the selections are separated by commas. If the value cannot fit onto one line, the content is truncated and an ellipsis placed at the end. The consumer can view the value between brackets in full by pressing the # key. Until the # key is released, the content that can fit on the screen is viewed. The soft keys are hidden while the content is viewed in full.

The option element specifies a single choice option in a select element. Options can be grouped with an <optgroup> element, which specifies a group of choice items in a select element. An <optgroup> element is displayed with an icon in front of the title. An <optgroup> element can be used in single-selection lists as well as in multiple-selection lists. Only in multiple-selection lists is it possible to have option groups that allow multiple selections.

Example - Select and optgroup

```
<wml>
<card id="phones" title="Information Request">
<p align="left">
Send me more information about:
<select name="models" title="Products" multiple="true">
<optgroup title="Phones">
<option value="Nokia 8310">
8310
```

```
</option>
<option value="Nokia 5510">
5510
</option>
<option value="Nokia 6310">
6310
</option>
</optgroup>
<optgroup title="Accessories">
<option value="Battery">
Battery
</option>
<option value="Desktop stand">
Desktop stand
</option>
<option value="Charger">
Charger
</option>
<option value="Headset">
Headset
</option>
</optgroup>
</select>
Please, provide your
<br/>
Name:
<input name="name" type="text" title="Name"
emptyok="false"/>
</p>
<do type="accept" label="Confirm" optional="false">
<go href="#confirm" method="get" sendreferer="false"/>
</do>
<do type="prev" optional="false">
<prev/>
</do>
</card>
</wml>
```

Optional WAP 1.2.1 Features

This chapter is an introduction to the optional WAP 1.2.1 features. These features are supported in most WAP1.2.1 compliant devices.

Push Service Indication

Push service indications are an ideal way to activate consumers. They can be used to notify consumers of updated content or provide alerts in their areas of interest. The service provider can push a service indication content type to the device display which is then saved to the Service Inbox in the Service menu. The consumer can view the indicated content afterwards by using the Service Inbox.

A service indication contains text that is displayed to the consumer and a URL for content which may be dynamically generated for each push message from the application server.

Messages that have already been sent can be replaced and deleted. Messages with the same message id can also be put in the correct order on the basis of timestamps. Service providers can also determine the consumer attention priority level.

The Service Inbox can be accessed through the options list under Services and under the options list belonging to the browser display. In the Service Inbox, the received service indications can be viewed, deleted, or downloaded. Note that receiving push services is off by default. It can be turned on in the Service Inbox settings.

Wireless Telephony Applications Interface

Three WTAI functions are supported. One can make a call while browsing, send Dial Tone Multi-Frequency (DTMF) tones, and save numbers and names to the phonebook. These functions, *MakeCall*, *SendDTMF*, and *AddPBEntry*, can be used anywhere in the WML code in the same way as when Uniform Resource Identifier (URI) or script references are used for normal non-WTAI references.

The *MakeCall* function is used for making a phone call directly from the WML browser application. A typical example of the usage of *MakeCall* is when the consumer selects an anchored link that initiates a phone call. When a *MakeCall* function is executed, the consumer is asked to confirm that the dial-up is to be made. If the phone number that is about to be called does not exist in the phonebook, a confirmation query with the phone number is displayed. If the number is in the phonebook, a confirmation query is displayed with the name fetched from the phonebook. If the consumer agrees to make the phone call, another confirmation query is displayed, with the text "*Quit browsing and make the call?*"

If the consumer accepts both times, the browser session will be terminated and the browser application will be closed down. The call will then be initiated. When the call is terminated, the device is left in idle state. If the consumer rejects the latter confirmation query, the call will be initiated from within the browser display and the consumer can browse cached content during the call. No in-call options (e.g., Mute and Hold) are accessible from within the browser application. The options list belonging to the browser display remains unaffected by the fact that a call is active.

Normal call handling applies when a call is initiated from the browser. The consumer can send DTMF tones within the phone call with the *SendDTMF* function. Just like *MakeCall*, a typical way of using *SendDTMF* is to assign the *SendDTMF* function to an anchored link. The consumer must have a voice call active. When the DTMF tone has been sent, the consumer returns to the card/deck where he/she initiated the sending. The voice call remains active.

The *AddPBEntry* function offers an easy way of storing a phone number and a corresponding name to the phone book application from a WML card. The name and number are provided by the service provider. When the consumer activates an *AddPBEntry* function and the service provider has declared a name and a number, the phone displays a confirmation query with the text "*Save name.*" When the consumer provides confirmation, another confirmation query, with the text "*With number +44 123 123 4567*" is displayed, and the number is stored in the phonebook application. When saving is done, the currently active card is displayed again. Note that the consumer does not have to be online or have any voice calls active in order to use the *AddPBEntry* function.

Accesskey

Service providers have the possibility of using the *accesskey* attribute of the <a> element and of the <anchor> element. This permits the consumer to open links with a long press of the associated accesskeys. The allowed keys for accesskey use are the 0-9 number keys. The service provider should indicate to the consumer which keys to press in order to open the desired links. The key can be indicated to the consumer by adding the label of the key to the link concerned.

Example - Using accesskey "2"

```
<a accesskey="2" href="phone.wml">(2)a </a>
```

Only one link can be associated with each accesskey. A key will also open its corresponding link if the service provider has assigned it as an accesskey but does not indicate this to the consumer. An accesskey has an effect on a link even if the link is not highlighted. The link chosen by the consumer is highlighted after the corresponding accesskey has been given a long press. This is visible while the terminal is fetching the content of the link. A long press of an accesskey also has an effect when a card contains both accesskeys and a highlighted input element. An input element can be activated by an associated accesskey through a long press in the same way as anchored links, as described above.

Cookies

Cookies enable the storage of data (e.g. consumer information) to ease the browsing process for the consumer by reducing the amount of information input required. For example, login can be configured dynamically so that it is displayed only if the application cannot identify the consumer.

Series 40 Browsing

This section provides information and practical examples for developers who want to optimize their existing Wireless Application Protocol (WAP) services for the Series 40 user interface. Series 40 is a UI category for Nokia 128 x128 pixel screen resolution. It comprises a passive matrix color screen with two soft keys. This section highlights the possibilities, limitations, and requirements of service development, and it provides a good introduction to the Nokia style of user interface design.

Series 40 User Interface

This chapter gives a short overview of the type of user interface seen in Series 40 devices. The main focus is on the WAP services element of the device. The WAP browser user interface is designed to comply with the user interaction handling of other applications on the device.

The user interface is a combination of specific user interface hardware like keys and display; user interaction conventions, which include input and output functions and their relationships; and audio-visual appearance that is used in user interaction conventions.

Series 40 Devices

The Nokia browser in Series 40 devices has a WAP browser with enhanced features and increased usability. The deck size is 2.8kbit and cache size in the device is 20kbit. Other WAP features include predictive text input (T9) and a picture viewer. Three different image formats are supported here: Wireless BitMap (WBMP), static Graphics Interchange Format (GIF), and animated GIF. The WAP1.2.1 compliant devices support push service indication, Wireless Telephony Applications Interface (WTAI) and cookies.

	Nokia 7210
WAP version	WAP 1.2.1
Network	GSM900/1800/1900
Bearers	CSD, HSCSD, GPRS
Keys	Two soft key UI

A Nokia Series 40 device and its browsing capabilities

Two Soft Key Display

The display is a high-resolution passive matrix color display, 4096 colors, with a display resolution of 128 pixels by 128 pixels. The display consists of the application area, header area, and the area used for the soft keys.

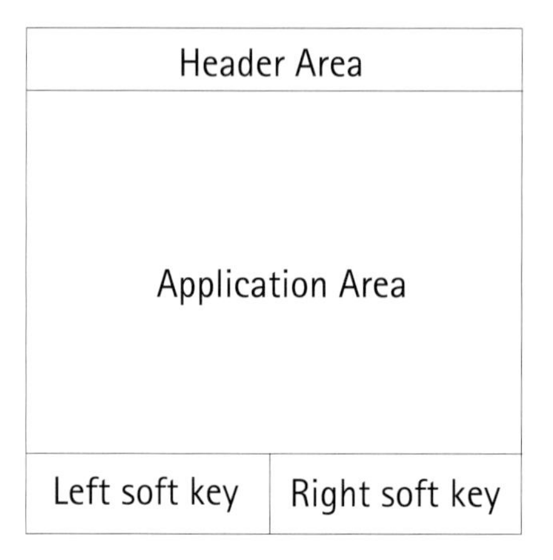

Structure of the browser screen in the Series 40 UI

The application area is 122 pixels (horizontal) by 96 pixels (vertical); it includes five lines for main text and can also be used for displaying graphics, which are scrollable in both dimensions up to the maximum deck size.

- **Send/Talk key** works as a selection key.
- **End key** exits a data call/General Packet Radio Service (GPRS) connection and takes the unit into idle state when pressed twice.
- **two soft keys**: The soft keys are assigned actions that enable the consumer to manipulate the user interface by making selections and entering, editing, and deleting text.
- **left soft key** is used as a yes/positive key. It is associated with options that execute commands and go deeper into the menu structure (e.g., Select, OK, and Options).
- **right soft key** is used as a no/negative key. It is associated with options that cancel commands, delete text, and go backwards in the menu structure, such as Back, Exit, and Clear.
- **Scrolling up/down** allows the consumer to scroll the options, text, and images in the current display up and down.
- **Scrolling left/right** allows the consumer to scroll the images in the current display in the horizontal direction.

Display Fonts

All fonts are proportional. Proportional fonts give a dynamic width for each character rather than assigning each character the same size block. They provide improved readability of displayed text and generally allow more characters to be displayed per line. On the other hand, using proportional fonts means that it is difficult to tell how many characters there can be in each line.

Header text
Choice item text
Choice item text
Choice item text
Choice item text
Choice item text
Options Back

	Height (pixels)
One line	19
Font	16
Margin Top	1
Margin Bottom	1
Underlining	1

Information for one line of text

Accessing WAP Browser

The browser is accessed by selecting Services from the menu and entering a home page defined for the currently active settings or a bookmark. For quick access to the browser, a long press of the "0" key will take the consumer to the home page that is defined in the currently active settings.

Navigation, Labels and Titles

The consumer should be provided with consistent card headers, element titles, and <do> element labels. The title of a <select> element is used in the header of a selection list or option groups list. The title of an <optgroup> element is used as an option group title and in the header of its selection list. The title of an input element is used in the title in the editor. The label of a <do> element is used in the Service options behind the Options soft key.

Scrolling

The consumer can move up and down in Card view when it contains elements and static text areas between them. This is done by *jumping* from element to element. Scrolling through long static sections is done line by line. The first element of a card is highlighted by default if it is on the first display.

Picture Viewer

The picture viewer offers the consumer the ability to perform horizontal and vertical scrolling of pictures/animations that are too wide/high for the display. The picture viewer can only be activated by selecting the options list item *View Picture* if the currently active page contains at least one picture/animation. In the picture viewer, pictures/animations are displayed similarly to the way they are displayed in the browser display except that only one can be viewed at a time.

Cache

The browser places viewed cards in cache. Therefore, previously visited cards can be quickly accessed, as there is no need to reload them. The cards stay in cache until it is manually cleared by the consumer or until the memory is full.

Content Elements for the Series 40 User Interface

This chapter is a guide for using WML 1.3 in designing services for Series 40 phones. It is an overview of general Graphical User Interface (GUI) elements, that is, the Wireless Markup Language (WML) elements that are critical from the point of view of rendering and the WML capabilities supported by the browser. All the elements introduced here are supported in Series 40 devices. However, this chapter does not include all possible WML elements and attributes. WAP service developers should pay special attention to TABLEs and IMAGEs when optimizing their existing services. The WML elements are briefly described and demonstrated with the use of screen shots.

Text Formatting

The contents of a WML card are displayed in the Card view. The card is a container for text, images, tables, and input elements. The order of elements in a card is significant, as they appear on the screen in the same order.

The paragraph element, <p>, enables word wrapping and content alignment. A paragraph always starts on a new line. Normal static text information is always wrapped on a display, unless word wrapping is turned off in the browser's settings.

Insignificant white space is ignored. If more than one white space separates the constituent sections of a text, these white spaces are ignored unless the <pre> element is used.

Content inside a paragraph can be aligned to the left, center, or right; left alignment is used by default. Alignment is determined in the paragraph attributes (e.g., <p align="right">). Word wrapping can be set to wrap or nowrap by using the *mode* attribute of the paragraph element.

Example - Alignment <align>

```
<p align="center">
Align &quot;center&quot;
</p>
<p align="right">
Align &quot;right&quot;
</p>
<p align="right">
<img alt="8310" src="file://…/7210.wbmp" align="top"
hspace="0" vspace="0"/>
</p>
```

New lines in text can be defined by a line break. The line break element, <br>, can be used inside other elements as well, as long as it belongs to a paragraph. If a line break is defined after an <a> element, the line break is ignored. If an empty line is needed between two links, it is necessary to add two line breaks between the <a> elements.

The <fieldset> element allows the grouping of related fields and text. The basic idea of grouping is to show the grouped items in the same screenful if possible. If the items cannot be displayed on the same screen, the user is not given any notification. A fieldset always starts a new line and ends with a line break.

The <pre> element is supported. When it is used, the content shown is rendered as pre-formatted to the extent that is possible. This implies that white space is left intact when rendered, that the font in the cards remains the same as for plain text in a card, and that word wrapping is enabled/disabled based on how the browser is set.

TABLE

The <table> element is used together with the <tr> elements and <td> elements to create sets of rows and columns of data (e.g., text and images). It is possible to have text, images, and tables on the same card. The cells are shown in bordered rows and columns.

The size of the cells is dynamic, based on the content of the cells. The widest cells affect the width of the other cells in the same column. A minimum cell width of 10 pixels is necessary in order for the columns to remain discernible. The width of the rows will be adapted so that all can fit. Where more cells are defined than can fit on the screen, the cells are all rendered at the defined minimum width. Where the content of a cell is too large to fit inside the cell, the content is truncated and three dots are added.

A maximum of one text, image, or link element can be shown in each cell when no row in the table has been selected. But otherwise, text, image, and link elements can be shown in a cell. In a text element, if line breaks are defined, several lines can be shown at a time. When no row has been selected, the longest line in a cell defines the width of the cell if the cell can be shown in full width. Otherwise, lines of excessive length are truncated and three dots added. The full content of each cell can be viewed by scrolling.

The title of the table is shown when a row is selected. If the table has no title, the title of the card in which the table is situated is used as the title for the table.

Example - table element

```
<table align="LCC" columns="3">
      <tr>
            <td>Date</td>
            <td>F'cast</td>
            <td>T °C</td>
      </tr>
      <tr>
```

```
            <td>
            <anchor title="date">M 6/7
            <go href="#date" method="get" sendreferer="false"/>
            </anchor>
            </td>
            <td>
            <anchor>
            <img alt="rain" src="rainy.wbmp" align="bottom"/>
            <go href="#descr" method="get" sendreferer="false"/>
            </anchor>
            </td>
            <td>25°C</td>
        </tr>
        <tr>
            <td>T 6/8</td>
            <td>
            <img alt="part cldy" src="file://…/partcldy.wbmp"
            align="bottom"/>
            </td>
            <td>27°C</td>
        </tr>
        <tr>
            <td>W 6/9</td>
            <td>
            <img alt="cloudy" src="file://…/cloudy.wbmp" align="bottom"/>
            </td>
            <td>24°C</td>
        </tr>
        <tr>
            <td>T 6/10</td>
            <td>
            <img alt="rainy" src="file://…/rainy.wbmp" align="bottom"/>
            </td>
            <td>28°C</td>
        </tr>
        <tr>
            <td>F 6/11</td>
            <td>
            <img alt="sunny" src="sunny.wbmp" align="bottom"/>
            </td>
            <td>29°C</td>
        </tr>
    </table>
```

Images

The graphic formats WBMP, static GIF, and animated GIF are supported. The static graphics area is a maximum of 122 pixels wide and 96 pixels high but is vertically and horizontally scrollable up to the maximum deck size. The animated GIF graphics area is the same as the static graphics area. Images fitting in the graphics area are centered unless specified otherwise by the service provider.

However, displaying images is optional and can be turned off in the appearance settings. Images can also be used inside a table and as links. An image that functions as a link is represented with a full-line frame around it. There cannot be text next to an image; the image will always start its own line.

Image and header text

If a requested image does not exist or could not be fetched, a small default picture will be shown. It is also recommended to use a value for the image element's alt attribute as an alternative, textual representation of the image.

Example - img element

```
<img alt="part cldy" src="file://.../partcldy.wbmp"/>
```

The most recent Nokia browsers support animated GIF image format. The maximum number of frames allowed is 13.

Links

The anchored link or <a> element specifies a hotlink. Links are underlined and colored blue. When a user selects a link, an associated task is performed. When the link is active, the options list of the browser display is extended with the *Open link* option. The consumer can also select a link by pressing the Send key.

The <a> element is a short form of the anchor element and is bound to a go task without variables. In general, it is recommended to use the <a> element instead of <anchor> where possible, to allow more efficient compression.

A hotlink is automatically followed by a line break. If a line break is defined after an <a> element, the line break is ignored. If an empty line is needed between two links, it is necessary to add two line breaks between the <a> elements. If a hotlink does not have a title or label, the Uniform Resource Locator (URL) address of the link is displayed in its full length and functions as a normal hotlink.

Example - Image as a link

```
<anchor>text<go href="#card2"/>
</anchor>
<anchor>
<img alt="part cldy" src="file://…/partcldy.wbmp"/>
<go href="#card2"/>
</anchor>
```

DO Element

The <do> element provides a general mechanism for the consumer to act upon the current card. The <do> elements are mapped behind the browser's options list together with the preloaded options. If a <do> element contains a prev task, the right soft key is labeled *Back* and the options list is extended with *Back*. Use of a prev task in every card is highly recommended because it enables backward navigation. <do> elements have a label that is the text of the item in the browser's options list, if the label is available, it is used as an option list item. If there is no label, a default text is displayed. However, it is highly recommended to use the label attribute.

Default Text in the DO Element Label

Type	Static text
Accept	OK
Prev	Back
Help	Help
Reset	Reset
Options	Options
Delete	Delete
Unknown	Unknown

The author of the WAP service is always responsible for the working navigation model within the given service. If there is a need for back functionality, it should be explicitly defined with the <prev> type <do> element. The WAP browser does not have any implicit back functionality.

The <do> element can be expressed in two ways: in card-wide scope or in deck-wide scope in a template. Do elements will be stored in the browser's options list together with the preloaded options.

Example - Deck-wide backward navigation, prev

```
<template>
<do type="prev" label="Back">
<prev/>
</do>
</template>
```

Example - Card-wide backward navigation

```
<do type="prev" label="Back">
<prev/>
</do>
```

Example - Do element

```
<wml>
<template>
<do name="help-button" type="options" label="Ask Help">
<go href="http://.../help.wml" method="get"/>
</do>
<do type="options" label="Contact">
<go href="http://.../contact.wml" method="get"
sendreferer="false"/>
</do>
<do type="prev" optional="false">
<prev/>
</do>
</template>
<card id="card1" title="Homepage" ordered="true">
<p align="left">
Please, register
<br/>
Username:
<input name="username" type="text" title="Username"
emptyok="false"/>
Password:
<input name="password" type="password"
title="Password" emptyok="false"/>
<do type="accept" label="Enter">
<go href="#confirm" method="get"
sendreferer="false"/>
</do>
</p>
```

```
</card>
<card id="confirm" title="Confirmation"
ordered="true" newcontext="false">
<p align="left">
$(username), thank you for registering.
</p>
</card>
</wml>
```

Input Processing

Input processing enables the consumer to input requested information to the service. There are two kinds of input element: text fields determined by an input element and selection lists determined by a <select> element. <option> elements are used to specify a single-choice option in a <select> element. <option> elements can be grouped by using an <optgroup> element.

The input element specifies a character entry object. The input element is displayed with brackets. By selecting the input element, the consumer invokes the editor. The editor is never displayed directly in Card view. The editor layout is alphanumeric data query layout. The options list of the browser display is then extended with the Edit option. The T9 option is enabled in the browser. The consumer can select the input element by pressing the Send key. The input element consists of a title, brackets, and a value. There can be a default value inside the brackets. The title of the element is only displayed when the editor box is displayed, which occurs after the input element has been selected. The value with the brackets is always wrapped to the next line. If the value cannot fit onto one line, the content is truncated and three dots added at the end.

The consumer can also select the input element by pressing any number key when the edit box appears, and this keystroke will be placed in the edit box. In other words, the consumer can just start inputting characters and the edit box will appear automatically. When T9 is activated, the soft keys are *Options* and *Back* when the editor is empty. Otherwise, the soft keys are *Options* and *Clear*. This also applies if T9 is deactivated. Input fields can be specified by the input element type and format attributes.

Example - Text input <input>

<template>

```
<do type="previous" label="Back" optional="false">
<prev/>
</do>
</template>
<card id="card1" title="Homepage">
<p align="left">
Please, register
<br/>
```

```
Username:
<input name="username" type="text" title="Username"/>
Password:
<input name="password" type="password" title="Password"/>
<do type="accept" label="Enter" optional="false">
<go href="#confirm" method="get" sendreferer="false"/>
</do>
</p>
</card>
<card id="confirm" title="Confirmation" ordered="true">
<p align="left">
$(username), thank you for registering.
</p>
</card>
</wml>
```

SELECT Element

Selection lists are elements that specify a list of options for the consumer to choose from. Two kinds of selection list are supported; single choice and multiple-choice lists. The consumer can select multiple options if the multiple attributes are set to true. The consumer can highlight and select the selection list item on a card. The options list of the browser display is extended with *Select*. The consumer can also select the selection list by pressing the Send key. That same item will be highlighted and displayed with an icon indicating *selected* in front of it, once the consumer re-enters the list during the same browsing session. A selection list item on a card looks similar to an input element item; it consists of a title, brackets, and a value. There is always a default value inside the brackets in a single selection list. If there are no options in the selection list, three dots are displayed between the brackets. The title is not displayed in the card itself. The value with the brackets is always wrapped to the next line, which means that there will never be text and a value with brackets on the same line. If the value cannot fit onto one line, the content is truncated and three dots added at the end. The title of the selection list is the first item of the card containing the selection list. If the value is a multiple-selection value, commas separate the options. If the value cannot fit onto one line, the content is truncated and the end replaced with three dots. The consumer can view the value between brackets in full by pressing the '#' key. Until the # key is released, the content that can fit on the screen is viewed. The soft keys are hidden while the content is viewed in full. The layout in full view is the same as that selected by the consumer.

The <option> element specifies a single choice option in a select element. Options can be grouped with an <optgroup> element, which specifies a group of choice items in a select element. An <optgroup> element is displayed with an icon in front of the title. An <optgroup> element can be used in single-selection lists as well as in multiple-selection lists. Only in multiple-selection lists is it possible to have option groups that allow multiple selections.

Example - Select and optgroup

```
<wml>
<card id="phones" title="Information Request">
<p align="left">
Send me more information about:
<select name="models" title="Products" multiple="true">
<optgroup title="Phones">
<option value="Nokia 8310">
8310
</option>
<option value="Nokia 5510">
5510
</option>
<option value="Nokia 6310">
6310
</option>
</optgroup>
<optgroup title="Accessories">
<option value="Battery">
Battery
</option>
<option value="Desktop stand">
Desktop stand
</option>
<option value="Charger">
Charger
</option>
<option value="Headset">
Headset
</option>
</optgroup>
</ >
Please, provide your
<br/>
Name:
<input name="name" type="text" title="Name"
emptyok="false"/>
</p>
<do type="accept" label="Confirm" optional="false">
<go href="#confirm" method="get" sendreferer="false"/>
</do>
<do type="prev" optional="false">
<prev/>
</do>
</card>
</wml>
```

Optional WAP 1.2.1 Features

This chapter is an introduction to the optional WAP 1.2.1 features. These features are supported on most WAP 1.2.1 compliant devices.

Push Service Indication

Push service indications are an ideal way to activate consumers. They can be used to notify consumers of updated content or provide alerts in their areas of interest. The service provider can push a service indication content type to the device display which is then saved to the Service Inbox, found in the Service menu. The consumer can view the indicated content afterwards by using the Service Inbox. The service indication should contain at least text with a URL address pointing to a service.

A service indication contains text that is displayed to the consumer, and a URL for content which may be dynamically generated for each push message from the application server.

Messages that have already been sent can be replaced and deleted. Messages with the same message ID can also be put in the correct order via timestamps. Service providers can also determine the consumer attention priority level.

The Service Inbox can be accessed through the options list under Services and under the options list belonging to the browser display. In the Service Inbox, the received service indications can be viewed, deleted, or downloaded. Note that receiving push services is turned off by default. It can be turned on in the Service Inbox settings.

Wireless Telephony Applications Interface

Three WTAI functions are supported. The consumer can make a call while browsing, send Dial Tone Multi-Frequency (DTMF) tones, and save numbers and names to the phonebook. These functions, *MakeCall*, *SendDTMF* and *AddPBEntry*, can be used anywhere in the WML code in the same way as when Uniform Resource Identifier (URI) or script references are used for non-WTAI references.

The *MakeCall* function is used for making a phone call directly from the WML browser application. A typical example of the usage of *MakeCall* is when the consumer selects an anchored link that initiates a phone call. When a *MakeCall* function is executed, the consumer is asked to confirm that the dial-up is to be made. If the phone number that is about to be called does not exist in the phonebook, a confirmation query containing the phone number is displayed. If the number is in the phonebook, a confirmation query is displayed with the name fetched from the phonebook. If the consumer agrees to make the phone call, another confirmation query is displayed, with the text "*Quit browsing and make the call?*"

If the consumer accepts both times, the browser session will be terminated and the browser application will be closed down. The call will then be initiated. When the call is terminated, the device is left in idle state. If the consumer rejects the latter confirmation query, the call will be initiated from within the browser display and the consumer can browse cached content during the call. No in-call options (e.g., Mute and Hold) are accessible from within the browser application. The options list belonging to the browser display remains unaffected by the fact that a call is active.

The consumer can send DTMF tones within the phone call by executing a WTAI function called *SendDTMF*. Just like *MakeCall*, a typical way of using *SendDTMF* is to assign the *SendDTMF* function to an anchored link. The consumer must have a voice call active. When the DTMF tone has been sent, the consumer returns to the card/deck where he/she initiated the sending. The voice call remains active.

The *AddPBEntry* function offers an easy way of storing a phone number and a corresponding name to the phonebook application from a WML card. The service provider provides the name and number. When the consumer activates an *AddPBEntry* function and the service provider has declared a name and a number, the device displays a confirmation query with the text "*Save name.*" When the consumer provides confirmation, another confirmation query, with the text "*With number +44 123 123 4567*", is displayed and the number is stored in the phonebook application. When saving is done, the currently active card is displayed again. Note that the consumer does not have to be online or have any voice calls active in order to use the *AddPBEntry* function.

Accesskey

Service providers have the possibility of using the *accesskey* attribute of the <a> element and of the <anchor> element. This permits the user to open links with a long press of the associated accesskeys. The allowed keys for accesskey use are the 0-9 number keys. The service provider should indicate to the consumer which keys to press in order to open the desired links. The key can be indicated to the consumer by adding the label of the key to the link concerned.

Example - Using accesskey "2"

```
<a accesskey="2" href="phone.wml">(2)a </a>
```

Only one link can be associated with each accesskey. A key will also open its corresponding link if the service provider has assigned it as an accesskey but does not indicate this to the consumer. An accesskey has an effect on a link even if the link is not highlighted. The link chosen by the consumer is highlighted after the corresponding accesskey has been given a long press. This is visible while the device is fetching the content of the link. A long press of an accesskey also has an effect when a card contains both accesskeys and a highlighted input element. An input element can be activated by an associated accesskey through a long press in the same way as anchored links.

Cookies

Cookies enable the storage of data (e.g., consumer information) to ease the browsing process for the consumer by reducing the amount of information input required. For example, login can be configured dynamically so that it is displayed only if the application cannot identify the consumer.

Content Download

Content download is a technology that is used to deliver digital content (e.g., entertainment and business applications) to mobile devices. Another important application is the personalization of devices according to a consumer's preferences and lifestyle. Content downloading can be initiated by a consumer or by a network application.

The content download mechanism between the mobile device and content source is based on open technologies (e.g., HTTP and Java). This technology allows the creation of an open, multivendor market for mobile device vendors as well as for network server and broker vendors.

Series 60 Browsing

This section provides information and practical examples for developers who want to optimize their existing WAP services for the Series 60 (resolution 176 x 208) User Interface (UI) category. This section highlights the possibilities, limitations, and requirements of service development and provides a good introduction to the Nokia style of user interface design. The screen shots in this section are taken with the emulator included in the Nokia Series 60 Platform SDK for Symbian OS.

Series 60 User Interface

This section gives a short overview of the user interface in 176 x 208-pixel screen resolution Series 60 devices. Emphasis is on the WAP services part of the device. The WAP browser user interface is designed to be consistent with user interaction handling familiar from other applications on the device.

The user interface style is a combination of specific user interface hardware like keys and display; user interaction conventions, which include input and output functions and their relationships; and audio-visual appearance that is used in the user interaction conventions.

Series 60 Devices

Series 60 devices have a WAP browser with enhanced features and increased usability. Predictive text input (T9) can be used in the WAP browser. Series 60 devices support push service indication, three Wireless Telephony Applications Interface (WTAI) public library functions, cookies, and content downloading. Applications created with C++ or Mobile Information Device Profile (MIDP™) can be downloaded to the device over the mobile network by pointing the WAP browser to a page which contains the actual file to be downloaded.

	Nokia 7650
WAP version	WAP 1.2.1
Network	GSM900/1800
Bearers	CSD, HSCSD, GPRS
Resolution	176 x 208
Keys	Two soft keys and 5-way joystick

A Nokia Series 60 device and its browsing capabilities

Keys and Display

Nokia 7650 keys

The Send/talk key initiates a data call.

The End key exits a data call.

The two soft keys: The soft keys are assigned actions that enable the consumer to manipulate the user interface by making selections and entering, editing, and deleting text.

- **The left soft key** is used as a yes/positive key. It is associated with options that execute commands and go deeper into the menu structure (e.g., Select, OK, and Options).
- **The right soft key** is used as a no/negative key. It is associated with options that cancel commands and go backwards in the menu structure (e.g., Back and Exit).

Navigation Key (five-way joystick):

- **Scrolling up/down** allows the consumer to scroll the options or text in the current display up and down.
- **Scrolling left/right** allows the consumer to scroll the options or text in the current display in the horizontal direction.
- **Pressing** selects the currently highlighted item.

Other Keys:

- **Application key** allows application swapping without closing current application.
- **Clear key** clears entered characters/numbers and deletes the selected item(s) in certain contexts. The Clear key is not used for back/exit operations.
- **Edit key** enables switching between input modes: character input, numbers, and T9. Press-and-hold with joystick selects text area. Pressing the key simultaneously with joystick enables multiselection in lists.

Display Areas

The Series 60 display is an illuminated graphical active matrix display with a resolution of 176 pixels (horizontal) by 208 pixels (vertical) and support for 4096 colors. The display consists of three areas: a status area, main area, and soft key area.

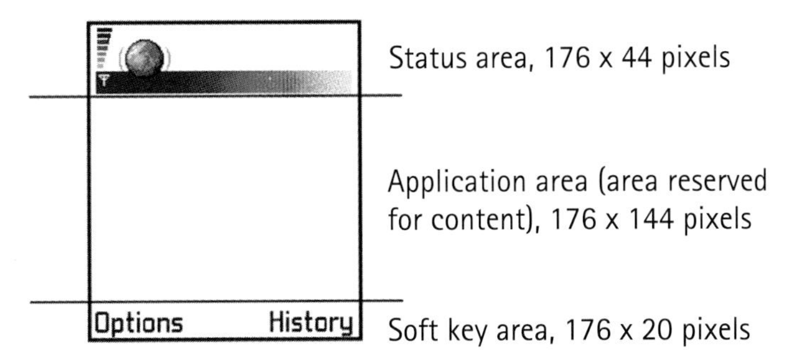

Physical dimensions of the browser screen

- o **Status area** displays status information of the current application and state as well as general information about the device status (e.g., signal strength and battery charge). The Status area occupies the top part of the screen and contains five sub-areas: signal, title, context, navi, and battery/universal indicator.
- o **Application area** is the principal area of the screen where an application can display its data. In the WAP browser, this area is reserved for the WML card content.
- o **Soft key area** occupies the bottom part of the screen and displays the labels associated with the two soft keys.

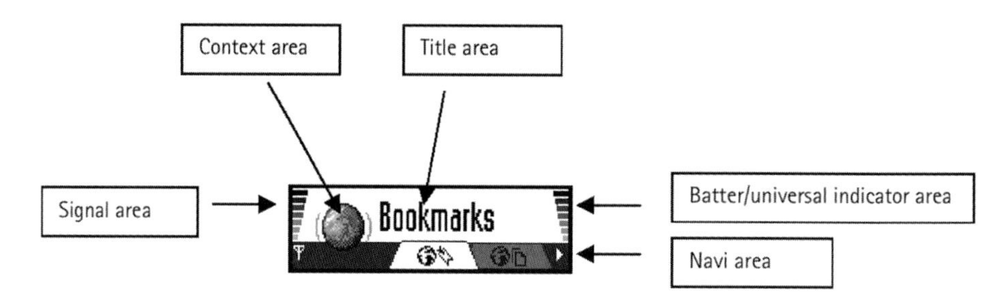

Different parts of the status area

The screen size reserved for content rendering is 176 x 144 pixels (width x height). Besides the content rendering area, there is also a status area (44 pixels high) and a soft key area (20 pixels high) visible.

Display Fonts

The browser has multiple text types and sizes. There are normal and large sizes, plain and bold type, and italic version of all of these. The font sizes are:

12 pixels (8 rows of text on the display)

- o normal plain text
- o normal bold text
- o normal italic plain text
- o normal italic bold text

13 pixels (7 rows of text on the display)

- o large plain text
- o large bold text
- o large italic plain text
- o large italic bold text

All fonts are proportional. Proportional fonts give a dynamic and minimized width for each character, providing improved readability of the display texts. They generally allow more characters to be displayed per line. On the other hand, use of proportional fonts means that it is difficult to tell how many characters there can be in each line.

WAP Browser View

The WAP browser is accessed via the Application shell by selecting Services. After Services is selected, two views are available. These are the Bookmarks view and the Saved cards view. When the consumer chooses to open WML content from one of the two views, the card is displayed in the main area on the screen. A WML card can contain hotlinks, input elements, selection list items, static text areas, and images.

The bookmarks view can include the following items:

- Start page, which is the home page of the service provider. The home page is related to the access point used. The access point and home page can be set in Settings.
- Last page visited. When the phone is disconnected from the service, the last visited page is kept in memory until a new page is visited during the next connection.
- Bookmarks showing the title or the Internet address of the bookmark. Bookmarks are displayed in alphabetical order.

WAP browser in the Bookmarks view

When scrolling through bookmarks, the consumer can see the address of the highlighted bookmark in the Go-to field at the bottom of the display.

The Saved card view contains saved cards and folders added by the consumer. The saved cards are sorted in alphabetical order, and folders inside the Saved cards view are displayed after saved cards, in alphabetical order. The consumer can open the saved card or folder by highlighting it and selecting Open or pressing the joystick.

The WAP browser uses the character sets defined and used in the Symbian platform, which includes the usage of Unicode as necessary. Where multiple character sets are found, the reference-processing model of the WML specification is used.

Character set encodings that are fully supported are US-ASCII, UTF-8, and ISO-8859-1.

Navigation, Labels and Titles

The consumer should be provided with consistent card headers, element titles, and do element labels. WML card title ID displayed in the title area of the screen. If the card does not have a title, the URL of the current deck is displayed. The title of a <select> element is used in the header of a selection list or option groups list. The title of an <optgroup> element is used as an option groups title and in the header of its selection list. The title of an <input> element is used in the editor title. The label of a <do> element is used in the Service options behind the Options soft key.

Scrolling

The consumer can move up and down and also horizontally in Card view when it contains elements with long static text areas between them. This is done by *jumping* from element to element using the joystick to scroll the view and to choose hyperlinks and elements.

Scrolling through long static sections is done line by line. The first element of a card is highlighted by default if it is on the first screenful.

Cache

The browser places viewed decks in the cache. Therefore, the previously visited decks are quick to access, as there is no need to reload them. The consumer can empty the cache by selecting the Clear cache option in the Options list in the WAP browser.

Content Elements for the Series 60 User Interface

This section is a guide for using WML in designing services. It is an overview of Graphical User Interface (GUI) elements, that is, the WML elements that are critical from the rendering point of view and their WML capabilities supported by the browser. The document does not include all possible WML elements and attributes. WAP service developers should pay special attention to TABLEs and IMAGEs.

Text Formatting

The contents of a WML card are displayed in the main area of the display. The card is a container for text, images, tables, and input elements. The order of elements in a card is significant, as they appear on the screen in the same order.

The following table contains all text layout formatting elements. These are described in greater detail later in this chapter.

Text Layout Formats

Element	**Formatting**
em	Italicized font
strong	Bold font
b	Bold font
i	Italicized font
u	Underlined font
big	Font size is set to big
small	Font size is set to small
p	A paragraph break is inserted in the text
br	A line break is inserted in the text

The browser supports all text formatting elements of WML. Table below displays how the emphasis elements map to the user interface.

Emphasis type	Rendering when font size setting as normal	Rendering when font size setting as large
Plain text	Normal	Large
Plain text with emphasis tag <em>	Italic normal	Italic large
Plain text with strong tag <strong>	Bold normal	Bold large
Plain text with italics tag <I>	Italic normal	Italic large
Plain text with bold tag <b>	Bold normal	Bold large
Plain text with underline tag <u>	Underlined normal	Underlined large
Plain text with tag <big>	Large	Bold large
Plain text with tag <small>	Small	Normal

Emphasis elements in the WAP browser

The paragraph element, <p>, enables word wrapping and content alignment. A paragraph always starts on a new line. Normal static text information is always wrapped on a display, unless word wrapping is turned off in the browser's settings.

Insignificant white space is ignored. If more than one white space separates the constituent areas of a text, these white spaces are ignored unless the <pre> element is used.

Content inside a paragraph can be aligned to the left, center, or right; left alignment is displayed by default. Alignment is determined in paragraph attributes (e.g., <p align="right">). Word wrapping can be set to wrap or nowrap by using the *mode* attribute of the paragraph element.

Example - Alignment <align>

```
<p align="center">
Align &quot;center&quot;
</p>
<p align="right">
Align &quot;right&quot;
</p>
<p align="right">
<img alt="7650" src="file://C:/USERS/wml/7650.gif"
align="top" hspace="0" vspace="0"/>
</p>
```

New lines in text can be defined by a line break. The line break element, <br>, can be used inside other elements as well, as long as it belongs to a paragraph. If a line break is defined after an <a> element, the line break is ignored. If an empty line is needed between two links, it is necessary to add two line breaks between the <a> elements.

The <fieldset> element allows the grouping of related field and text. The basic idea of grouping is to show the grouped items in the same screenful of information if possible. If the items cannot be displayed at the same time, the consumer is not given any notification. A fieldset always starts a new line and ends with a line break.

The <pre> element is supported. When the <pre> element is used, the content shown is rendered as pre-formatted to the extent possible. This implies that white space is left intact when rendered, that the font in the cards remains the same as for plain text in a card and that word wrapping is enabled/disabled according to how the browser is set.

Table

The <table> element is used together with the <tr> elements and <td> elements to create sets of rows and columns of data (e.g., text, images, and links). It is possible to have text, images, and tables on the same card. The cells are shown in bordered rows and columns.

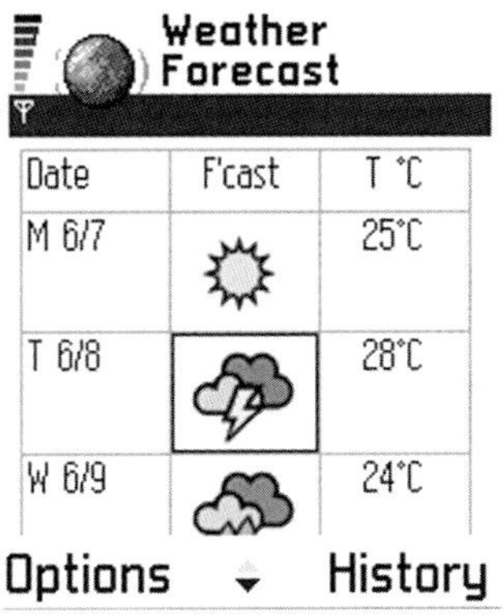

Weather Forecast

Date	F'cast	T °C
M 6/7		25°C
T 6/8		28°C
W 6/9		24°C

Options History

Table element with three columns, one of which is selected

A table consists of cells whose width (horizontal) is fixed but whose length (vertical) may vary. The length of a table row is determined by the length of the content in the longest cell in the row.

The fixed width of a table cell and its border is one third of the display width if the table contains three or more cells in the rows. The fixed width of a table cell and its border is half the display width if a table row has two cells and is the display width if the table only contains one cell in its rows. A maximum of three columns can be displayed simultaneously on the display. If the content does not fit into the largest possible cell size, it is truncated.

Table cells can be highlighted and selected like any other element on a card. When focus on a card moves into a table from an element above a table, the top left cell is always the first highlighted cell. The top left cell is also highlighted by default if there is no content above the table. When focus moves into a table from an element below it, the bottom left cell is always the first cell highlighted. All table cells are highlightable - including those that fit into the display and thus do not contain truncated content. However, it is not possible to highlight more than one cell at a time. The border around a cell is displayed in bold when a cell is highlighted. The content of the cell remains as if the cell were not highlighted.

The consumer can scroll a table cell by cell, in both vertical and horizontal directions. The consumer can select a highlighted cell by pressing the joystick or by selecting Open in the Options menu. When a highlighted cell has been selected, the cell content is displayed as a card in the main area.

The title of the table is displayed in the Navi Area whenever a table cell is highlighted. The title is surrounded by left and right arrow indicators telling the user if one or more cell exists to the left and right of the currently highlighted cell.

Example - table element

```
<table columns="3" align="LCC">
      <tr>
            <td>Date</td>
            <td>F&apos;cast</td>
            <td>T &#xB0;C</td>
      </tr>
      <tr>
            <td>M 6/7</td>
            <td><img src="sunny.gif" alt="sunny"/></td>
            <td>25&#xB0;C</td>
      </tr>
      <tr>
            <td>T 6/8</td><td><img src="thunder.gif"  alt="thunder"/></td>
            <td>28&#xB0;C</td>
      </tr>
      <tr>
            <td>W 6/9</td><td><img src="rain.gif" alt="rain"/></td>
            <td>24&#xB0;C</td>
      </tr>
      <tr>
            <td>T 6/10</td><td><img src="cloudy.gif" alt="cloudy"/></td>
            <td>23&#xB0;C</td>
      </tr>
</table>
```

Images

The Series 60 devices support all the image formats that the Symbian Media Server supports. These are:

- Wireless BitMap (WBMP)
- Symbian bitmap (MBM)
- Joint Photographic Experts Group (JPEG), including progressive JPEG
- static Graphics Interchange Format (GIF) and animated1, interlaced, and transparent GIF
- Portable Network Graphics (PNG)
- Tagged Image File Format (TIFF), generally used by faxes

The graphics area is vertically scrollable. Images can be scrolled vertically without cutting/ truncation. If an image does not fit into the remaining width of the current line, a line break is inserted before the image is rendered.

The user can use the WAP browser settings to choose whether he/she wants to automatically load images or not. When there is an image visible in the card, it can be sent to the image viewer application for further processing (e.g., editing and printing). Images can also be saved to the photo album in the device directly from the WML page. Images can be used inside a table and as hotlinks. Images that act as links have borders in blue and when highlighted; borders are in boldface.

If an image for some reason could not be fetched, a broken image icon and the `ALT` text is displayed. The `ALT` text is truncated if it exceeds the horizontal space left for the text on the line in use.

Links

The anchored link element specifies a hotlink. Anchored links are shown underlined. A link that points to a deck/card which does not exist in the cache is colored blue while a link that points to a deck/card which exists in the cache is colored violet. If there is an image and text declared inside an anchored link, the image is displayed with a border around it and the text is shown underlined. If highlighted, the border turns bold and the text is displayed with highlighting.

When a consumer selects a hotlink, an associated task is performed. When the hotlink is active, the options list of the browser display is extended with the option "Select". The consumer can also select a hotlink by pressing the joystick.

The <a> element is a short form of the <anchor> element and is bound to a go task without variables. In general, it is recommended to use the <a> element instead of anchors where possible, to allow more efficient parsing into tokens.

If a hotlink does not have a title or label, the Uniform Resource Locator (URL) address of the link is displayed in its full length and functions as a normal hotlink.

Example - Link text is underlined and image which is a link is given a border.

```
<anchor>Nokia Mobile Internet Toolkit<go
href="#card2"/>
</anchor>
<anchor>
<img alt="Forum Nokia" src="file://.../forum.gif"/>
<go href="http://forum.nokia.com"/>
</anchor>
```

Do Element

The <do> element provides a general mechanism for the consumer to act upon the current card. These elements are mapped behind the browser´s options list together with the preloaded options. If a <do> element contains a <prev> task, the right soft key is labeled *Back*. Use of a <prev> task is highly recommended for every card because it enables backward navigation. <do> elements have a label, i.e. the text of the item in the browser's options list. If the label is available, it is used as an option list item. If there is no label, a default text is displayed, on the basis of table below. However, it is highly recommended to use the "label" attribute.

Default Text in the Do Element Label

Type	Static text
Accept	OK
Prev	Back
Help	Help
Reset	Reset
Options	Options
Delete	Erase
Unknown	Unknown

The author of the WAP service is always responsible for the working navigation model inside the given service. If there is a need for back functionality, it should be explicitly defined with the <prev> type <do> element. The WAP browser does not have any implicit back functionality.

The <do> element can be expressed in two ways: in card-wide scope or in deck-wide scope in a template. Do elements will be stored in the browser's options list together with the preloaded options.

Example - Deck-wide backward navigation, prev

```
<template>
<do type="prev" label="Back">
<prev/>
</do>
</template>
```

Example - Card-wide backward navigation

```
<do type="prev" label="Back">
<prev/>
</do>
```

Example - Do element

```
<wml>
<template>
<do name="help-button" type="options" label="Ask Help">
<go href="http://.../help.wml" method="get"/>
</do>
<do type="options" label="Contact">
<go href="http://.../contact.wml" method="get"
sendreferer="false"/>
</do>
<do type="prev" optional="false">
<prev/>
</do>
</template>
<card id="card1" title="Homepage" ordered="true">
<p align="left">
Please, register
<br/>
Username:
<input name="username" type="text" title="Username"
emptyok="false"/>
Password:
<input name="password" type="password" title="Password"
emptyok="false"/>
<do type="accept" label="Enter">
<go href="#confirm" method="get" sendreferer="false"/>
</do>
</p>
</card>
<card id="confirm" title="Confirmation" ordered="true"
newcontext="false">
<p align="left">
$(username), thank you for registering.
</p>
</card>
</wml>
```

Input Processing

Input processing enables the consumer to input requested information to the service. There are two kinds of input elements: text fields determined by an input element and selection lists determined by a select element. <Option> elements are used to specify a single choice option in a <select> element. Option elements can be grouped by using an <optgroup> element.

Input Elements

The input element specifies a character entry object. Input elements may be formatted, meaning that the consumer has to make input that corresponds to the format applied to the input element by the service provider.

An input element is identified by a rectangular editing box, whose position on the display depends on whether or not it is empty, if there is a default value or if the consumer has entered characters in the box. If the input element is empty, a constant-size input box is displayed. The empty input box is moved to the next line if it does not fit on the current line.

The editing box will automatically wrap to the necessary number of lines as the consumer inputs characters, or there can be a default value given in the element's *value* attribute.

When the consumer has filled one line of the editing box and enters another character, the input box will take up two whole lines and the last entered character will be displayed on the second line. The editing box may be bigger than can be displayed on the screen at once. The consumer can input characters to an input element after highlighting and selecting it. The consumer selects an <input> element by pressing the joystick on the highlighted editing box or by selecting the options list item Open when the editing box is highlighted. When the consumer is entering text for an input field, the left soft key is Done. The consumer can confirm his/her entry by pressing Done or quit the editing box by pressing the right soft key, Cancel.

It is possible to start to key in characters when the editing box is highlighted. After selection of the input element, a cursor becomes visible in the editing box and the consumer can start (or continue) typing characters. This means that the consumer keys in characters directly on the card.

Example - Text input <input>

```
<template>
<do type="previous" label="Back" optional="false">
<prev/>
</do>
</template>
<card id="card1" title="Homepage">
<p align="left">
Please, register
<br/>
Username:
```

```
<input name="username" type="text" title="Username"/>
Password:
<input name="password" type="password"
title="Password"/>
<do type="accept" label="Enter" optional="false">
<go href="#confirm" method="get" sendreferer="false"/>
</do>
</p>
</card>
<card id="confirm" title="Confirmation"
ordered="true">
<p align="left">
$(username), thank you for registering.
</p>
</card>
</wml>
```

Select Element

Selection lists are elements that specify a list of options for the consumer to choose from. There are two kinds of selection lists supported: single-choice and multiple-choice lists. The consumer can select multiple items if the multiple attribute is set as true.

A selection list item on a card is a rectangular box that looks similar to an input element item. Inside the selection box, there is a static arrow pointing to the right. This arrow is positioned at the very end of the last line of the selection box. This arrow differentiates the selection box from the editing box.

The consumer can open a selection list by entering the Options menu and selecting the item Open or by pressing the joystick when a selection list is highlighted. These lists can have a title and a predefined value. The title is used as a label for the list of values from which the consumer can choose one or more values. The predefined value can be used as the value that is selected by default.

The selected value(s) will be displayed in the selection box. If more than one value is selected in a multiselect list, the values are separated with commas.

The size of the selection box fits the size of the selected value(s). The selection box will automatically wrap its content and extend itself to two or more lines if necessary. An exception to this is when the consumer has set content not to wrap, in which case the selected values will be displayed in the one-line box in truncated format. If no selections have been made, a constant-size selection box is displayed to the consumer.

The option element specifies a single choice option in a select element. Options can be grouped with an <optgroup> element, which specifies a group of choice items in a <select> element. An <optgroup> element is displayed with an icon in front of the title of the element. An <optgroup> element can be used in single-selection lists as well as multiple-selection lists. Only in multiple-selection lists is it possible to have optgroups that allow multiple selections.

Example - Select and optgroup

```
<wml>
<card id="phones" title="Information Request">
<p align="left">
Send me more information about:
<select name="models" title="Products" multiple="true">
      <optgroup title="Phones">
      <option value="Nokia 7650">
            7650
      </option>
      <option value="Nokia 9210">
            9210
      </option>
      <option value="Nokia 6310">
            6310
      </option>
      </optgroup>
      <optgroup title="Accessories">
      <option value="Battery">
            Battery
      </option>
      <option value="Desktop stand">
            Desktop stand
      </option>
      <option value="Charger">
            Charger
      </option>
      <option value="Headset">
            Headset
      </option>
      </optgroup>
</select>
Please, provide your
<br/>
Name:
<input name="name" type="text" title="Name" emptyok="false"/>
</p>
<do type="accept" label="Confirm" optional="false">
<go href="#confirm" method="get" sendreferer="false"/>
</do>
<do type="prev" optional="false">
<prev/>
</do>
</card>
</wml>
```

Optional WAP 1.2.1 Features

Push Service Indication

Push service indications are an ideal way to activate consumers. They can be used for notifying consumers of updated content or providing alerts in their areas of interest. The service provider can push a service indication content type to the device into the Service Inbox. Pushed notifications point to downloadable content. The consumer can also view the indicated content later by using the Service Inbox and the browser application. The service indication contains text with a URL address for a service. The link is opened with the WAP browser using the currently active settings.

The service provider can assign an Identity Code (ID) to an indication, which is used to separate different kinds of service indications. Several service indications may contain the same ID.

A service indication contains text that is displayed to the consumer and a URL for content, which may be dynamically generated for each push message from the application server.

Messages that have already been sent can be replaced and deleted. Messages with the same message ID can also be put in the correct order via timestamps. Service providers can also determine the priority level for the consumer.

The Service Inbox can be accessed through the options list under Services and under the options list belonging to the browser display. In the Service Inbox, the received service indications can be viewed, deleted, or downloaded. Note that receiving push services can be turned off using the Service Inbox settings.

Wireless Telephony Applications Interface

The WAP browser supports three WTAI functions: making a call while browsing, sending Dial Tone Multi-Frequency (DTMF) tones, and saving numbers and names to the phonebook. These functions, *MakeCall*, *SendDTMF*, and *AddPBEntry*, can be used anywhere in the WML code in the same way as when Uniform Resource Identifier (URI) or script references are used for non-WTAI references.

The *MakeCall* function is used for making a phone call directly from the WML browser application. A typical example of the usage of *MakeCall* is when the consumer selects an anchored link that initiates a phone call. When a *MakeCall* function is executed, the consumer is asked to confirm that the dial-up is to be made. If the phone number that is about to be called does not exist in the phonebook, a confirmation query with the phone number is displayed. If the number is in the phone book, a confirmation query is displayed with the name fetched from the phonebook. If the consumer agrees to make the phone call, another confirmation query is displayed, with the text "*Quit browsing?*" If the consumer answers in the affirmative to both queries, the browser session will be terminated and the browser application will be closed down. The call will then be initiated. When the call is terminated, the device is left in idle state. If the consumer rejects the latter confirmation query, the call will be initiated from within the browser display and the consumer can browse cached content during the call. No in-call options (e.g., Mute and Hold) are accessible from within the browser application. The options list belonging to the browser display remains unaffected by the fact that a call is active.

Normal call handling applies when a call is initiated from the browser part.

The consumer can send DTMF tones within the phone call by executing a WTAI function called *SendDTMF*. Just like *MakeCall*, a typical way of using *SendDTMF* is to assign the *SendDTMF* function to an anchored link. The consumer must have a voice call active. When the DTMF tone has been sent, the consumer returns to the card/deck where he/she initiated the sending. The voice call remains active.

The *AddPBEntry* function offers an easy way of storing a phone number and a corresponding name to the phonebook application from a WML card. The name and number are provided by the service provider. When the consumer activates an *AddPBEntry* function and the service provider has declared a name and a number, the phone displays a confirmation query with the text "*Save name.*" When the consumer answers the confirmation query in the affirmative, another confirmation query, with the text "*With number +44 123 123 4567*", is displayed and the number is stored in the phonebook application. When saving is done, the currently active card is displayed again. Note that the consumer does not have to be online or have any voice calls active in order to use the *AddPBEntry* function.

Cookies

Cookies enable the storage of data (e.g., consumer information) to make browsing easier for the consumer by reducing the amount of information the user must enter. For example, login can be configured dynamically so that it is displayed only if the application cannot identify the consumer.

Cookies in cached files are ignored.

Nokia 9210 Communicator WAP Browsing

This section provides information and practical examples for developers who want to develop Wireless Application Protocol (WAP) services for the Nokia 9210 Communicator. The Communicator is an advanced communications device with a feature-rich WAP services application. This chapter highlights the possibilities, limitations and requirements of service development and provides a good introduction to the Nokia style of user interface design.

WAP services screen size in the Nokia 9210 Communicator differs from that of common devices and should be taken into account when designing services that are fast and easy to use and that allow the consumer maximum enjoyment.

Nokia 9210 Communicator User Interface

Communicator interface, WAP browser display

This section gives a short overview of the Nokia 9210 Communicator user interface. The Nokia 9210 Communicator is a device with both a communicator interface and a phone interface. The WAP services application is implemented in the communicator interface together with Internet services. The phone interface part does not contain a WML browser.

Display

The Nokia 9210 Communicator display contains the following (from left to right): an indicator area, application area, and Command Button Area (CBA) with four soft buttons.

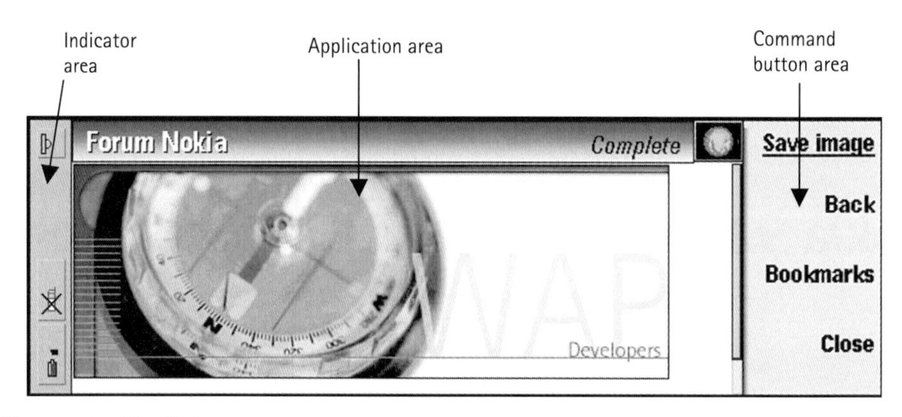

Different parts of the display

The indicator area has two widths: narrow (32pixels) and wide (92 pixels). The narrow indicator area is displayed with the WAP browser, is 32 pixels. A space is reserved for various other kinds of information (e.g., inbox and outbox, clock and profile).

The width of the command button area is dynamic and depends on the longest command text in the view. The width changes only if the whole view changes; that is, the width remains the same when only the button texts change in the given view. The command texts are right-justified. The minimum width of the command button area is 80 pixels and the maximum 130 pixels.

The width of the application area is 490 pixels. In full screen mode, the width is 625 pixels. Height is always 165 pixels.

The Nokia 9210 Communicator supports 4096 colors. *True color* is specified by 24 bits, 8 bits for each color component (red, green and blue). The Nokia 9210 Communicator uses the most significant four bits of each of the color components, resulting in a color depth of 12 bits. All other colors are either dithered or mapped to the closest color available, depending on the application.

Although WAP does not support color, the Nokia 9210 Communicator WAP browser supports image formats which use color.

WAP Browser Display

There are two views in the WAP browser: the Bookmarks view and the Card view. The Card view consists of a rendered card, options list and title bar. The Bookmarks view consists of a hierarchical list of saved bookmarks and a title bar. Both views have their own menus that provide access to the view's different functions.

WML cards are displayed in the Card view. Only one card of a WML deck is shown at a time. The vertical scroll bar is visible when the vertical length of the active card exceeds the screen size. The horizontal scroll bar is visible when a table or a non-breaking paragraph exceeds the screen width.

On the left side of the card is an options list, which lists all currently active <do> element labels. The narrow indicator area and CBA are visible except in full screen mode. The consumer can switch focus between the card and the options list with the tab key and the left and right arrow keys.

The browser remembers the focus of both the card and the options list. For example, if the focus on a card is on an anchor and the consumer focuses on the options list and then returns the focus to the card, the focus is automatically returned to that same anchor. The same applies to the options list. The browser also remembers whether the focus was on the card or on the options list if the consumer initiates a task that causes another card to be loaded. Once the new card has been displayed, the focus is set to the card area if it had focus before the action. If the consumer had focused on the options list before the action, it retains the focus after the card has been displayed. The focus on the options list is on the first item after the card has been fetched. The focus is not moved after refreshing, however.

The first button is a context-sensitive *action* button; that is, when a <select> or an <anchor> element has the focus, the first CBA will be *select*. If no appropriate element has been selected, the button label is dimmed. The first CBA button is always the default button in the Card view and may be launched by pressing <ENTER> key.

In the Bookmarks view, the consumer creates and manages WAP connections. The Bookmarks view is opened when the browser is launched without a Uniform Resource Locator (URL). The consumer can switch to the Bookmarks view from the Card view by selecting the third CBA button, Bookmark. The Bookmarks view consists of a hierarchical list of saved bookmarks and a title bar.

When the consumer focuses on a bookmark, its URL will be displayed in an info message. The URL address may be abbreviated; that is, part of the path name may be replaced with three dots, if necessary. The first and the last components of the URL are visible. If there is no space for both the first and the last component of the URL, the first is displayed and the URL is simply truncated. If the scheme of the URL is different than *http://*, it is displayed before the domain.

Only one bookmark item can be selected at a time. Zooming is not possible in the Bookmarks view. The first CBA button is always the default button in the Bookmarks view and may be launched by pressing <ENTER> key.

Content Elements for the Nokia 9210 Communicator

This section describes how to use Wireless Markup Language (WML) in designing services aimed at the Nokia 9210 Communicator. It gives an overview of the Graphical User Interface (GUI) elements and the WML capabilities supported by the browser. The document does not include all possible WML elements and attributes. The Nokia 9210 Communicator supports WML v1.1.

Browser Display

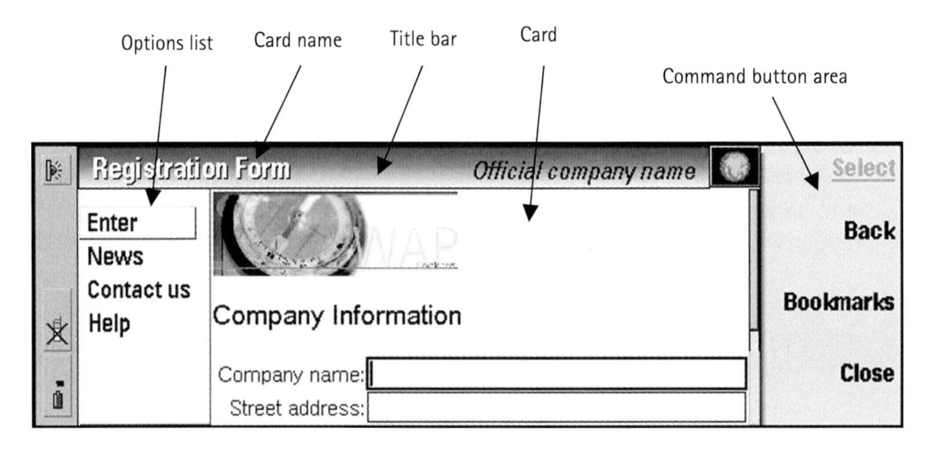

WML browser Card view with different display areas

The Nokia 9210 Communicator has a high-quality active matrix display. In the WAP browser, the application area is divided as follows: 30-pixel title bar on the top, a WML rendering area, and an options list on the left side. The width of the options list is 100 pixels, but it is displayed only if there are active <do> elements on the card. So, depending on whether the options list is present, the WML rendering area's width is between 390 and 490 pixels. In full-screen mode, the dimensions are 525 and 625 pixels. The height is always 165 pixels.

The vertical scroll bar is visible when the vertical length of the active card exceeds the screen size. The horizontal scroll bar is visible only when a table or a non-breaking paragraph exceeds the screen width.

On the left side of the card is the options list, which lists all currently active <do> element labels, along with any icons and hotkeys they may have. The narrow indicator area and CBA are visible except in full-screen mode. The consumer can switch focus between the card and the options list with the tab key.

The title bar is divided in two parts. On the left, the title of the card is shown. On the right, the title of the active element is shown. If both titles are too long to fit the title bar, the entire title of the active element is displayed and the title of the card is truncated or both are truncated. If there is no card name, the URL is displayed instead.

Formatting Elements

The table below contains all text layout formatting elements.

Text Layout Formats

Element	Formatting
em	Italicized font, red color
Strong	Bold, italicized font, green color
b	Bold font
I	Italicized font
U	Underlined font
Big	Font size is set to big
Small	Font size is set to small
P	A paragraph break is inserted in the text
Br	A line break is inserted in the text

The browser supports all WML specification text formatting elements. <Emphasis> and <strong> elements are shown in color. The figure below demonstrates the information in graphical form.

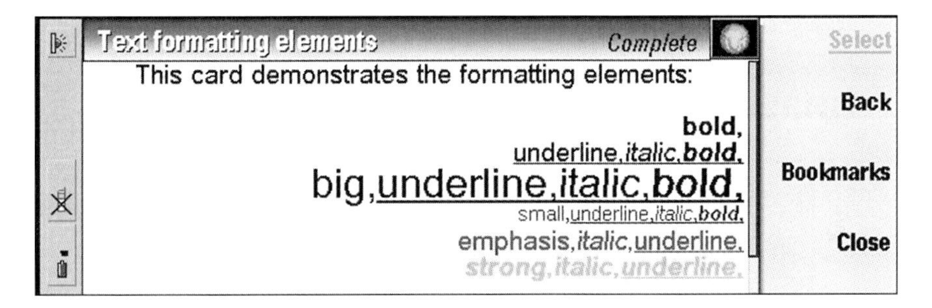

Card demonstrating text formatting elements

The paragraph element, <p>, determines text grouping. A new paragraph always starts on a new line. Text inside a paragraph can be aligned to the left, center or right. Left alignment is used by default. Alignment is determined in paragraph attributes (e.g., <p align="right">).

New lines in text can be defined by the line break element <br>. The <br> element can be used within other elements as long as it belongs to a paragraph.

The <fieldset> element can be used for grouping elements. It implies a paragraph break between the elements, and the title of the element is used as the active element's title if it has no title of its own. Note that fieldset titles are not supported for text; that is, text in a card cannot be given a title by using the <fieldset> element.

Tables

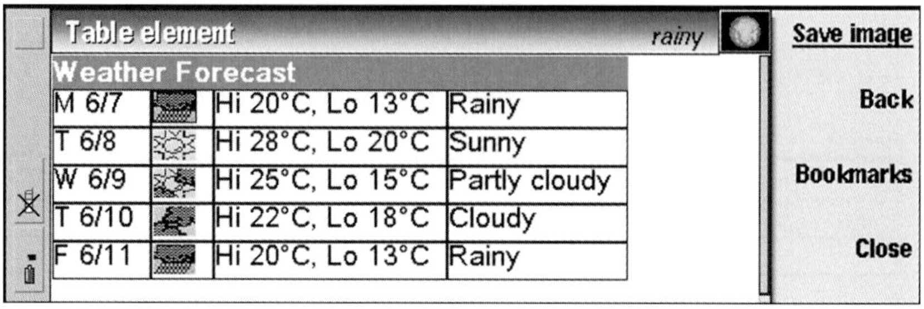

Table element
rainy
Save image
Back
Bookmarks
Close
Weather Forecast
M 6/7
Hi 20°C, Lo 13°C
Rainy
T 6/8
Hi 28°C, Lo 20°C
Sunny
W 6/9
Hi 25°C, Lo 15°C
Partly cloudy
T 6/10
Hi 22°C, Lo 18°C
Cloudy
F 6/11
Hi 20°C, Lo 13°C
Rainy

A sample table

A table element, <table>, and its content elements <tr> and <td> are used to create columns and rows of text and images in a card, surrounded by a gray border. Table elements do not specify column or intercolumn widths; the width of the column is the same as the width of the widest cell in the column. If there is a "title" attribute in the table element, it will be rendered as the first row of the table, in boldface and in a white color on a blue background. There can be multiple tables in one card. A line break is inserted before and after each table. The table may also contain images and links, which are given the focus in order from left to right and from top to bottom. The maximum number of columns in a table is 30. The contents of any columns beyond column 30 are all rendered in the last column of the table.

Images, Links and Timers

Image element
Nokia 6210 - Streched!
Save image
Back
Bookmarks
Close
Format:GIF
JPEG
Stretched JPEG:

Different types of images

In addition to Wireless BitMap (WBMP) image format, the Nokia 9210 Communicator supports all the most commonly known image formats.

The image element, <img>, is used for displaying an image in a card. Image sizes may be 60 kB or less. Although there are no absolute limits to an image's physical measurements. However, for taller images, the consumer must scroll down, and images wider than the browser area are scaled down to fit the screen. Images can also be used inside a table and as links.

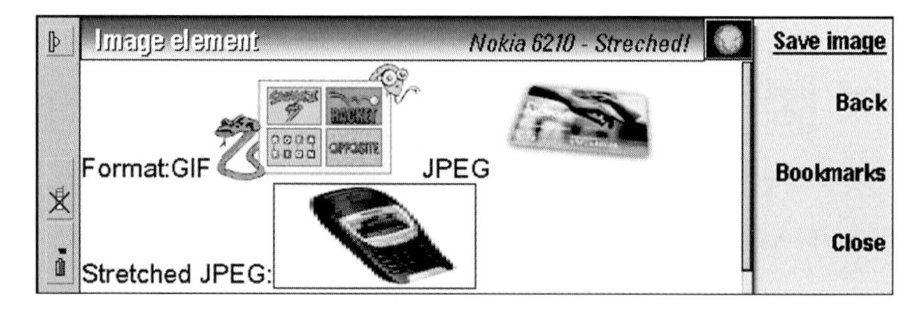

The <img> element should have width and height attributes defined in pixels. If one or both of the width and height attributes have been defined in pixels, they are used as the size of the image and the placeholder. A fetched image is scaled to fit the specified size.

Width and height attribute values specified in percentages are ignored. An image is always forced into the horizontal space available. That is, if the image is wider than the screen, it will be scaled to fit the horizontal space available.

If the horizontal margin or vertical margin has been defined for the <img> element, the specified number of pixels is left as a margin between the surrounding text flow and the image. Again, margins specified in percentages are ignored.

When the consumer focuses on an image and it has not been fetched and is not inside an anchor element, the first CBA button will change to *Load Image*. If the consumer selects this, the image will be fetched and displayed as it arrives from the network. If the image is inside an anchor or <A> element, the anchor's UI behavior will override the image's behavior.

If the consumer focuses on a completely loaded image, or if the focus is on an image when fetching is completed, the first CBA button will change to *Save Image*. If the consumer presses it, the standard *Save As* dialog box opens and the consumer can save the image in its original format.

Anchors

Anchor elements, <a>, specify the head of links to another card or deck. A link allows easy navigation through an application. An anchor may consist of text, an image, or a combination of text and an image. The <a> element is a short form of the <anchor> element. In general it is recommended to use the <a> element instead of anchor elements where possible. An unselected anchor is rendered as underlined, while the color of a selected anchor is inverted.

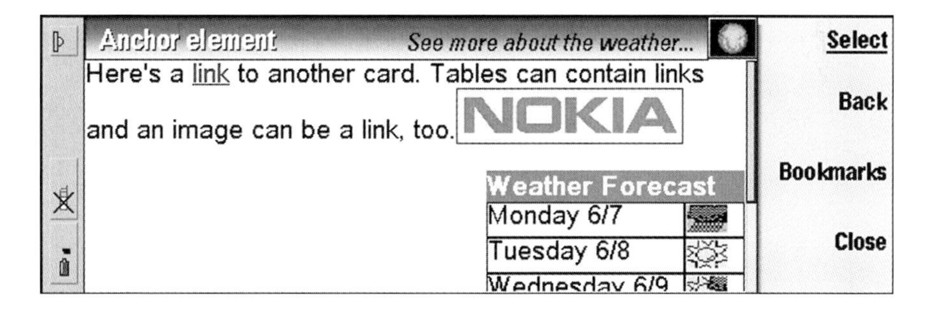

Text and image links. An image within a table is selected.

Timers

The timer element, <timer>, defines a card timer, which processes inactivity or idle time. Timer starts the count immediately after the card is loaded. This element can be used only once in card, and its unit is 1/10 s.

Dynamic Buttons

The <do> element, <do>, binds a task to a user action, which can be executed in an options list on the left side of the screen. The options list contains all currently accessible <do> elements. The text representing each <do> element is the <do> element's *label* attribute value or, if it has not been defined, the UI string corresponding to the element's "type" attribute value. The labels are updated with current values whenever a refresh task is executed but the focus in a list is not changed.

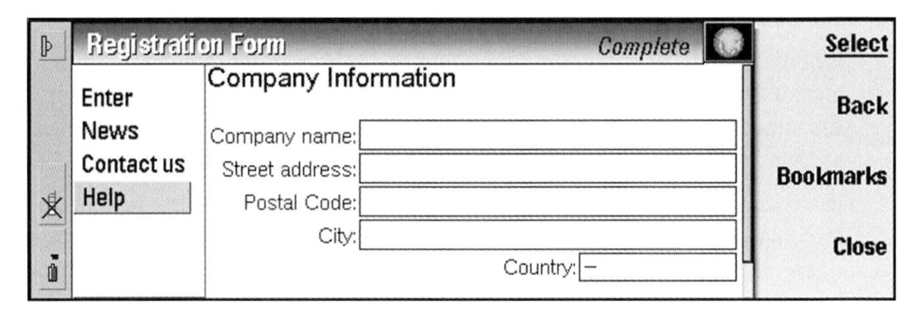

<do> elements in an options list. The options list has the focus.

Each WML deck can have a template element. The template contains <do> elements that are to be displayed on each card of the deck. A card's <do> elements can either override or hide the template's <do> elements. Hidden <do> elements will not be shown.

The order of the card's <do> elements in the options list is the same as that in which they are defined in the card, unless they override the template's <do> elements. The template's <do> elements are last on the options list, that is, after all the card's <do> elements. If a <do> element of a card overrides the <do> element on a template, the card's <do> element replaces the template's <do> element in the list.

All optional <do> elements are displayed, with the exception of <do> elements of the *prev* type.

Whenever a new card is shown, a new history list item is created. When the "prev" task is activated on a WML card, the target URL is the previous history list item and the current card is not retained in the history list.

In contrast to other types of <do> elements, <do> elements of the type "prev" have special behavior. If there is only one *prev* type <do> element active, it is not shown on the options list. Instead, it is bound to the second CBA button and is labeled as *Back*. The second CBA is dimmed if there is none, or more than one *prev* type do element active, and <do> elements are displayed on the options list like all other <do> elements.

The author of the WAP service is always responsible for the working navigation model within the service. If there is a need for back functionality, it should be explicitly defined with the *prev* type <do> element. The WAP browser does not have any implicit back functionality.

WML Input Processing

Input Elements

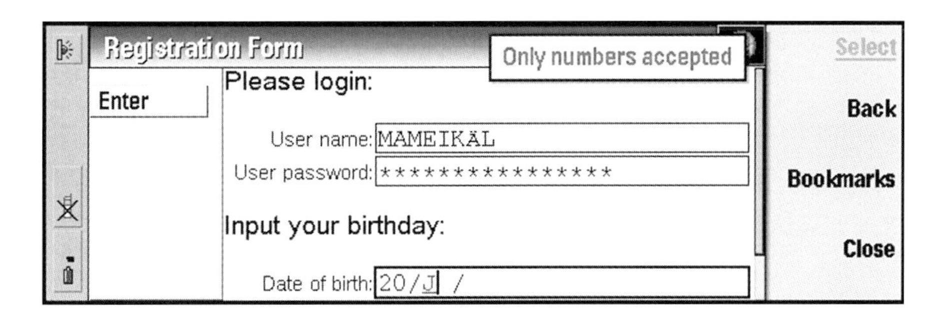

Input element - focus is in the input box with numeric format

An <input> element specifies a text entry object for data input. It is shown as an input box in a card. The text entered in the <input> element can be determined by the *format* attribute. The format string specifies that a particular character must be, for example, a number, an uppercase character, or a lowercase character.

The consumer can enter any characters in the input field, but characters that do not match the specified format are in red and are underlined. In addition, every time the consumer enters a different type of input than the browser was expecting, an appropriate message in an *Incorrect input* dialog box will be displayed. All characters that do match the specified format are in black.

The author can specify a maximum length for the entry, with either the format or the maxlength attribute. If the maximum length is reached, the <input> element will not insert any characters in the field but will cause a beep and the display of an info message.

The author can specify with the *emptyok* attribute that the entry must match the format mask. If there are input elements that do have that requirement but the entry for those elements does not match the mask and a task is initiated, the *Missing Input* dialog box will appear. Once the consumer has closed the dialog box, the focus will move to the first of those input elements on the card. Note that the consumer can exit the card only if all input elements have a valid value or if they are allowed to be empty.

Selection Lists

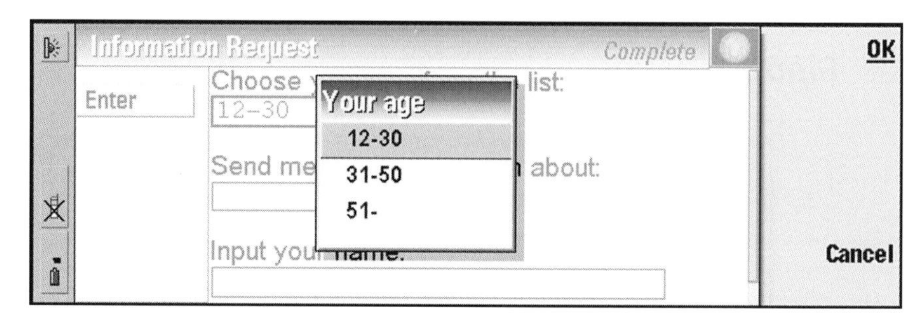

Simple single-selection list

Selection lists specify a list of options for the consumer to choose from. The selection list can be either a single-selection or multiple-selection element. Each option is specified by an <option> element. Options can be organized into groups by using the <optgroup> element.

A selection list is opened by focusing on the input box and pressing the first CBA button for Change. The selection list appears. A single-selection list has the title from the *title* attribute; if it has not been defined, the title displays the text *Selection* by default. A multiple-selection list has two windows; the left one is for unselected items and the right one contains the selected items. The title of the pane for non-selected items is the <select> element's title or, if one has not been defined, the default text displayed is *Not selected.* The title of the pane for selected items is *selected.* The consumer can switch focus between the two dialog boxes with the tab key.

If the options have been grouped with an< optgroup> element, the optgroup title will be shown as a bold item in the selection list. All options under the <optgroup> element are intended and shown under the optgroup item. Note that the Nokia 9210 Communicator only supports one level of optgroups. Optgroup on a deeper level is ignored and its options are handled as if they were under the first-level optgroup.

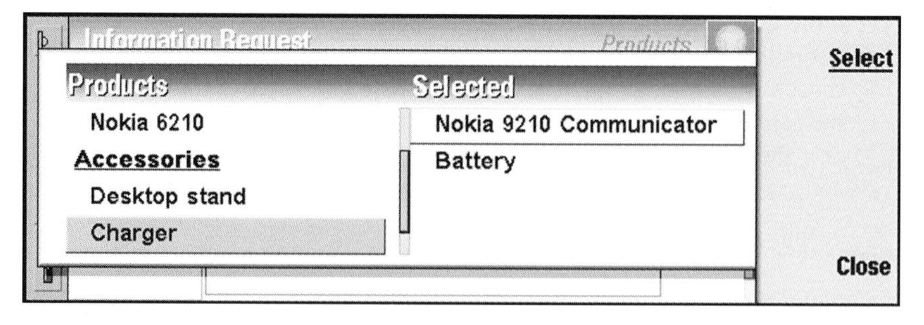

Multiple-selection list

Titles and Labels

A title bar is divided into two parts; on the left is the card title, and on the right is space for element titles, which are shown only when the element has the focus. The card title is displayed continuously. If there is no card title, the actual URL of the card is displayed instead. Below is a list of element titles that use the right side of the title bar.

- Link, attribute "title"
- Image, attribute "alt"
- Input, attribute "title"
- Select, attribute "title"

In addition, there are elements that have a title that is not shown on the main title bar. These are tables whose *title* attribute value is shown on its own title bar. A <select> element's *title* attribute value is shown on the main title bar when the input box has the focus. After the selection list is opened, the same title is shown on the select list's own title bar. The optgroup *title* attribute's value is shown as a bold item in the selection list.

The only element with a *label* attribute is the <do> element. Cards' currently accessible <do> elements are listed in the options list on the left side of the application area, where their *label* attribute values are shown. An exception to this is the *prev* type <do> element.

Nokia 9210 Communicator Web Browsing

This section is a style guide for creating Web browsing services for the Nokia 9210 Communicator device. The Nokia 9210 Communicator is an advanced communications device with a feature-rich Web browser. However, the screen size and the wireless communication link should be taken into account in order to design services that are both fast and easy to use as well as offering maximum enjoyability for consumers.

Web Browser Features

The Nokia 9210 Communicator Web Browser supports:

- HyperText Transfer Protocol version 1.1 (HTTP/1.1).
- HyperText Markup Language version 3.2 (HTML 3.2), except some features listed below.
- HTML frames, as specified in HTML 4.0 document, except for the <iframe> element and target frames.
- HTTP over Secure Sockets Layer protocol version 3 (SSLv3), also known as the https: URL scheme.
- Transport Layer Security protocol version 1 (TLSv1) is also supported by the e-mail client.
- Support for Joint Photographic Experts Group (JPEG) and Graphics Interchange Format (GIF) images, including progressive JPEG and interlaced GIF, plus several other image formats (e.g., Portable Network Graphics (PNG), Wireless Bitmap (WBMP), Windows Bitmap (BMP), the Symbian OS native MBM bitmap format, and Tagged Image File Format (TIFF/F)).
- Java™ applets are not supported.
- JavaScript™ is not supported.
- Plug-in interface for third-party plug-ins written for the Symbian OS.
- Native support for Uniform Resource Locators (URL), mailto:, sms: and fax:. Possibility of adding third-party URL handlers with add-on software.
- Possibility to launch other programs based on the Multi-purpose Internet Mail Extensions (MIME) type of incoming data and a way to store downloaded data in a local file.

Features Not Supported:

- <isindex> element is not supported. It is used to create very simple search pages. HTML forms offer better usability and more possibilities for tailoring a query page for consumer's needs.
- Background images are not supported. Background images, especially when shown on a small screen, easily distract the consumer and make the page harder to read. However, background colors are supported.

General Web Usability Issues

Validate the HTML

There are several HTML validators available that validate documents against the HTML Document Type Definition. It is recommended that authors validate their Web pages because valid HTML is always less prone to incompatibilities and unintended behavior than pages which contain non-compliant HTML, regardless of the browser used.

Web Site Organization

The consumer is accessing the Web site via a Global System for Mobile Communications (GSM) data call and pays per second. It is not recommended to use a "doormat" or an "intro" page as the front page, as such pages have no functionality other than perhaps to greet the visitor and to display a logo. It is better to go to the service directly.

Automatically Detect the Browser

Consumers do not generally want to select which browser they are using. And they certainly do not want to be told that their browser is not supported and that they should upgrade. If the designer is using a modern Web site hosting environment, it is usually possible to detect the browser and supply correct content transparently, without direct consumer input. This depends on the capabilities of the Web hosting environment.

The Nokia 9210 Communicator Web browser identifies itself as *EPOC32-WTL/2.2 Crystal/6.0 STNC-WTL/6.0(build)* in the HTTP user-agent header, where *build* is a number. This string will be available in an environment variable in most Web publishing environments. The important parts are *EPOC32*, which identifies the operating system as the Symbian OS, and *Crystal*, which indicates that the browser is operating on a half-VGA screen. The *STNC-WTL* indicates the features and requirements for the browser below the user interface level. Depending on the purpose for which this information will be used, one should try to seek the correct substring of this header.

Optimize for Size

The size of the content is critical. If the documents are large (e.g., listings, large tables), consider splitting them into multiple parts for faster download. Large comment sections within HTML should be avoided. In particular, the use of scripting languages within a page may cause the page to be littered with very long comment blocks, which may slow down the download.

As for the total download time, some studies place an upper limit for acceptable delay at 10 to 15 seconds, including all images, on a PC-based browser. Even if the consumers are accustomed to the somewhat slower transmission speeds of GSM data, this could still be used as a rough guideline when judging the usability of a Web page.

The following table shows the transmission speeds that can be expected over HTTP in optimal conditions with good network coverage. The values given include the HTTP request and should be taken as approximations; they depend on the GSM network, Internet service provider's configuration and equipment, other Internet Protocol traffic, server and client load, compression, encryption and other factors. Note that the high-speed transfer modes are generally more expensive than normal GSM data and might, for example, be used only when downloading large amounts of data in a continuous stream.

	10 kB HTML document	10 kB JPEG image	100 kB JPEG image
Normal GSM data, 9 600 bps, analog modem pool	12 seconds	14 seconds	98 seconds
Two high-speed slots, 14 400 bps each, ISDN connection	6 seconds	8 seconds	39 seconds
Three high-speed slots, 14 400 bps each, ISDN connection	5 seconds	7 seconds	27 seconds

Use Frames Sparingly

As the screen is relatively small, frames quickly eat up screen area. Frames also make it more difficult for the consumer to navigate on or bookmark the page. The consumer may also opt not to view frames the way they are usually viewed. The Nokia 9210 Communicator supports three different frame styles. The Web site designer cannot know how the frames are shown, so it is unwise to use them for page layout. Avoid frames if possible, and note that the IFRAME element and target frames are not supported.

However, if the designer does choose to use frames, they should be given descriptive names and not be used solely for page layout purposes. If possible, provide a way to access the page without frames. If linking to another page, avoid the situation where a new set of frames is loaded inside a frame, as then the usability quickly deteriorates on a small display.

When one uses frames, a black background color is not recommended, as it is easier for the consumer to resize frames when using a light-colored background.

Also, favor frames that split the screen horizontally instead of frames that divide it vertically. This is because the horizontal resolution of the screen is much greater than the vertical resolution.

Choose Descriptive Page Titles and Document Names

Page titles have much more of a visual impact on the Nokia 9210 Communicator than they usually have on a PC-based browser. It is very useful to give a descriptive name to the page. It might be a good idea to start the title with the service's name and keep the total length of the title short.

It also pays to use meaningful URLs since the consumer sees the URL of the currently selected link on the screen and can use it as an aid to navigation, especially when images have not been loaded.

It is very common for a consumer of a PDA-type device to bookmark a page in order to return directly to it later. Web hosting systems that generate ephemeral URLs effectively foil this usage scenario. Best results are obtained if all subpages on the site can be bookmarked and in cases where the page is created dynamically from form data, an invalid URL will redirect the consumer to a sensible page.

The URL of the currently selected link flashes on the screen

Pay Attention to the First Screenful

The Nokia 9210 Communicator's screen size depends on user settings as follows:

	Horizontal viewable area	Vertical viewable area
Default	478 pixels	170 pixels
No title bar	478 pixels	195 pixels
Full screen mode	635 pixels	170 pixels
Full screen mode and no title bar	635 pixels	195 pixels
Full screen mode, no title bar and scroll bars disabled	640 pixels	200 pixels

Some of the available area is also taken up by rendering margins.

The number of text lines depends on a user-selectable zoom factor. The user can select a font size between 8 and 12 points.

	Zoom factor 1	Zoom factor 2 (default)	Zoom factor 3
Font size 10 (default)	12 lines of normal text	10 lines of normal text	7 lines of normal text

Because the default rendering area in the Nokia 9210 Communicator is 478 x 170 pixels, the first (topmost) screenful of any page is the most important one. All of the frequently used navigational links, search fields, login screens and bulk of the information should reside there if at all possible. The consumer is then able to navigate forward before the rest of the page has been loaded, and the consumer does not have to scroll down the page.

When tables or frames are used, the use of absolute values is not recommended. Sizes should be specified as percentages of the total width or height. More specifically, do not expect that the consumer have a 640-pixel horizontal resolution.

Avoid wasting the top of the page on banner advertisements or non-informative graphics. It is better to place the advertisements at the right edge than on the top. When tables are used, the left edge should be reserved for the most important links, as the consumer will be able to navigate there quickly with the tabulator key.

Avoid Large Tables

Rendering an HTML table requires the whole table to be downloaded before it can be viewed onscreen, as the browser needs to know the dimensions of the table. If the whole page is inside a table, all of the HTML code has to be downloaded before the page can be viewed. On a large page, this may cause a considerable pause before the consumer can read the page. If possible, split the page into several smaller tables.

Take Tabbing Order into Consideration

The consumer usually "tabs" through the page using the tab and shift+tab keys. This will highlight each image and link, one at a time, in the order that they appear in the HTML source.

Try to group all of the most important links as the first ones in the HTML source, so that the consumer does not have to "tab" through the whole page.

The same design principle applies to frames. If it is really necessary to use frames, always try to make the first frame the one that the consumer is most likely to access first. Otherwise the consumer needs to change the active frame before being able to select links.

Support the Use of a Pointer

The Nokia 9210 Communicator has a pointer, which looks like a mouse pointer but which can be moved with the cursor keys. It is a very good practice to test all of the clickable content on the page to make sure that the items are large enough to facilitate easy navigation with the pointer. As a rule of thumb, items less than ten pixels in width or height are difficult to select using the pointer.

Interactive and Dynamic Content

Applets and content that depend on a pointing device can be used on the Nokia 9210 Communicator, as the consumer can invoke a pointer that can be moved around with cursor keys.

The Nokia 9210 Communicator does not support JavaScript™. Pages using JavaScript should not rely on it and should work without it.

As an example, when designing input forms, always provide a submit button and when using JavaScript for automatic browser detection, specify a timeout that will force a redirection to a non-JavaScript page if it is not supported.

The Nokia 9210 Communicator Web browser has a plug-in interface that third parties can use to implement their plug-ins. If a plug-in is required for the Web content, please contact the vendor of the plug-in and request that it be ported to the Symbian OS.

Note that plug-ins that are compiled for other operating systems (e.g., such as Linux®, MacOS or Microsoft Windows), do not run under the Symbian OS.

When using an automatic page refresh after a certain period, it is necessary to change the file name of an inline image if it is to be reloaded from the server instead of the cache (e.g., Web cams). This is due to internal cache organization.

Pictures, Fonts and Color

The downloading of images takes time, and many consumers may switch the loading of images off for more speed. Try to optimize the size of images. Use JPEG format with a high compression ratio for photographic images and PNG or GIF for images that require lossless compression, or use uniform fills or fewer colors. If the site contains large pictures, consider using thumbnails for the image index. The use of interlaced or progressive images is encouraged, as the consumer can get an overview of the image more quickly this way.

Always give a text alternative for images that convey information. Always use a null alternative text (ALT="") for images which do not convey information or are used for page layout or decorative purposes only.

The use of a number of small, transparent images is discouraged because each image on the page causes a new HTTP request. If running over a 9,600 bps data call, this may slow down page loading.

Always specify the correct image width and height in <img> elements. This speeds up the layout process as the layout engine can reserve the right amount of space on the screen even before downloading the image. It avoids unnecessary screen refreshes.

Imagemaps are not the best alternative when navigating with a keyboard. Split images with appropriate "alt" attributes are preferable. If one has to use imagemaps, it is preferable to use client-side imagemaps with descriptive names for the clickable areas, via the "alt" attribute. Also, provide textual links for all of the imagemap links in case the consumer does not wish to download the image.

The Nokia 9210 Communicator supports 4096 colors. Full "true color" is specified by 24 bits, eight bits for each color component (red, green and blue). The Nokia 9210 Communicator uses the most significant four bits of each of the color components, resulting in a color depth of 12 bits. All other colors will be either dithered or mapped to the closest color available, depending on the application.

When creating graphics with uniform fills, use only colors that will not be dithered. Some image processing tools may be able to reduce the size of images if the number of colors is restricted to the exact 4096 colors supported by the Nokia 9210 Communicator.

Do not use colors which are too close to each other. This may result in the colors being mapped to the exact same color.

If using transparent images, one should be sure to set the background color in the HTML document accordingly. If the transparency relies upon a dark background image, a dark background color should also be specified.

For added accessibility, one might wish to review the images in grayscale and take the requirements of color blind users into account.

Server Configuration

Character Sets

The Web server should always supply the correct character set information in the HTTP response headers. This is important for any future browsers that may contain more internationalized features.

The Nokia 9210 Communicator encodes all form submissions as per the HTML 4.01 specification, using a language-specific character set. For Western European and Nordic language versions, the ISO 8859-1 character set is used. Elsewhere, the character set may change according to the characters available in that specific language version.

If the language version uses characters that are not available in the ISO 8859 standard series, the device may use the Unicode character set with UTF-8 encoding. The server should not just assume that all incoming forms are in ISO 8859-1. Supporting Unicode server-side has the additional benefit of adding another layer of international compatibility to the Web site.

MIME Types

Some Web servers tend to use the generic MIME type for most downloaded files that are not HTML or text. The Nokia 9210 Communicator, however, uses and stores the MIME type information, so the Web server should always be configured to return the correct MIME type for a given file. If, however, the generic MIME type is used, the Nokia 9210 Communicator tries to guess the file format from the filename suffix and the contents.

The Nokia 9210 Communicator supports a number of MIME types, either in its Web browser or through a separate application. For some of the MIME types, there may be more than one application that can view the file, and these applications may use different MIME types as some of the MIME types are not standard. To maximize interoperability, when configuring the server, use the first MIME type listed for any given file type. It also helps to use one of the listed suffixes for the filename.

Of course, one should take into account the size of the file. In particular, files containing graphics may be extremely large, and downloading them over a wireless connection could prove to be very uncomfortable.

In most cases, the files must be saved on the Nokia 9210 Communicator before they can be viewed. Some files open directly in the Web browser (e.g., HTML files, text files and most picture formats). For most other files, the user needs to install a viewer separately.

Supported MIME Types

MIME type	Description	Filename extensions
application/msexcel application/vnd.ms-excel application/x-excel application/xlc application/x-msexcel	Microsoft Excel spreadsheet	.xls, .xlc
application/msword application/vnd.msword application/vnd.ms-word	Microsoft Word document	.doc, .wri
application/rtf	Rich text format	.rtf
application/vnd.lotus-1-2-3 application/x-lotus123	Lotus 1-2-3	.wq1, .wku, .wk1, .wk3, .wk4, .wk5, .wk6, .123
application/vnd.ms-project	Microsoft Project file	.mpp
application/vnd.nokia.ringing-tone	Nokia ringing tone	.rng
application/vnd.symbian.install	Symbian installation file	.sis
application/vnd.visio	Visio drawing	.vsd
application/wordperfect5 application/wordperfect5.1 application/x-wordperfect6	WordPerfect document	.wpd
application/x-gzipapplication/gzip	UNIX GNU Zip (gzip)	.tgz
application/x-mspowerpoint application/mspowerpoint application/pot application/pps application/ppt application/vnd.ms-powerpoint	Microsoft PowerPoint slide show	.ppt, .pot, .pps
application/x-tar	UNIX Compress/tar	.tar, .taz
application/zip	PkZip archive	.zip, .exe
audio/basic	Sun audio file	.au
audio/x-sibo-wve	Symbian audio file	.wve
audio/x-wav	WAV audio file	.wav
image/cgm	Computer graphics metafile	.cgm
image/gif	GIF image file	.gif
image/jpeg	JPEG JFIF image file	.jpeg, .jpg, .jif
image/png	Portable Network Graphics file	.png

MIME type	Description	Filename extensions
image/tiff	TIFF/F (Fax) image file	.tif
image/tiff	TIFF image file	.tif
image/vnd.wap.wbmp	WAP monochrome bitmap	.wbmp
image/wmfimage/x-win-metafileimage/x-wmf	Windows metafile	.wmf
image/x-amidraw	Lotus AMI Draw file	.sdw
image/x-bmpimage/bmpimage/x-MS-bmpimage/x-win-bitmap	Windows bitmap	.bmp, .rle, .ico, .cur
image/x-cgm	Computer graphics metafile	.cgm
image/x-epoc-mbm	Symbian multi bitmap file	.mbm
image/x-pc-paintbrush	Paintbrush image file	.pcx, .dcx
image/x-png	Portable Network Graphics file	.png
image/x-presentations	Corel/Novell Presentations	.shw
image/x-wordperfect-graphics	WordPerfect document	.wpg
None specified	Nokia OTA image file	.ota
None specified	Symbian Sheet document	None specified
None specified	Symbian Word document	None specified
text/html	HTML hypertext file	.html, .htm, .shtml, .shtm
text/plain	Text file	.txt
text/rtf	Rich text format	.rtf
text/vnd.symbian.ebookmark	Symbian Web bookmark file	.ebm
text/x-vcalendar	Vcalendar	.vcs
text/x-vcard	Vcard	.vcf

Secure Web Connections

The Nokia 9210 Communicator's Web browser supports the SSLv3 protocol. To guarantee interoperability, the Nokia 9210 Communicator uses SSL for Web connections for the time being.

When the connection is secure, the user sees a lock icon in the title bar and can see the "encrypted" status in the menu.

The lock icon is visible for pages retrieved over SSL (https://)

In order to authenticate the server to the Web browser, one needs a certificate from a Certification Authority (CA). Nokia does not endorse any specific CA. The authenticity of the server's certificate is checked against a so-called root certificate, which is installed in the certificate management application. Root certificates from the most popular commercial CAs are factory-installed in the Nokia 9210 Communicator. Users can install new root certificates themselves if required.

It is important to make sure that the server's name is present in the *common name* element of the certificate. Otherwise, the Web browser will display a warning message about the name not matching the Web site's name.

When installing a new root certificate on the Nokia 9210 Communicator, it must be in raw DER encoded form (not base64 encoded). The certificate has to be downloaded to the device and opened from the certificate manager tool. After that, the consumer needs to set the trust settings appropriately.

Client certificates are not supported. If a server requires client authentication using certificates, a null certificate is automatically sent.

Nokia Mobile Internet Toolkit

Nokia Mobile Internet Toolkit is a suite of related tools that facilitate the development of applications for the mobile browsing. These include a set of editors for creating content of various content types that are supported in mobile browsers, as well as the debugging, logging and testing facilities required for true application development.

In addition, the Toolkit is a Mobile browser. Developers and content designers can use the Toolkit to view mobile browsing content using a device simulator, just as if a real mobile device were being used. For example, a developer can access Mobile browsing sites (e.g., CNN or MapQuest), in the same way as could be done from a mobile device outside or in a car.

The Toolkit provides two device simulators in its basic installation but also provides for the use of additional simulators as well. A device simulator is a graphical interface that simulates the display screen, keys and controls of a mobile device. Capabilities vary among the various simulators; these differences are outlined in subsequent sections.

Content Creation, Editing and Testing Facilities

The mobile browser is designed to support existing and newly emerging content types. Some of the earliest content types defined by the WAP Forum were Wireless Markup Language (WML), WMLScript and Wireless BitMap (WBMP); and later the push message and multipart message content types. Most recently, there has been movement toward the adoption of content types more closely aligned with those used for the Web (e.g., Extensible HyperText Markup Language (XHTML) Basic and Cascading Style Sheets (CSS)).

The Toolkit provides editors for convenience in developing mobile browsing applications. Several editors are provided, most designed for authoring content consisting of a particular Multipurpose Internet Mail Extensions (MIME) content type.

Most editors enable the immediate processing of content as it is developed. For example, within the WMLScript editor, the content designer can compile a file, view compilation messages, or call the function directly. In addition, most editors enable the viewing of content on a simulator simply by pressing a button. The following table summarizes the capabilities of these editors.

Editor	Description
WML Deck	Used for creating WML content. Supports any of the WML 1.1, 1.2, and 1.3 Document Type Definitions.
WML Script	Used for creating WML Script content. WML Script is a derivative of ECMA Script and is used to add programmatic features to WML deck (e.g., calculations).
WBMP Image	Used for creating Wireless BitMap (WBMP) content. Similar to most image editors, the WBMP editor enables the creation and editing of WBMP images, as well as conversion of existing images from Graphics Interchange Format (GIF) and Joint Photographic Experts Group (JPEG) formats to WBMP format.
Multipart Content	Used for creating Multipart content. A multipart content message is often used as a kind of Push message consisting of more than one part, each of which is separately processed by the user agent. The editor enables the incorporation and ordering of already existing parts into a single Multipart message.

Editor	Description
Push Content	Used for creating a Push message with any of the content types SI, SL, or CO. The Push editor facilitates the creation of a Push message, while the Toolkit's Push Message Inbox is used to receive and process the resultant message.
XHTML File	Used for creating XHTML Basic content. Supports the XHTML Basic DTD.
CSS File	Used for creating and editing CSS. The CSS contains formatting style definitions that will be applied to the elements specified in an XHTML Basic file.

The Toolkit uses encoders to encode text-based content for transmission over the air, as well as decoders to convert encoded data to text for display on the device simulator.

The content is encoded if necessary and usually immediately displayed upon use of the Show button in most editors. However, with push and multipart messages, the developer can choose whether they are immediately displayed or instead placed in the Push Inbox where their content can be verified prior to its processing by the user-agent. The developer can also save push and multipart messages in binary format from within the editor itself.

When the developer chooses Show or otherwise specifies encoding of newly edited content, compilation status messages are displayed at the bottom of the editing window. If there are errors due to invalid coding, the line numbers of the offending code are displayed so it is easy to find the errors immediately and correct them.

All Toolkit tab views provide information; however, the following tab views are particularly useful for debugging: the Browser Session/Cache view and the Current view with source, browser context variables and history. In addition, the Toolkit Message Log is a separate window within which the developer can view Toolkit messages and set the desired level of detail to be viewed.

The Toolkit provides sample applications in the /samples directory. The /Wap subdirectory contains WML examples, and the /Xhtml subdirectory contains XHTML and CSS examples. The developer can view these on emulator as well as copy code for use in applications.

Browsing Facilities

In addition to being an application development environment, the Toolkit is a mobile browser. It can be used to browse Mobile Internet content, add and edit bookmark locations, load locations, stop loading, go back and so on, just as a user can do with an Internet browser (e.g., Netscape Navigator).

Facility	Description
Compile Errors	Real-time viewing of compilation errors is available at the bottom of the editing window.
Current Document View	In this view, the developer can view the current content of any content type as source text. The developer can also view WAP-based content types (but not XHTML content) as bytecode or as an element tree by choosing from the "View type" drop-down list box.
History In the Current Document view	In the History area, the developer can set the context of the content currently being executed, in effect resetting the state of the stack, for example, by returning to a previous card in the same deck. The developer can also remove previous contexts - in effect, starting over.

Facility	Description
Variables In the Current Document view	The developer can view the values of current variables in the browser context, change current values and add new variables.
Session View	It is possible to view all the data specified in an HyperText Transfer Protocol (HTTP) request made through the Toolkit, as well as all data received as a response to this request. The data is presented in a folder structure which allows revealing or hiding details as appropriate. The developer can also view content stored in the local cache.
Toolkit Log	Shows user-determined levels of processing information (e.g., parsing results, execution flow and errors).

Content to be read is displayed on the current device simulator. Browsing controls are all accessible from the main Toolkit window.

Go Location Bar

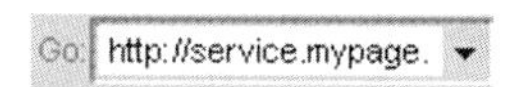

Below the main menu bar in the Toolkit is the Go location bar:

The Go Location bar displays the Uniform Resource Locator (URL) or file name of the currently displayed content. Clicking the down arrow to the right displays a list of recently visited content; choose from the list to load that content. If a URL is typed in the text box, the Toolkit loads the content.

Browser Buttons

At the top right of the main Toolkit window are the following buttons:

Displays the previous content.

Stops loading the current content.

Reloads the current content.

Loads the home page.

Bookmarks Button

At the top left of the main Toolkit window, adjacent to the Location bar, is the Bookmarks button:

Bookmarks

Displays the Add Bookmarks and Open Bookmarks menu items, as well as the currently defined bookmarks. Add Bookmarks adds the current location to the bookmark list and enables one to name it and provide a comment. Open Bookmarks displays the Bookmarks view within which the developer can edit and organize all the bookmarks.

Bookmarks View

The Bookmarks view provides access to all bookmarking functions on one tab view. Be sure the view is turned on by choosing the View menu item to ensure that the Browser Bookmarks item is checked. When it is checked, there will be a Bookmarks tab in the main Toolkit window.

Toolkit Windows

Toolkit functions can be broadly categorized as application development functions and browsing functions. To perform these functions efficiently and in a manner suited to individual working styles, the Toolkit also provides configuration and customization functions, which are accessible through the Settings menu item.

PART 4.5

Terminals

- Java™ on Nokia 9200 Series Communicators
- Java™ on Nokia 9210 Communicator
- Series 60 Platform

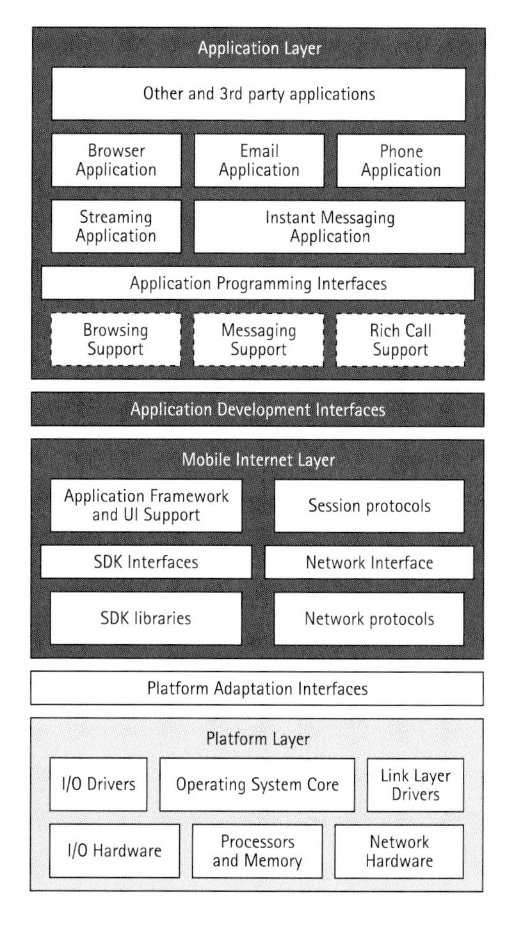

Java™ on Nokia 9200 Series Communicators

This section offers an introduction to creating Java™ applications for Nokia 9200 Series Communicators, including the Nokia 9210 Communicator in Europe and the Nokia 9290 Communicator in the Americas. These devices are based on the Symbian OS.

With full native Java support, there is no need to learn a new language in order to develop applications for Symbian OS. Java developers are immediately productive, thanks to their existing skills and experience. Java is expected to become the preferred language for developing third-party applications and services on Symbian OS. It provides a powerful programming environment, and key Symbian OS technologies (e.g., telephony, management of contacts, calendar functions, datagram messaging and IR communications) are exposed through the JavaPhone™ APIs.

It is assumed that the reader has no prior specific knowledge of Symbian OS, but it does presume familiarity with Java and the Nokia 9200 Series Communicator SDK for Symbian OS. The SDK is essential for developing, testing and debugging Java applications. It provides documentation, tools and sample code to assist developers, along with a Microsoft Windows® hosted emulator of the Nokia 9200 Series Communicators.

Java Capabilities of Nokia 9200 Series Communicators

The Java functionality available in Nokia 9200 Series Communicators is similar to, and indeed exceeds in a number of areas, that which is typically available in a desktop environment. Furthermore, it rivals the capabilities available to native C++ application developers, while the support available for Java Native Interface programming reduces this gap still further.

The Java environment on Nokia 9200 Series Communicators is based on the PersonalJava™ Application Environment. PersonalJava™ is similar to Standard Java as embodied in JDK 1.1. The main difference is that certain functional components (e.g., packages, classes or methods) that are obligatory in Standard Java are optional in PersonalJava, reducing the minimum ROM budget. Symbian's PersonalJava implementation also adds some functionality (e.g., timers). However, Symbian has opted for a fairly complete PersonalJava API set, implementing virtually all optional components, including Remote Method Invocation (RMI) and Java Database Connectivity API (JDBC) support.

Over and above the standard Java functionality, Symbian OS also provides an implementation of the JavaPhone 1.0 API that gives Java programs access to a selection of invaluable native services on the device.

Java Telephony API:

- o Create and terminate calls
- o Listen for and answer incoming calls
- o Detect changes in call state

Calendar and address book API:

- o Read, write and modify contact details, calendar items and to-do items
- o Work transparently with data in native Symbian format
- o Search across all entries in calendar or address book

Point-to-Point wireless datagram API:

- o Exchange datagrams with other devices via User Datagram Protocol (UDP) or Short Message Service (SMS)
- o Keep a specified port open for incoming datagrams

javax.comm:

- o Discover and configure available ports (serial and infrared)
- o Send and receive data
- o Listen for events on monitored ports

Forum Nokia is also making available the J2ME Mobile Information Device Profile (MIDP) runtime environment for Nokia 9200 Series Communicators.

Development Environment

Nokia 9200 Series Communicators SDK

The Nokia 9200 Series Communicators SDK must be installed on a PC for developing Java applications for the Nokia 9200 Series Communicator. The SDK provides the following:

- o Emulator
- o PersonalJava Application Environment
- o Classes.zip archive providing the necessary Java classes customized for the Nokia 9200 Series Communicators
- o JavaPhone.jar archive
- o Useful utilities

- Tools required to package an application
- JRE 1.2.2.
- Full documentation

Emulator

The emulator is designed to run on a PC with Windows NT® 4.0 or Windows 98®. The Java installation will require approximately 200 MB of free hard disk space.

JDK 1.1.8

To compile Java source code, the programmer will need to install a copy of Sun's Java Development Kit (JDK). The recommended version is JDK 1.1.8, since the PersonalJava Application Environment implemented on the Nokia 9200 Series is close to a full implementation of the JDK 1.1.8 specification.

Phone with Infrared Modem

An optional requirement is a GSM phone with infrared modem for testing the telephony and communication features offered in the JavaPhone API. This modem can communicate with the emulator via a Jet Eye infrared pod which plugs into the serial port of the PC.

In order to use the serial port in PC to drive the infrared link to a mobile device, one must make sure nothing else is using the port.

Integrated Development Environment (IDE)

The previous procedure provides all the tools necessary to develop and deploy Java applications on Symbian OS. In order to use the Symbian for Java alongside with Integrated Development Environment (IDE), the IDE should support pluggable virtual machines so that applications can be launched in a Symbian OS environment emulating a Nokia 9200 Series Communicator and have access to the custom User Interface (UI) and JavaPhone™ functionality.

It should be noted that Metrowerks and Symbian are creating CodeWarrior™ for the Symbian OS product line. The first of these integrated IDEs will target PersonalJava development on the Nokia 9200 Series Communicators, while later products will support both C++ and Java development.

Another partnership, between Borland and Nokia, has produced Java development tools for the Nokia 9200 Series Communicators. There are now two development toolkits available: the Nokia Developer's Suites for the Java 2 Platform, Micro Edition (J2ME™) as well as PersonalJava Application Environment (PJAE) tools, in conjunction with Borland JBuilder and Sun Forte™ for Java, create a complete environment for application development.

Running the Application on the Emulator

The SDK documentation provides full instructions for building and deploying a simple "Hello World" application. A screen shot of the application running on the Nokia 9210 emulator is shown below:

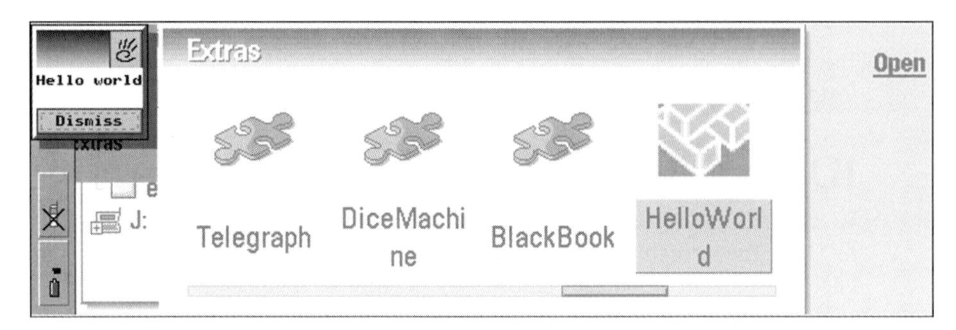

A Hello World icon on the Nokia 9210 emulator

The documentation also includes an introduction to the AIFBuilder tool on the SDK, which enables Java applications to be launched from the emulator or target hardware in the same manner as a native application.

Porting the Application to the Nokia 9200 Series Communicator

Assuming the "Hello World" application ran successfully on the emulator, it can now be transferred to the target hardware. To do this, one must have installed the Connectivity software that is on the CD accompanying the Nokia 9200 Series Communicator. Next, ensure that the device is connected to the PC via the serial cable and that the connection is active. Then, using PC Suite for the Nokia 9210 Communicator, simply copy the files from the emulator to the Nokia 9210 Communicator.

The application can then be launched from the Extras screen view shown above in the same way the application was launched in the emulator.

Customized APIs for Nokia 9200 Series Communicators

Custom API for the Command Button Array

As Nokia 9200 Series Communicators do not by default have a pointer, user input is via the keyboard or the Command Button Area (CBA). To ensure a satisfying user experience, developers will have to familiarize themselves with the API used to program the CBA. Therefore, it is appropriate to look at the code for a simple "Hello World" application that uses the CBA correctly, and also introduce some of the issues involved.

The code for the main Frame class is shown below:

```
import java.awt.*;
import com.symbian.epoc.awt.*;
public class HelloWorldDemo extends Frame implements CBAListener
{
      private EikCommandButtonGroup cbg = new EikCommandButtonGroup();
      public HelloWorldDemo(String title)
      {
            super(title);
            add(cbg);
            show();
            setBounds(CKONToolkit.getAvailableScreenRect());
            setFrameCBA();
      }
      /** Sets up the Command Button Area */
      public void setFrameCBA()
      {
            cbg.addCBAListener(this);
            cbg.setEnabled(EikCommandButtonGroup.BUTTON1, true);
            cbg.setText(EikCommandButtonGroup.BUTTON1, "Say Hello");
            cbg.setEnabled(EikCommandButtonGroup.BUTTON4, true);
            cbg.setText(EikCommandButtonGroup.BUTTON4, "Quit");
      }
      public void cbaActionPerformed(CBAEvent ae)
      {
            /* Show SayHello Dialog */
            if (ae.getID() == EikCommandButtonGroup.BUTTON1)
            {
                  //remove listener from this Frame
                  cbg.removeCBAListener(this);
                  //pass reference to CBA
                  SayHelloDialog mydialog = new SayHelloDialog(this, cbg);
            }
            /* Quit application */
            else if (ae.getID() == EikCommandButtonGroup.BUTTON4)
            {
                  System.exit(0);
            }
      }
      public static void main(String[] args)
      {
```

```
                try
                {
                      Thread.sleep(25000);
                } catch(InterruptedException ie) { }
                new HelloWorldDemo("My Frame");
          }
    }
```

It will now be helpful to go through the code pointing out features specific to the Nokia 9200 Series Communicator UI. The appropriate classes controlling the CBA and other specific features of the device are contained in the `com.symbian.epoc.awt` package, so this needs to be imported. The CBA responds to `CBActionEvents`, hence the Frame implements a `CBAListener` interface, which extends the `EventListener` interface.

The line

```
private EikCommandButtonGroup cbg = new EikCommandButtonGroup();
```

creates a new CBA. It is important to note that each application can only support one instance of `EikCommandButtonGroup`.

The line

```
setBounds(CKONToolkit.getAvailableScreenRect());
```

uses a static method of the CKONToolKit class to find out how much screen real-estate is available to the Frame.

The `setFrameCBA` method is used to set up the required buttons of the CBA for this Frame, as well as to add the current `CBAListener` (which is this Frame) to the CBA.

The `cbaActionPerformed` method of the `CBAListener` interface must be implemented, and in this case it responds to presses of the first and fourth buttons of the CBA, generating a new `SayHelloDialog` or exiting the application, respectively. Carefully note the code required to produce the `SayHelloDialog`:

```
if (ae.getID() == EikCommandButtonGroup.BUTTON1)
{
      cbg.removeCBAListener(this); //remove listener from this Frame
      SayHelloDialog mydialog = new SayHelloDialog(this, cbg);
}
```

The first line removes the current `CBAListener` from the CBA, since the current listener is this frame, which is about to be put in the background behind a new dialog which will become the new listener. The new dialog takes a reference to the `EikCommandButtonGroup` as an argument to its constructor. Since each application can support only one instance of `EikCommandButtonGroup`, it is necessary to pass this to the new dialog.

Here is the source code for the dialog:

```
import java.awt.*;
import com.symbian.epoc.awt.*;
public class SayHelloDialog extends Dialog implements CBAListener
{
      private HelloWorldDemo parent;
      private EikCommandButtonGroup cbg;
      private TextField text
            = new TextField("Hello from the Nokia 9210 Communicator");
      public SayHelloDialog
            (HelloWorldDemo _parent, EikCommandButtonGroup _cbg)
      {
            super(_parent,"Hello Folks", false);
            parent = _parent;
            cbg = _cbg;
            add(text);
            Rectangle r = CKONToolkit.getAvailableScreenRect();
            int y = r.y;
            int x = r.x;
            int width = (int)(3*r.width/4);
            int height = r.height/2;
            setBounds( x + width/8, y + height/4, width, height );
            show();
            setDialogCBA();
      }
      public void setDialogCBA()
      {
      cbg.addCBAListener(this);//add listener to Dialog
      cbg.setEnabled(EikCommandButtonGroup.BUTTON1, false);
      cbg.setText(EikCommandButtonGroup.BUTTON1, "");
      cbg.setEnabled(EikCommandButtonGroup.BUTTON4, true);
      cbg.setText(EikCommandButtonGroup.BUTTON4, "Close");
      }
      public void cbaActionPerformed(CBAEvent ae)
      {
            if (ae.getID() == EikCommandButtonGroup.BUTTON4)
            {
            cbg.removeCBAListener(this);
            dispose();
            parent.setFrameCBA();
            }
      }
}
```

The structure of this class is similar to that of the Frame class with regard to handling the CBA. The constructor receives a reference to the CBA from the previous view. The `setDialogCBA` method uses this reference to set up the CBA for the current view and, of course, makes the dialog the current listener.

Again, pay special attention to the body of the `cbaActionPerformed` method. This responds to the fourth button of the CBA by disposing of the dialog. First, it removes the current listener, then after disposing of the dialog it resets the CBA of the parent Frame since this is now the active view.

To make it easier to program the CBA for multiple views, the SDK installation includes the `CBAHandler` utility. This class provides a wrapper around `EikCommandButtonGroup` and, among other things, ensures that the appropriate `CBAListener` is active for a given view. This avoids the need to explicitly add and remove listeners upon changing views. Further information on programming for the Crystal reference design is contained in the Symbian Press book Wireless Java for Symbian Devices.

Two screen shots of this "Hello World" application running on the emulator are shown below. The first screen shot depicts the main frame of the application, showing the two activated CBA buttons.

The second screen shot shows the dialog displayed as a result of selecting the "Say Hello" CBA button.

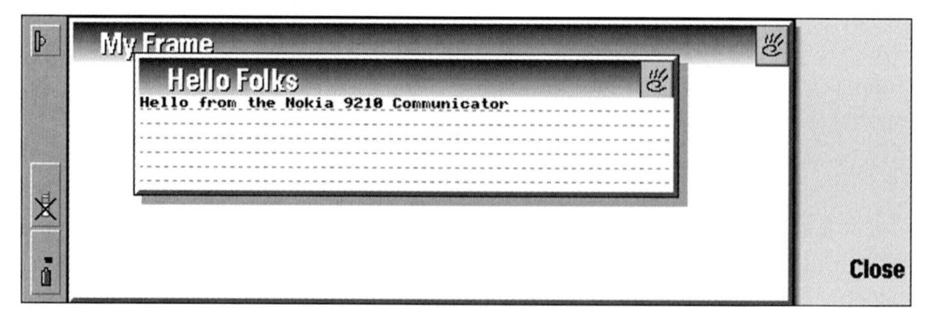

Note how the CBA has been reset for the dialog view.

JavaPhone™ API

JavaPhone™ is a Sun API that is designed to give Java full access to the telephony features of a mobile device. The Symbian OS Java offering is the reference implementation of this API. JavaPhone comprises a number of extension packages from Sun and, as with other extension packages from Sun, the intention is that the required functionality be provided by the host operating system. The following packages are provided in the current Symbian OS implementation:

```
javax.net.datagram
javax.pim.addressbook
javax.pim.calendar
javax.pim.database
javax.pim.userprofile
javax.power.monitor
javax.telephony
javax.telephony.mobile
javax.telephony.capabilities
javax.comm
```

Packages included in the JavaPhone API but not included in the current implementation are listed below:

```
javax.ce.install
javax.power.management
javax.telephony.callcontrol
javax.telephony.phone
javax.net.ssl
```


Packaging Applications

Finished applications ready for general release should be packaged into an installation file (.sis) using the Symbian Installation System. This provides a simple and consistent user interface for installing applications, data or configuration information on Symbian OS devices. Consumers install components packaged in installation files either from a PC, by using the installer or from a mobile device, using the Add/remove Control Panel applet.

The first stage in generating an installation file is to create a package file. A minimal package file for a token "Hello World" Java application would look something like this:

```
#{"Minimal application"},(0x01000000),1,0,0
; files to be installed
"HelloWorld.app"-"!:\system\apps\HelloWorld\HelloWorld.app"
"HelloWorld.txt"-"!:\system\apps\HelloWorld\HelloWorld.txt"
"HelloWorld.jar"-"!:\system\apps\HelloWorld\HelloWorld.jar"
```

The package header defines the application name ("Minimal application"); UID (0x01000000); major and minor build numbers (1, 0); and build number (0). The second line, preceded by a semicolon, is a comment. The final three lines specify the location of the files, which should be put in the installation file, and their destination on the target machine. The UID uniquely identifies this application. For testing purposes, one can use any UID desired, the first hex digit of which is a "0". Those who want to redistribute the code they should obtain a unique number by making an e-mail request to uid@symbiandevnet.com.

To create the installation file (HelloWorld.sis), place the package file (HelloWorld.pkg) in a directory along with the files to be packaged, and then launch a command prompt from that directory and type

```
makesis HelloWorld.pkg
```

The installation file can then be transferred to the target machine and installed as an application by clicking on it in the file manager and following the instructions. After installation, the application may be run by selecting the HelloWorld icon from the Extras view.

The installation system provides many options, including creating digitally signed installation files. For full details, refer to the SDK documentation.

Hints and Tips

1. Applications launched directly from a command prompt with *pjava_g.exe* or *pjava.exe* will often be put in the background behind the desk view presented on launching the emulator. This problem can be overcome by adding the line

   ```
   Thread.sleep(25000);
   ```

   to the `main` method. If this line is omitted, the application view will usually be put in the background behind the desk view presented on launching the emulator. In practice, programmers are advised to write the `main` method of the application to test for a flag, which can be passed on as an argument when the application is launched from a command prompt.
2. In the application, one should take care to include only classes that are supported by the PersonalJava Application Environment. Also, remember to compile the source code against Symbian *classes.zip* as opposed to the version of *classes.zip* in the JDK or Java 2 SDK.
3. It is a limitation of the emulator that when a Java application running on the emulator is closed down, the emulator is also closed down. This is to ensure that all threads associated with the application are terminated.
4. It is only possible to run one Java application at a time on the emulator. On the Symbian OS emulator, multiple Java virtual machines cannot run simultaneously. When a Java application starts up, it loads *pjavai.dll* (or *pjavai_g.dll*) and starts up the Java virtual machine. Because the emulator runs as a single process, a second Java application will find it is running in the same process as the first, so it cannot load another instance of

that DLL. Instead, it will attempt to share the global variables associated with the existing DLL instance. Unlike native applications, the Java DLLs are not designed to be reentrant in this manner, so this operation will fail. Currently, there is no way to work around this situation. There is, however, no problem with separate instances of the emulator both running Java applications, as the two emulators run as separate processes.

On a target Symbian OS device, which supports multiple processes, more than one instance of the Java virtual machine can be loaded simultaneously from a single instance of javai.dll in ROM or RAM. The only restriction is the amount of RAM available.

5. One common source of confusion for Java developers new to Symbian OS arises between the two methods of launching a Java application, namely, from the command prompt via *pjava.bat* (or *pjava_g.bat*) and from the emulator Extras view. After developing a Java application in the erj directory, then packaging it using the AIFBuilder and installing it in the system\apps\ directory, the user may choose to launch the application from the command prompt using pjava.bat. The emulator fires up, but the Java application appears not to start - since it has been put in the background. If the user proceeds to select the application icon in a mistaken attempt to launch the application, the application will display a *"Could not create the Java™ virtual machine"* message. This happens because an instance of the JVM is already running the application, and selecting the application icon tries to start a second instance of the JVM. The emulator, as previously discussed, cannot support this, hence the error message. One can avoid this problem if the application is launched from the Extras, moved to the background, then re-launched, since the system is smart enough to recognize that the desired application is already running and only needs to be moved to the foreground.

6. Programming for the Nokia 9200 Series Communicators user interface requires a little getting used to. To assist developers in working with the CBA, two useful utility classes are provided with the SDK. `CFrame` can be used instead of Frame in applications to provide the correct look and feel, including a CBA. The `CBAHandler` class can be used for the correct handling of the reference to the `EIKCommandButtonGroup` and in particular takes care of passing it between different views.

7. The keyboard-driven user interaction paradigm of Nokia 9200 Series Communicators can affect the way a developer programs interaction with certain components (e.g., lists). Consider the following code, which can be used to navigate a list using a pointer:

```
...
public class ListDialog extends Dialog implements ItemListener {
      ...
      private List carList;
      public ListDialog(Frame parent){
            super(parent);
            carList = new List(6);
            carList.add("Ferrari");
            carList.add("Volvo");
            ...
            carList.addItemListener(this);
```

```
            add(carList);
            ...
        }

        public void itemStateChanged(ItemEvent ie){
            String car = carList.getSelectedItem();
            //do something with selected car
            ...
        }
        ...
    }
```

This represents the standard way to choose an item from a list on a mouse-driven desktop system. Although the code also works satisfactorily on the emulator, which has access to the PC's mouse, it proves unsatisfactory on the real hardware since, to navigate the list, it is necessary to use the four-way keypad. However, the instant a key on the keypad is pressed, an `ItemEvent` is generated and the `itemStateChanged` method triggered, with the selected item being the next one in the list, though it may not be the one desired. Therefore it is not possible to directly select the desired item.

The recommended way to choose an item from a list when developing for the Nokia 9200 Series Communicators is to use the CBA to select the item as follows:

```
    ...
    public class ListDialog extends Dialog implements CBAListener {
        ...
        private List carList;
        private EikCommandButtonGroup cbg;
        public ListDialog(Frame parent, EikCommandButtonGroup cbg){
            super(parent);
            this.cbg = cbg;
            carList = new List(6);
            carList.add("Ferrari");
            carList.add("Volvo");
            ...
            add(carList);
            ...
            cbg.addCBAListener(this);
            cbg.setEnabled(EikCommandButtonGroup.BUTTON1, true);
            cbg.setText(EikCommandButtonGroup.BUTTON1, "Select");
            ...
        }
        public void cbaActionPerformed(CBAEvent ae){
            String car = carList.getSelectedItem();
            //do something with selected car
```

```
                ...
            }
            ...
        }
```

In this example, the first button of the CBA is enabled for selection of the item, and a `CBAListener` is added to the dialog. The list can now be navigated correctly using the four-way keypad. When the required item is highlighted, the user presses the "Select" button of the CBA. This selection triggers the `cbaActionPerformed` method, and the correct item is selected via the `getSelectedItem` method of the list class.

8. There are problems accessing the infrared and RS232 serial ports from the JavaPhone *javax.comm* API. By design, the RS232 port on Nokia 9200 Series Communicators is configured to listen continually for a remote link to a PC, so as to allow the Nokia Connect software to work seamlessly. In other words, do not try to use the RS232 port on Nokia 9200 Series Communicators.

   In the case of the infrared port, the problem stems from a defect in the *javax.comm* JavaPhone package that shipped with the Nokia 9210 Communicator and corresponding SDK, whereby the wrong name for the infrared port (IrComm) rather than the correct (IRCOM1) was hard-coded. The solution is to patch this class with an updated version available from the Symbian OS Knowledge Base.

   It should then be possible to initialize the infrared port successfully from the SerialChat application.

9. To test the JTAPI or SMS datagram API of the JavaPhone API on the emulator requires an infrared-enabled GSM phone connected via an infrared Jet Eye pod to the PC's serial port. If the phone is absent, the application will generate exceptions.

10. In the Symbian OS implementation of the JavaPhone 1.0 specification, not all the JTAPI methods have been implemented, although the respective package is one of the supported packages. Invoking unsupported methods will result in a *MethodNotSupportedException.* The JTAPI command set is further limited under emulation by what the emulator's device driver and GSM phone allow.

11. The AIFBuilder tool requires a JRE 1.2.2 to be installed. The JRE 1.2.2 is supplied on the SDK and, if not detected by the SDK installer, must be installed. Note that this is required in addition to the installation of JDK 1.1.8, which is needed to compile PersonalJava applications.

12. For Java applications launched from the Extras view, *System.out* and *System.err* messages are not visible. This is true for both the emulator and the mobile device. To see this output, use the Redirector application. An emulator version comes pre-installed with the SDK. A version that can be installed on a Nokia 9200 Series Communicator is included with the SDK.

    When redirector application is activated by launching from Extras, *System.out* and *System.err* text is channeled to it and can be subsequently viewed by moving the Redirect application to the foreground. Alternatively, one can configure Redirect to send output to permanent storage by specifying a target file name.

Java™ on the Nokia 9210 Communicator

Java Implementation

The Nokia 9210 Communicator is the first Java-capable Nokia phone. At a general level, the objectives of using Java in the Nokia 9210 Communicator are:

- To start fulfilling the promise of the Java language: ease of programming, portability and safety. A simpler and safer language means easier programming, fewer errors, less testing and less debugging.
- Applet support: The Nokia 9210 Communicator Web browser does not support applets, but an applet viewer is included.
- Allowing more third-party software: the Nokia 9210 Communicator has enough power for PersonalJava applications.
- Downloadable applets and applications: Java is a safe technology for this. A key feature of the current legacy Internet industry is downloading applications free of charge from the Web.
- JavaPhone implementation: The JavaPhone API is a vertical extension to the PersonalJava platform. JavaPhone APIs can only be used in applications, and not in applets, for security reasons.

The Nokia 9210 Communicator Java implementation is based on the Sun reference implementation. It includes all optional functionality except printing. Java applications and applets can be run on both, on the device and the emulator. Customization is needed only for the *look and feel* of the Device Family Reference Designs (DFRD).

Development Guidelines

The Java SDK contains an emulator for Windows NT® 4.0, Windows 95®, and Windows 98®, documentation with examples and tools, and additional tools to support native method development using Java Native Interface (JNI). A Java compiler/Integrated Development Environment (IDE) is not included in the SDK. One must download free Java Development Kit™ (JDK) 1.1.8 and PersonalJava compatibility classes from the Sun Web site. The PersonalJava compatibility classes are additional classes available in the PersonalJava API, which are not available in the corresponding Java Development Kit. JNI development will also need Microsoft Visual C++®, version 6.

The SDK documentation contains a Quick Start tutorial for creating a simple Hello World application and detailed information about developing Java applications for the Crystal platform. The Crystal platform is one of three Symbian DFRDs, and it is designed for Communicator-like devices.

User Interface Principles

The Nokia 9210 Style Guide is included in the SDK. It contains details on the look and feel of the Crystal platform on the device. Certain matters should be considered when developing applications for the Nokia 9210 Communicator. The interactive elements in the Crystal Platform consist of four command buttons, a menu and a Personal Digital Assistant (PDA) keyboard. No real pointing device or touch screen exists, but it is possible to use the pointer instead.

Screen size (resolution 640 x 200) should be taken into account. The developer should also notice that certain areas in the display make use of the screen. The following figure shows a typical screen shot of the Nokia 9210 Communicator display. The Indicator and Command Button Areas may be one of two different sizes or hidden altogether.

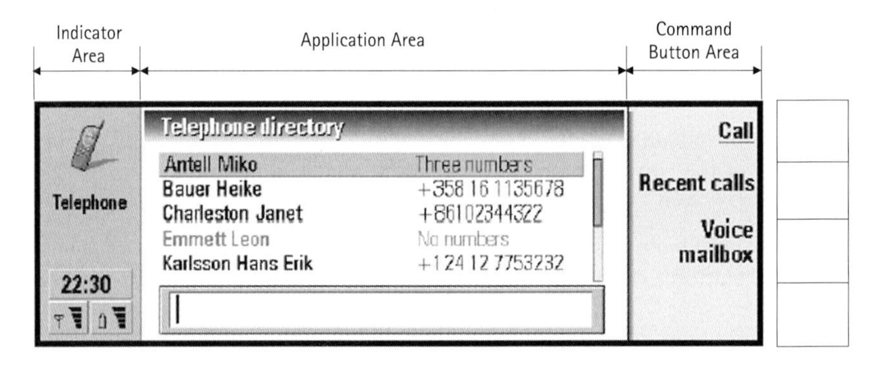

Typical view of the Nokia 9210 Communicator screen

Abstract Window Toolkit

The Java programming language provides a class library called the Abstract Windowing Toolkit (AWT) that contains a number of common graphical widgets. These widgets can be added to the display area and positioned with a layout manager.

A typical UI designed for a PC screen may not be efficient enough for the screen of the Nokia 9210 Communicator. It is recommended that application developers take advantage of all the UI features in the Nokia 9210 Communicator. Certain APIs for Nokia 9210 Communicator specific display features are included:

- Command Button Area API
- Status Pane API
- Virtual Cursor API

Command Button Area API

The Command Button Area is the recommended method of allowing the user to choose commands simply and rapidly. Crystal provides a class that allows Java programs to create Command Button Areas and receive events from them. The API can be used by both applets and applications.

Status Pane API

The Status Pane API provides access to the Crystal UI Status Pane. The API can be used by both applets and applications. The Status Pane is dedicated to providing different kinds of important information (e.g., connection, battery and field strength indicators). The API allows one to set the style (size) of the Status Pane. There are two styles for the Status Pane: the wide area, which is 92 x 200 pixels, and the narrow one, which is 32 x 200. The wide area also has a place for the time and the application's icon and name.

Virtual Cursor API

The Virtual Cursor (VC) is a useful UI extension providing consumers with a software pointer in the absence of a hardware pointer. The Pointer is useful in applications that explicitly require pointer events. For example, image maps on a Web browser which require pointer events can be handled by the VC Pointer.

Crystal provides a class that allows Java programs to control the Pointer and receive pointer events from it. The API can be used by both applets and applications.

Further Information

1. Nokia 9210 Style Guide (included in the SDK CD-ROM)
2. Java Developer's Guide for Crystal (included in the SDK CD-ROM)
3. Forum Nokia Web site http://www.forum.nokia.com
4. Java Web site http://java.sun.com
5. Symbian Developer Net http://www.symbiandevnet.com
6. Professional Symbian Programming, Martin Tasker et al, Wrox Press Ltd., 2000
7. Example applications included in the SDK (C:\Symbian\6.0\NokiaJava\erj\examples)
8. PersonalJava™ Web site http://java.sun.com/products/personaljava/spec-1-1-1/index.html

Series 60 Platform

Since its inception, mobile device technology has relied on software for many functions. Today, the technology depends on software for functionality (e.g., the Graphical User Interface (GUI), data services and downloadable software applications). With the introduction of the Series 60 Platform, mobile device technology is now opening up for software applications. Finally, the mobile device market is within the reach of the software industry, as independent software vendors (ISV) can develop and market applications for mobile devices.

The Series 60 Platform is targeted at a new class of mobile devices, smartphones. It includes a graphical UI and a suite of applications all built on the Symbian Pperating System (OS). The Series 60 Software Development Kit (SDK) enables the development of applications in Java or C++, and the downloading and running of the same applications. The platform allows software developers, carriers, and device manufacturers to create their own solutions, which will be interoperable across different devices and networks.

The technology intelligence firm IDC estimates that in 2005, in Western Europe alone, 49 million smartphones will be shipped to consumers. This will be more than all other handheld devices, PDAs and industrial handheld devices together. By 2005, IDC expects Symbian OS to have the largest market share in smartphone operating systems.

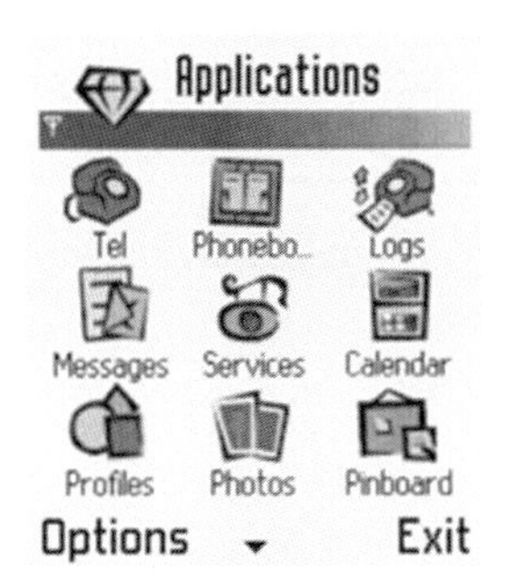

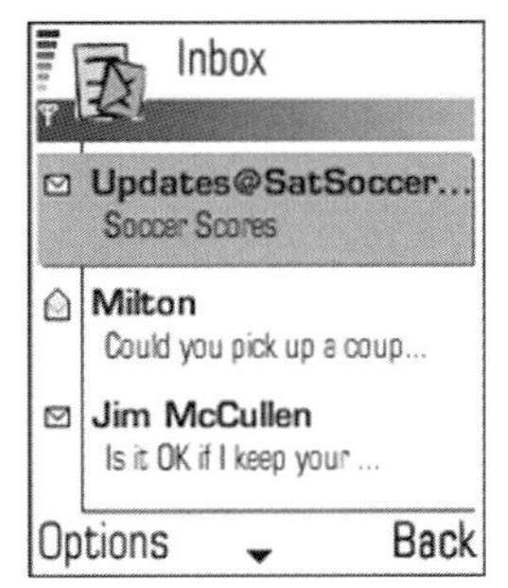

Graphical user interface of the Series 60 Platform

The Series 60 Platform draws its design and functionality from the experience of Symbian and Nokia. Combining an operating system designed from the beginning for small mobile devices with the most popular user interface components in the industry produces an environment in which applications thrive.

As a standards-based platform, Series 60 and applications developed for it can run on any participating manufacturer's hardware, creating a new growing market for the software industry and a safe platform to invest in for a software vendor.

The Mobile World is now open for all innovators who envision a future driven by applications and services - on an open architecture globally shared by software companies, content providers, carriers and device manufacturers.

Introduction

For mobile devices, new technologies, services, device types and functions are constantly moving forward. With different screen sizes, keypads, browsers and other elements, manufacturers are trying different approaches in order to find a product that most appropriately meets the needs of the consumers. Applications, services and content must all be adapted to different devices much like traditional content is adapted for newspapers, magazines, radio and television.

Industry leaders are committed to creating a global and open architecture for interoperable applications, content and services in the Mobile domain. The scope of this action covers both device client software modules for mobile device vendors, and the corresponding server solutions for carriers. This offers carriers, systems integrators, Information Technology (IT) suppliers, mobile device manufacturers and application developers new avenues of growth and revenue generation by enabling a multi-vendor ecosystem, built on open global standards (e.g., Wireless Application Protocol (WAP) 2.0/Extensible HyperText Markup Language (XHTML), Multimedia Messaging Service (MMS), SyncML and other Third Generation Partnership Project (3GPP) -compliant technologies). Additional important components of the initiative include the use of Java™ technology and Symbian OS.

An application developer who wants to reach the widest possible market adheres to standards and uses popular programming languages (e.g., Java and C++). These crucial standards and development tools, among many other protocols and utilities, have been implemented in the Series 60 Platform, which offers open architecture for smartphones.

In mobile devices, the screen and keyboard hardware dictate how the UI portion of the software is designed. To promote interoperability from the start, the Series 60 Platform defines a common UI that is one-hand operated and has a 176 x 208 screen size. This creates a uniform UI and screen format enabling simplification and savings in development costs.

Application designers can use the Series 60 SDK to create both stand-alone and server-connected applications. Also, separate Java and WAP/XHTML toolkits can be used for designing applications.

In addition to mobile devices, developers can find opportunities in designing software products for servers (e.g., carriers and service providers can offer content and application services to their subscribers). Enterprises need software that connects their mobile employees to the intranet, and applications for customer service and mobile commerce.

Reference Applications

The Series 60 Platform includes ready-to-run applications, which hardware manufacturers typically embed in their Series 60 devices. These applications not only illustrate the possibilities of the platform, but they also guide developers in designing software that complies with the UI style.

Reference applications provide public Application Programming Interfaces (APIs) for accessing the services from other applications (e.g., the Phonebook application has a service for displaying a list of contacts, the Photo Album application a service for locating images, and the Messages application a service for sending e-mail).

Some of the applications in the Series 60 Platform: Phonebook (left) and Calendar (right)

Phonebook	Contact database integrated with messaging and other applications. Supports vCard.
Calendar	Scheduling application, supports vCalendar data format.
To-Do List	vCalendar items can be downloaded into this to-do list.
Notepad	For text entries.
Photo Album	Storage for multimedia messages and images.
Pinboard	Application management tool for the multitasking environment.
Clock, Calculator, Games, Unit Converter	World clock, business calculator, and a selection of entertainment.
Composer	Allows consumers to compose new tunes for applications.
E-mail, SMS and MMS	Client software for messaging applications.
Telephony applications	Voice Recorder, Telephone Settings, Call Logs & Message Indicators,User Profiles, Call Forwarding, Speed Dialing, and Voice Dialing and Voice Tags.
Application installation	Installing new software via the PC Connectivity suite or over network.
Synchronization	SyncML 1.0.1 synchronization engine. Supports data transfer over mobile networks, Bluetooth and infrared (IrDA). vCal 1.0 and vCard 2.1 data formats.
Security	Security settings and software certificate management.

Platform Architecture

Symbian OS components provide data management, communications, graphics, multimedia, security, application engines, a messaging engine, Bluetooth support, browser engines and support for data synchronization and internationalization. Generic Technology is the Symbian release used as the base system.

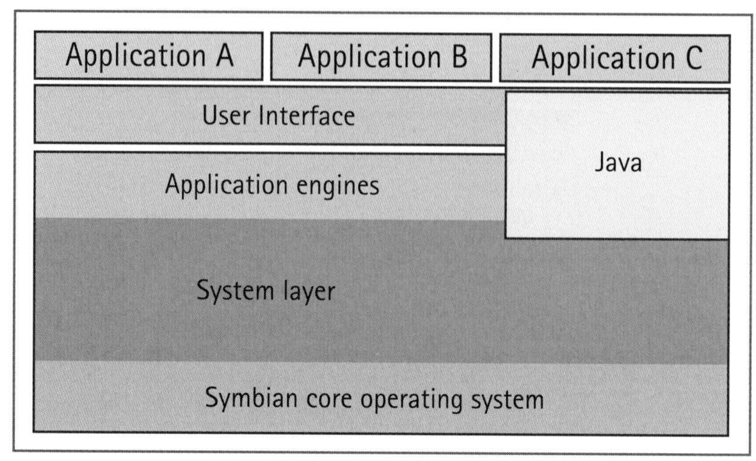

The Series 60 Platform Architecture

The kernel, file server, memory management and device drivers are located in the Symbian core operating system layer.

The system layer provides communication and computing services (e.g., Transmission Control Protocol (TCP/IP), Internet Message Access Protocol (IMAP), Short Message Service (SMS)), and database management.

The application engines allow software developers to create their own UIs to the application data and databases. Data synchronization is provided through the PC Connectivity Suite.

The UI software created on top of Symbian OS is adapted for a particular device category. The ready-to-run and custom developed applications make up a fully functional mobile device.

The Java runtime environment allows the download and deployment of Java MIDP™ applications in Series 60 devices.

Symbian OS

The Symbian OS is a 32-bit multitasking operating system, in which applications are designed to interact with one another (e.g., if a phone call interrupts a consumer from composing an e-mail message, the consumer can switch from e-mail to a calendar application in the middle of a telephone conversation or an incoming SMS may trigger the consumer to access the contact database and forward the SMS).

By complying with the platform architecture and software design guidelines, application designers can routinely manage such occurrences in the daily lives of consumers.

From the start, the Symbian OS was designed for small battery-powered mobile devices. The design cornerstones of the Symbian OS have been:

- Performance - the Symbian OS is designed to make minimal demands on batteries and to have low memory consumption.
- Multitasking - telephony and universal messaging are fundamental components of the Symbian OS. All applications are designed to work seamlessly in parallel.
- Standards - the use of technologies based on agreed standards is a basic principle of Symbian. This ensures that applications are portable and interoperable.
- Object-oriented software architecture
- Memory management optimized for embedded software environment
- Security mechanisms for enabling secure communications and safe data storage
- Application support for international environments, built-in Unicode character sets

User Interface

A Series 60 device is primarily a mobile device, a fact reflected in the UI optimized for one-handed operation. However, it is also a handheld device for data communication, even though the graphical UI does not require a pen or a keyboard. This is a crucial distinction when compared to Personal Digital Assistants (PDAs), which require the use of both hands for viewing or modifying content.

The design criteria underlying the Series 60 UI is that anyone who can use a mobile phone, can use a Series 60 device. The platform has been optimized for voice services, data communication and information viewing. The Series 60 Platform supports a 176 x 208 pixel screen size.

The UI design of an application typically starts from dividing the structure into browsing elements and detailed views. When the consumer activates an entry, the respective detailed view displays the selected data.

A wide selection of UI elements is available for developers, ranging from list boxes, standard dialogs, pop-up menus, check boxes and radio buttons to rich text and graphics.

The platform specifies a 12-key numeric keypad with function keys. The function keys include two softkeys, a 4-way navigation key, an application launch-and-swap key, and Send and End keys. For improving text input, the keyboard also specifies a clear key and an alpha toggle key.

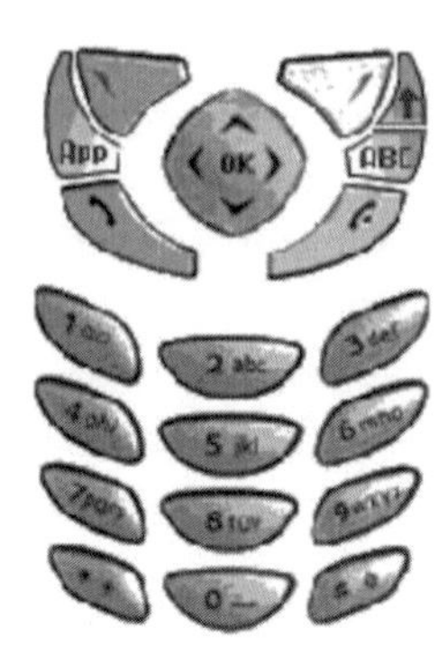

A keypad with Series 60 supported keys

Communication

Application designers who create solutions that communicate with other systems need standards to ensure interoperability. The Series 60 Platform relies on standard protocols that have been defined for communication, messaging, browsing and data synchronization.

In addition to stand-alone applications designed for Series 60 devices, server applications, server utilities and middleware software represent a market for software companies. Server applications may be hosted by a carrier who provides them as services to subscribers. Mobile portals, payment solutions, location-based solutions, advertising and virtual communities are examples of these services.

For enterprises, General Packet Radio Service (GPRS) means Internet Protocol (IP) connectivity to mobile devices through mobile networks. Server software for mobile applications can reside in corporate networks, allowing intranet applications to reach employees who are out of the office, and helping mobile commerce applications reach corporate customers.

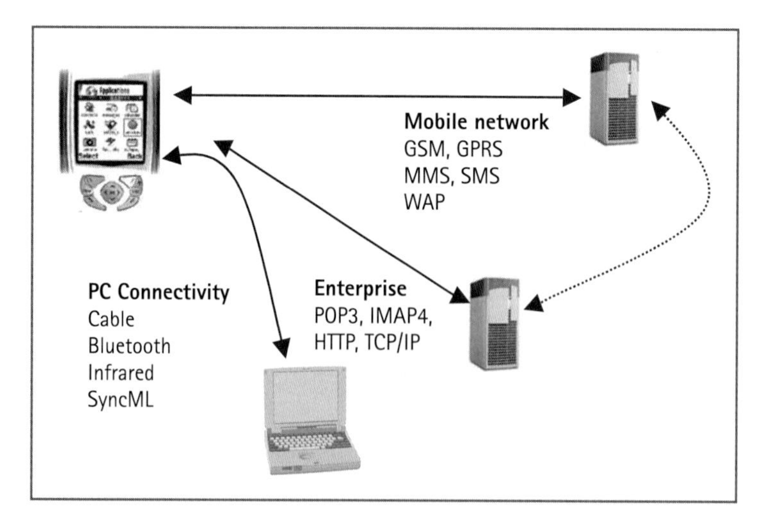

Series 60 Platform communication technologies

Data transfer between applications in different devices is enabled by standards that define the syntax and format for data. The Series 60 Platform features a SyncML engine, which can be accessed through a public API. PC Connectivity over a wireless or cable connection can be used for data synchronization and application installation.

Developing Applications

Application developers from the computer, networking and telecommunications worlds are looking at smartphones as a new platform paradigm. However, developers can still use familiar programming tools together with new toolkits for turning their ideas into innovative new applications. The Series 60 Platform is packaged as an SDK for developers. The SDK features APIs, documentation and an emulator that allow software to be tested before it is downloaded into an actual device.

The supported programming tools are C++ and the Java platform. Depending on the software's intended use, it can be designed as a Java application, a Symbian C++ application, a messaging application, or a content browsing application.

Java Applications

Java has become popular as a programming language and runtime environment from small devices to network servers. Nokia intends to deliver more than 50 million mobile devices supporting the Java platform to all segments of the consumer market by the end of 2002.

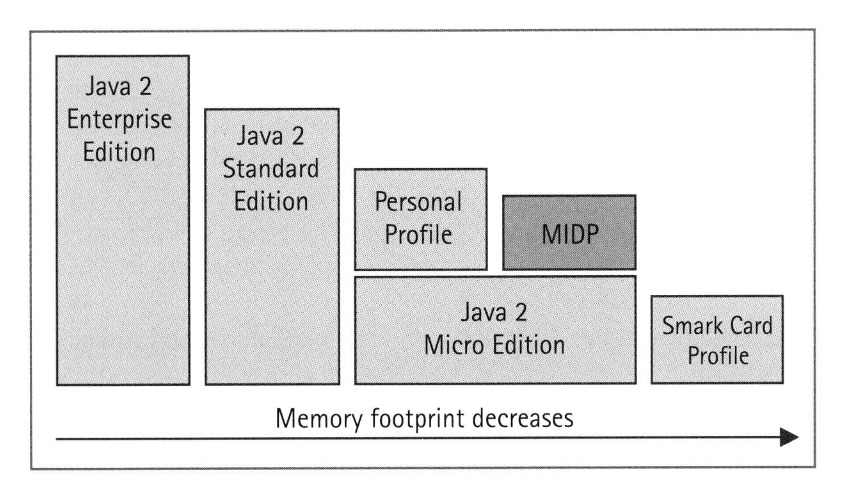

Java technology platforms

The Series 60 Platform accommodates the J2ME™ environment according to the Mobile Information Device Profile (MIDP) profile of the Connected Limited Device Configuration (CLDC) configuration definition. The CLDC is designed to be a small-footprint configuration for resource-constrained devices. MIDP is a functional extension to the CLDC, defining the profile for mobile devices. MIDP applications, MIDlets, can be downloaded from the Internet over the air and executed in mobile devices.

For application developers, Java offers hardware independence, the support of a large development community and built-in security.

Examples of downloadable applications include the following:

- Interactive information applications (e.g., maps and city guides, corporate information tools).
- Entertainment applications (e.g., games, animated characters, virtual pets).
- Financial applications (e.g., banking and stock trading applications).

In a Series 60 device, Java is best used in applications for which time to market is critical, the client application acts as an extension to a server application, application requirements change frequently, and the deployment of the application in different platforms is important.

Series 60 devices can be connected to the Internet, and consumers can download the applications and data of their choice into their devices. Java has a built-in sandbox security model to protect the system from malicious software. The security is achieved by setting clear boundaries on what applications can do in the device.

Since Java has been designed to run on any device equipped with a Java engine, there are some compromises in its generic functionality. A Java application cannot access all features of a device (e.g., the contact database or the calendar). Full functionality on the Series 60 platform is available in the C++ development environment.

Native Symbian Applications

C++ is the native programming language of Symbian OS, so all Series 60 Platform APIs are available for C++ programmers. Designing the application in C++ gives the best performance and facilitates lower memory consumption.

A Series 60 application could be kept running for weeks, which makes memory management critical for the operating system. Symbian provides programming methods (e.g., heap checking, asserts, naming convention and leave-trap mechanisms), which enforce good memory management.

Messaging

Messaging is ideal for mobile communication applications that do not require immediate response from a server. A client application puts together the message, sends it away and lets the store-and-forward system of the mobile network take care of the rest. Messaging also frees the consumer for other tasks while waiting for a response.

The success of SMS has proved how beneficial it is for the whole industry when an application is available on the mobile devices of different manufacturers and across different carrier networks. Mobile messaging is now evolving from SMS text messaging to a Multimedia Messaging Service

(MMS). Practically all existing, commercially successful SMS services can also be implemented with MMS. New infotainment, chatting, instant messaging, and person-to-person messaging services are opportunities for developers who understand the consumer demand for instant content creation and consumption.

In the corporate world, e-mail is a vital tool for corporate users, who can now access their e-mail and other messaging-enabled corporate applications by using their mobile devices. For example a database application that keeps consumers up-to-date via e-mail can communicate with corporate users who have a secure connection from the mobile device to the corporate intranet.

Application Programming Interface	**Function**
Application Engines	Access to the data of the service applications (e.g., Calendar, To-Do list and Contacts).
Application Framework	Core frameworks and libraries for application software.
Application Services	Utility services for applications, including alarms, logging, system information, and vCard and vCalendar handling.
Communication	Frameworks and system services for communications, such as sockets.
Infrared	Infrared communications.
Messaging	Framework for multi-protocol messaging, for example, e-mail, MMS and SMS.
Multi Media Server	Music and image manipulation and format conversion. Supports graphics, animation, audio files and video clips.
Networking	TCP/IP and dial-up networking services.
PC Connectivity	Backup, restore, file format conversions, application installation and printing.
Serial Communication	Framework for serial communications services.
System	System functions, such as security, clipboard, date and time, database management, file server, graphics, locale settings, memory management, thread and process management and timers.
Telephony	Interface for initiating, controlling and terminating telephone calls.
User Interface	User interface library for Series 60.
WAP Stack	Access to the WAP protocol stack.

Developers can make full use of the messaging facilities of the Series 60 Platform. Messaging offers plenty of opportunities for creating messaging-enabled client applications, and for creating plug-in modules to support customized messaging types. The built-in messaging framework in Series 60 provides an API for sending and receiving SMS, MMS and e-mail.

A feature useful for programmers is the Send-As API, which helps create outgoing messages in client applications. It provides a common method for composing messages, regardless of the used message type or transportation method, and features a simple UI module for sending the message on its way.

Browsing

It is well understood that browsing on a mobile device is very different from browsing on a PC. A mobile device must show essential, personally relevant information, in a compact and visually appealing manner.

The WAP is a global standard for Mobile Internet applications and browsing. Functionally similar to the World Wide Web, it is designed to accommodate the limited memory and small screens of mobile devices, which are connected to servers over low bandwidth connections. WAP over GPRS makes the spontaneous use of mobile data services a reality.

Examples of applications that involve real-time interaction or long sessions are interactive games, online auctions, chat applications and newsgroups. A banking transaction on a mobile device is an example of an application that requires a secure, online connection between the client and the server throughout the transaction. A secure session over a browser connection is a proven way to implement such an application.

The Series 60 Platform supports WAP 1.2.1/Wireless Markup Language (WML) browsing. Supported features include the push functionality, over-the-air configuration of WAP settings, content download, Wireless Telephony Applications Interface (WTAI) and Wireless Transport Layer Security (WTLS) security. Nokia has made a Mobile Internet Toolkit available to application designers and content producers for creating both XHTML and WML content.

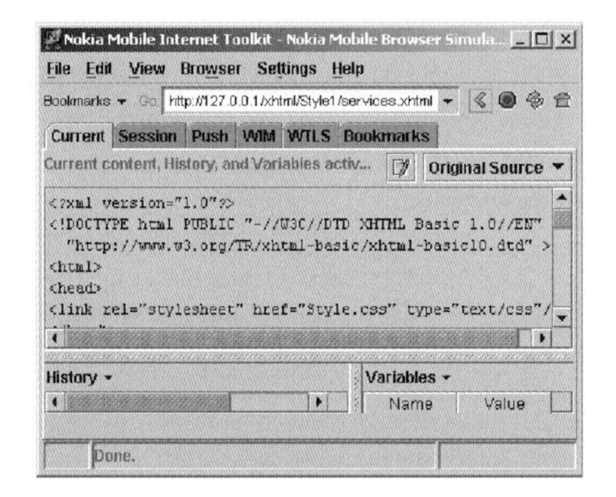

Mobile Internet Toolkit: scripting and application screens

The Mobile Internet Toolkit runs on a PC and provides a complete scripting, testing, and simulation environment for developers. The included emulator can be adjusted for different screen sizes, including the 176 x 208 used in the Series 60 Platform. Developers can thus create content and applications without an XHTML device, and without having access to a carrier infrastructure.

V EPILOGUE

Epilogue

The Mobile Internet does not simply refer to accessing the conventional Internet from a mobile device. We will not spend our time browsing Internet pages for content as we do today, although this will still be possible. Instead, we will use services and applications to access content, make transactions, do business, link up with friends and family, play games, watch videos and listen to and download music. More importantly, we will use the Mobile Internet to help control our lives and give us more time to do the things we choose to, regardless of our location.

The new environment is about enabling people to shape their own Mobile World through personalized communication technology. It is also a place where companies do business by matching consumer needs with their service portfolio or product offering. To ensure the success of services in the Mobile World, they must be highly user-friendly. The consumer should be able to ignore the underlying technologies and enjoy the richness of the services regardless of the access method.

Three success factors for enabling service consumption are:

- Consumer acceptance of the services,
- A healthy business system, and
- Understanding technology life cycles and maturity levels.

Nokia has a good understanding of the mobile device consumer segments, the general attitudes and needs of these segments and the characteristics of technology adoption in each of them. This knowledge is applied to new services and, through product and user interface categorization, enables an optimal consumer experience and ease of use in each of the segments.

Understanding the profit-making logic of the Mobile and Web domains, and applying this knowledge to the innovation possibilities in the Mobile World will combine the best of these domains. It is important for all constituents of the Mobile World to unlock innovation potential through solid business models, so that the flow of new services and evolving consumer needs match. This consumption of new services benefits carriers through volume and through higher average revenue per user.

All technology choices should emphasize service enabling; technical architectures can be perceived as end-to-end service enablers. These technical architectures should lead technology evolution and the related selections, establish a framework for standardization efforts, and enable early system verifications with reference implementations.

Having a common framework for services and understanding this technical foundation will be important when companies interact with each other and consider introducing new services to consumers. To facilitate this, Nokia is active in open global standardization fora, such as Open Mobile Alliance, to develop a comprehensive application and service architecture for the Mobile Internet. The ultimate objective of the initiative is to create a user-friendly Mobile Internet experience for everyone.

The Mobile Internet Technical Architecture aims to provide seamless interoperability between all interaction modes, any network environment and with any type of access. Identifying the relevant communication modes, defining the required supporting key technologies and driving industry participation to develop a common Mobile Internet platform are steps towards the needed solutions. MITA is a common Mobile Internet platform for applications, a technical framework for Mobile services, and a technical foundation for an evolution path to the Mobile World.

In the solutions section we presented our baseline in path to Mobile World. We started with the Introduction to Key Service Enablers, yet at this time with the Nokia viewpoint i.e. describing how Nokia has approached these technologies and also to give an insight on how these Nokia solutions are composed.

The tools section described few challenges that application developers should solve when implementing solutions for Mobile Internet. The section also gave an overview of Nokia developer process, tools and support services.

We are in middle of an IP Convergence-driven technology evolution from three network environments: mobile networks, the Internet and Intranets towards a unified Mobile Internet. The role of end-to-end solutions, new technologies, such as SIP and Web services, together with increasing programmability in mobile devices will lead us to a personalized Mobile World where the requirements of consumers drive the development of the Mobile Internet. To achieve this goal, mobile devices, networks and service solutions must work together as one and developers must have access to develop new services.

An open solution benefits all (e.g., profitable business scenarios call for interoperability, short development cycles, large volumes and, most of all, global reach). Unless there is a commonly accepted architectural solution, markets will be fragmented and require separate parameters, and be much smaller than a single global market.

As part of the open architecture development, Nokia invites all developers, service providers, carriers and other industry players to participate in further clarifying and specifying the market requirements and technical solutions required to provide the Mobile Internet needed for superior end-to-end services.

VI APPENDIX

- Glossary

Appendix A: Glossary

2G	Second Generation
3DES	Triple DES
3G	Third generation
3GPP	Third Generation Partnership Project
3GPP2	Third Generation Partnership Project 2
A/D	Analog-to-digital
AAA	Authentication, Authorization, and Accounting
AAC	Advanced Audio Coding
AAP	Alternative Approval Process
ABNF	Advanced Backus-Naur Form
AC	Admission Control
ACID	Atomicity, Consistency, Isolation and Durability
ACIF	Australian Communications Industry Forum
AD	Area Director
ADI	Application Development Interface
ADPCM	Adaptive Differential Pulse Code Modulation
AES	Advanced Encryption Standard
A-GPS	Assisted Global Positioning System
AH	Authentication Header
AIC	Access Independent Connectivity
AII	Access Independent Interface
AKA	Authentication and Key Agreement
All-IP RAN	All-IP Radio Access Network
ALF	Application Level Framing
ALG	Application Level Gateway
AMR	Adaptive Multi-Rate
AMR-NB	AMR Narrowband
AMR-WB	AMR Wideband
AMS	Application Management Software
ANSI	American National Standards Institute
AO	Application Originated
AOA	Angle Of Arrival
AP	Access Point
API	Application Programming Interface

ARIB	Association of Radio Industries and Businesses
ARL	Authority Revocation List
ARP	Address Resolution Protocol
ARPU	Average Revenue Per User
ARQ	Automatic Repeat Request
AS	Announcement Server
AS	Application Server
AS	Authentication Server
ASCII	American Standard Code for Information Interchange
ASN.1	Abstract Syntax Notation One
ASP	Application Service Provider
AT	Access and Terminals
AT	Application Terminated
ATM	Asynchronous Transfer Mode
ATM	Automatic Teller Machine
ATM-F	ATM Forum
AtoM	Any Transport over MPLS
AVT	Audio/Video Transport
AWT	Abstract Windowing Toolkit
B2B	Business-to-Business
B2BUA	Back-to-Back User Agent
B2C	Business-to-Consumer
BARB	Bluetooth Architecture and Review Board
BBTAG	BroadBand Technical Advisory Group
BCH	Basic Call Handling
BCP	Best Current Practices
BDT	Telecommunication Development Bureau
BE	Best Effort
BEC	Backward Error Correction
BEP	Bit Error Probability
BG	Border Gateway
BGCF	Breakout Gateway Control Function
BGP	Border Gateway Protocol
BizCom	Business Committee
BLER	Block Error Ratio
BMP	Windows Bitmap
BNEP	Bluetooth Network Encapsulation Protocol

BOF	Birds of a Feather
BOV	Business Operational View
BPF	Berkeley-Packet-Filter
BPSK	Binary Phase Shift Keying
BQA	Bluetooth Qualification Administrator
BQB	Bluetooth Qualification Bodies
BQRB	Bluetooth Qualification Review Board
BQTF	Bluetooth Qualification Test Facility
BR	Radiocommunication Bureau
BRAN	Broadband Radio Access Networks
BS	Base Station
BSA	Binding Security Association
BSC	Base Station Controller
BSD	Berkeley Software Distribution
BSS	Base Station System
BSS	Basic Service Set
BSSGP	Base Station System GPRS Protocol
BTAB	Bluetooth Technical Advisory Board
BTI	Bluetooth Test and Interoperability Committee
BTP	Business Transaction Protocol
BTS	Base Station
BWA	Broadband Wireless Access
CA	Certification Authority
CA	Collision Avoidance
CAMEL	Customized Applications for Mobile Network Enhanced Logic
CAR	Candidate Access Router
CBA	Command Button Area
CBR	Constant BitRate
CC	Call Control
CCK	Complementary Code Keying
CC/PP	Composite Capability/Preference Profiles
CCIF	International Telephone Consultative Committee
CCIR	International Radio Consultative Committee
CCIT	International Telegraph Consultative Committee
CCITT	International Telegraph and Telephone Consultative Committee
CCS	Cascading Style Sheets
CCU	Channel Codec Unit

CD	Collision Detection
CD	Compact Disc
CDC	Connected Device Configuration
CDMA	Code Division Multiple Access
CDR	Call Detail Record
CDR	Common Data Representation
CEK	Content Encryption Key
Cell-ID	Cell Identity
CENELEC	European Committee for Electrotechnical Standardization
CEPT	Conference of European Postal and Telecommunications Administrations
CGI	Common Gateway Interface
CGL-WG	OSDL Carrier Linux Work Group
cHTML	Compact HTML
CIDR	Classless Inter-Domain Routing
CIF	Common Intermediate Format
CIR	Carrier-to-Interference Ratio
CL	Convergence Layer
CLDC	Connected Limited Device Configuration
CLI	Command-Line Interface
CLIP	Classical IP
CLP	Common Line Protocol
CLR	Certificate Revocation List
CMT	Cellular Mobile Telephone
CN	Core Network
CoA	Care-of Address
COD	Content Object Descriptor
COFDM	Coded Orthogonal Frequency Division Multiplex
COPS	Common Open Policy Service
CORBA	Common Object Request Broker Architecture
CoT	Care-of Address Test
CoTI	Care-of Address Test Initiate
CPA	Collaboration Protocol Agreement
CPCS	Common Part Convergence Sublayer
CPIM	Common Profile for Instant Messaging
CPL	Call Processing Language
CPP	Collaboration Protocol Profile
CPS	Connection Processing Server

CPU	Central Processing Unit
CR	Change Request
CRC	Cyclic Redundancy Check
CRL	Certificate Revocation List
CRM	Customer Relationship Management
CS	Circuit Switched
CSCF	Call State Control Function
CSD	Circuit Switched Data
CSMA	Carrier Sense Multiple Access
CSP	Client-Server Protocol
CSS	Cascading Style Sheets
CTP	Cordless Telephony Profile
CTS	Clear To Send
CWM	Common Warehouse Metamodel
CVM	Java™ virtual machine supporting CDC
CVOPS	C Virtual Operating System
CWTS	China Wireless Telecommunication Standard Group
D/A	Digital-to-Analog
DAB	Digital Audio Broadcasting
DAD	Duplicate Address Detection
DAML	DARPA Agent Markup Language
DCF	Distributed Coordination Function
DCOM	Distributed Component Object Model
DECT	Digital European Cordless Telecommunications
DER	Distinguished Encoding Rules
DES	Data Encryption Standard
DFRD	Device Family Reference Design
D-G	Director-General
DHCP	Dynamic Host Configuration Protocol
DiffServ	Differentiated Services
DIFS	Distributed InterFrame Space
DLC	Data Link Control
DLPI	Data Link Provider Interface
DM	Device Management
DMCA	Digital Millennium Copyright Act
DNS	Domain Name System
DNS-Sec	DNS Security

DoD	Department of Defense
DPIT	Designated Profile Interoperability Test platform
DPSCH	Dedicated Physical SubChannel
DRM	Digital Rights Management
DS	Distribution System
DSA	Digital Signature Algorithm
DSCP	Differentiated Services Code Point
DSL	Digital Subscriber Line
DSP	Digital Signal Processor
DSUI	Differentiated Services Urgency/Importance
DSS	Distribution System Services
DSSS	Direct Sequence Spread Spectrum
DTC	Domain Technology Committee
DTD	Document Type Definition
DTMF	Dial Tone Multi-Frequency
DUNP	Dial-Up Networking Profile
DVB	Digital Video Broadcasting
DVB-T	Digital Video Broadcasting Terrestrial
DVD	Digital Versatile Disc
E.164	International public telecommunication numbers for ISDN, ITU-T
E2E	Enterprise-to-Enterprise
EAIF	External Application Interface
EAP	Extensible Authentication Protocol
EBU	European Broadcasting Union
ebXML	Electronic Business XML
EC	Executive Committee
ECDSA	Elliptic Curve DSA
ECMA TC32	Communication, Networks and Systems Interconnection
ECML	Electronic Commerce Modeling Language
ECN	Encoding Control Notation
ECN	Explicit Congestion Notification
ECSD	Enhanced Circuit Switched Data
EDGE	Enhanced Data Rates for Global Evolution
EDI	Electronic Data Interchange
EE	Environmental Engineering
EEMA	European Forum for Electronic Business
EFI	External Functionality Interface

EFR	Enhanced Full Rate
EFTA	European Free Trade Association
EGW	Multimedia E-mail Gateway
EGPRS	Enhanced GPRS
EIRP	Effective Isotropic Radiated Power
EIS	Enterprise Information System
EJB	Enterprise JavaBeans™
EMC	Electromagnetic Compatibility
EMS	Enhanced Messaging Service
EMV	EuropayMastercardVisa payment protocol
ENUM	E.164 Number Mapping
E-OTD	Enhanced Observed Time Difference
EP	ETSI Project
EP BRAN	ETSI Project Broadband Radio Access Networks
EP TIPHON	ETSI Project TIPHON
EPC	Enhanced Power Control
ERC	European Radiocommunications Committee
ERM	EMC and Radio Spectrum Matters
ESMTP	Extended Simple Mail Transfer Protocol
ESO	European Standards Organization
ESP	Encapsulating Security Payload
ESS	Extended Service Set
E-TCH	Enhanced Traffic Channel
ETIS	E- and Telecommunication Information Services
ETSI	European Telecommunications Standards Institute
EU	European Union
FACCH	Fast Associated Control Channel
FAX	Facsimile
FaxP	Fax Profile
FBWA	Fixed Broadband Wireless Access
FC	Finance Committee
FCC	Federal Communication Commission
FDD	Frequency Division Duplex
FH	Frequency Hopping
FHSS	Frequency Hopping Spread Spectrum
FOTAG	Fiber Optics Technical Advisory Group
FP	File Transfer Profile

FR	Full Rate
FRF	Frame Relay Forum
FSG	Free Standards Group
FSV	Functional Service View
FTP	File Transfer Protocol
GA	General Assembly
GAP	Generic Access Profile
GCC	GNU C Compiler
GERAN	GSM/EDGE Radio Access Network
GFSK	Gaussian Frequency Shift Keying
GGSN	Gateway GPRS Support Node
GIF	Graphics Interchange Format
GIOP	Generic Inter-Object Request Protocol
GMA	Gateway Mobility Agent
GMM	GPRS Mobility Management
GMPCS	Global Mobile Personal Communications by Satellite
GMSK	Gaussian Minimum Shift Keying
GMT	Greenwich Mean Time
GOEP	Generic Object Exchange Profile
GPL	General Public License
GPRS	General Packet Radio Service
GPS	Global Positioning System
GRA	GERAN Registration Area
GRX	GPRS Roaming Exchange
GSA	Global Mobile Suppliers Association
GSC	Global Standards Collaboration
GSM	Global System for Mobile Communications
GT	Generic Technology
GTD	Geometric Time Difference
GTP	GPRS Tunneling Protocol
GTP-U	GTP for the user plane
GUI	Graphical User Interface
GUP	Generic User Profile
GW	Gateway
HA	Home Agent
HAck	Handover Acknowledgement
HC	Handover Control

HF	Human Factors
HI	Handover Interface
HILI	High Level Interface
HIPERACCESS	High Performance Radio Access
HIPERLAN	High Performance Radio Local Area Network
HIPERLAN2	High Performance Radio Local Area Network type 2
HIPERMAN	High Performance Radio Metropolitan Area Network
HLR	Home Location Register
HoT	Home Address Test
HoTI	Home Address Test Initiate
HR	Half Rate
HSCSD	High Speed Circuit Switched Data
HSDPA	High Speed Downlink Packet Access
HSP	Handset Profile
HSS	Home Subscriber Server
HTML	HyperText Markup Language
HTTP	HyperText Transfer Protocol
IAB	Internet Architecture Board
IACC	In-Advance Credit Check
IANA	Internet Assigned Numbers Authority
IAP	Internet Access Provider
IAPP	Inter Access Point Protocol
IC	Integrated Circuit
ICL	Interoperability Certification Lab
ICMP	Internet Control Message Protocol
I-CSCF	Interrogating CSCF
ICTSB	Information and Communications Technologies Standards Board
ID	Internet Draft
ID	User Identification
IDE	Integrated Development Environment
IDL	Interactive Data Language
IDL	Interface Definition Language
IEC	International Electrotechnical Commission
IEEE	The Institute Of Electrical And Electronics Engineers
IEEE-ISTO	IEEE Industry Standards and Technology Organization
IEEE-SA	IEEE Standards Association
IETF	Internet Engineering Task Force

IESG	Internet Engineering Steering Group
IFH	Intelligent Frequency Hopping
IFRB	International Frequency Registration Board
IGMP	Internet Group Multicast Protocol
IIOP	Internet Inter-Object Request Broker Protocol
IKE	Internet Key Exchange
ILP	Integrated Layer Processing
IM	Instant Messaging
IM/P	Instant Messaging and Presence
IMAP	Internet Message Access Protocol
IMEI	International Mobile Station Equipment Identity
IMPACT	International Marketing and Promotional Activities
IMPP	Instant Messaging and Presence Protocol
IMPS	Instant Messaging and Presence
IMR	IP Multimedia Register
IMS	IP Multimedia Subsystem
IMSI	International Mobile Subscriber Identity
IMT-2000	International Mobile Telecommunications 2000
IMTC	International Multimedia Telecommunications Consortium
IN	Intelligent Network
IntP	Intercom Profile
IntServ	Integrated Services
IOPCom	Interoperability Committee
IOT	Interoperability Testing
IP	Internet Protocol
IPDC	IP Datacasting
IPDL	Idle Period Down Link
IPDR.org	Internet Protocol Detail Record Organization
IPNG	Internet Protocol Next Generation
IPR	Intellectual Property Right
IPSec	IP Security
IPv4	Internet Protocol, version 4
IPv6	Internet Protocol, version 6
IR	Incremental Redundancy
IR	Infrared
IRC	Internet Relay Chat
IrDA	Infrared Data Association

IRTF	Internet Research Task Force
ISDN	Integrated Services Digital Network
ISLAN	Integrated Services LAN
ISM	Industrial, Scientific and Medical
ISO	International Organization for Standardization
ISOC	Internet Society
ISP	Internet Service Provider
ISV	Independent Software Vendor
IT	Information Technology
ITU	International Telecommunication Union
ITU-D	ITU Telecommunication Development Sector
ITU-R	ITU Radiocommunication Sector
ITU-T	ITU Telecommunication Standardization Sector
IWE	Interworking Element
IWF	Interworking Function
IVR	Interactive Voice Response
J2EE™	Java™ 2 Platform, Enterprise Edition
J2ME™	Java™ 2 Platform, Micro Edition
J2SE™	Java™ 2 Platform, Standard Edition
JAD	Java™ Application Descriptor
JAIN	Java™ APIs for Integrated Networks
JAM	Java™ Application Manager
JAR	Java™ Archive file
JAXM	Java™ API for XML Messaging
JAXP	Java™ API for XML Processing
JAXR	Java™ API for XML Registries
JAX-RPC	Java™ API for XML-based RPC
JCP	Java™ Community Process
JCTEA	Japan Cable Television Engineering Association
JDBC	Java™ Database Connectivity API
JDK	Java™ Development Kit
JMS	Java™ Messaging Service
JNDI	Java™ Naming and Directory Interface
JNI	Java™ Native Interface
JPEG	Joint Photographic Experts Group
JSPA	Java Specification Participation Agreement
JSPTM	JavaServer™ Pages

JSR	Java Specification Request
JTC	Joint Technical Committee
JTC Broadcast	Joint Technical Committee on Broadcasting
JVM	Java™ Virtual Machine
KVM	Java™ Virtual Machine supporting CLDC
L2	Layer 2
L2CAP	Logical Link Control and Adaptation Protocol
L3	Layer 3
LA	Link Adaptation
LAN	Local Area Network
LAP	LAN Access Profile
LC	Load Control
LCD	Liquid Crystal Display
LCDUI	Limited Capability Device User Interface
LDAP	Lightweight Directory Access Protocol
LGPL	Library GNU Public License
LIF	Location Interoperability Forum
LLC	Logical Link Control
LMA	Leaf Mobility Agent
LMM	Local Mobility Management
LMP	Link Manager Protocol
LMSC	IEEE 802 LAN/MAN Standards Committee
LMU	Location Measurement Unit
LSB	Linux Standards Base
LSP	Label Switched Path
LSR	Label Switched Router
M2M	Machine-to-Machine
MAC	Media Access Control
MAC	Message Authentication Code
MAN	Metropolitan Area Network
MANET	Mobile Ad Hoc Networking
MAP	Mobile Application Part Protocol
MarCom	Marketing Committee
MBM	Multi Bitmap file
MCC	Mobile Competence Center
M-COMM	Mobile Commerce
MCS	Modulation Coding Scheme

MCU	Multiparty Conferencing Unit
MCU	Multipoint Control Unit
MD5	Message Digest 5
MDA	Model Driven Architecture
MEO	Medium Earth Orbit
MESA	Public Safety Partnership Project
MeT	Mobile Electronic Transactions
MExE	Mobile Station Application Execution Environment
MFN	Multi Frequency Network
MG	Media Gateway
MGC	Media Gateway Controller
MGCF	Media Gateway Control Function
MGW	Media Gateway
MHP	Multimedia Home Platform
MIBA	Mobile Internet Business Architecture
MIDI	Musical Instrument Digital Interface
MIDP	Mobile Information Device Profile
MII	Mobile Internet Interfaces
MIME	Multi-purpose Internet Mail Extensions
MITA	Mobile Internet Technical Architecture
MLD	Multicast Listener Discovery for IPv6
MM	Mobility Management
MMA	Multimedia Message Adaptation
MMAC	Multimedia Mobile Access Communications Promotion Council
MMCTL	Mobility Management Controller
MMS	Multimedia Messaging Service
MMSC	Multimedia Messaging Service Center
MMS-IOP	MMS Interoperability Group
MMU	Multimedia Unit
MMUSIC	Multiparty Multimedia Session Control
MO	Mobile Originated
MOF	Meta-Object Facility
MOTO	Mail Order/Telephone Order
MoU	Memoranda of Understanding
MPE	Multi-Protocol Encapsulation
MPEG	Moving Pictures Experts Group
MPEG-4	MPEG version 4

MPI	Mobile Internet Protocol Interfaces
MPLS	Multi-Protocol Label Switching
MRFC	Media Resource Function Control
MRFP	Media Resource Function Processing
MRP	Market Representation Partner
MRV	Mobile Rights Voucher
MS	Mobile Station
MSC	Mobile Services Switching Center
MSDU	MAC Service Data Unit
MSF	Multiservice Switching Forum
MSG	Mobile Standards Group
MSI	Mobile Internet Software Interfaces
MSISDN	Mobile Station International ISDN Number
MSS	Media Subsystem
MSS	Mobile Satellite Services
MT	Mobile Terminated
MTP3B	Message Transfer Part 3 Broadband
MTS	Methods for Testing and Specification
MTU	Maximum Transmission Unit
MVC	Model-View-Controller
MWIF	Mobile Wireless Internet Forum
MX	Mail eXchange
N-ISDN	Narrowband Integrated Services Digital Network
NACC	Network Assisted Cell Change
NAMP	Nokia Artuse Messaging Platform
NAPTR	Naming Authority Pointer
NAR	New Access Router
NAS	Network Access Server
NAT	Network Address Translation
NATP-PT	Network Address/Port Translation - Protocol Translation
NAT-PT	NAT - Protocol Translation
NesCom	New Standards Committee
NGN	Next Generation Networks
NIST	National Institute of Standards and Technology
NLOS	Non Line Of Sight
NNA	Naming, Numbering and Addressing
NNI	Network-Node Interface

NNTP	Network News Transfer Protocol
NOKOS	NOKia Open Source license
NRT	Non-Real-Time
NSIS	Next Steps In Signaling
NTA	Sofia Transaction API
NTP	Network Time Protocol
NTR	Sofia Transaction API for RTSP
NUA	Sofia User Agent API
O&M	Operations and Maintenance
OBEX	Object Exchange
OCG	Operational Coordination Group
OCSP	Online Certificate Status Protocol
OFDM	Orthogonal Frequency Division Multiplexing
OID	Other Input Document
OIF	Optical Internetworking Forum
OMA	Open Mobile Alliance
OMC	Operations and Maintenance Center
OMG	Object Management Group
OP	Organizational Partner
OPP	Object Push Profile
OR	Octal Rate
ORB	Object Request Broker
OS	Operating System
OSA	Open Service Architecture
OSDL	Open Source Development Lab
OSI	Open Source Initiative
OSI	Open Systems Interconnection
OSPF	Open Shortest Path First
OSPFv6	Open Shortest Path First for IPv6
OSS	Open Source Software
OSS	Operation Support Systems
OTA	Over The Air
OTD	Observed Time Difference
OTDOA	Observed Time Difference Of Arrival
OWL	Ontology Web Language
OWLAN	Operator Wireless Local Area Network
PACCH	Packet Associated Control Channel

PAI	Platform Adaptation Interface
PAN	Personal Area Networking
PAR	Previous Access Router
PAR	Project Authorization Request
PC	Power Control
PC	Personal Computer
PCF	Point Co-ordination Function
PCG	Project Co-ordination Group
PCM	Pulse Code Modulation
PCMCIA	PC Memory Card International Association
P-CSCF	Proxy-Call State Control Function
PDA	Personal Digital Assistant
PDC	Personal Digital Communication
PDCP	Packet Data Convergence Protocol
PDH	Plesiochronous Digital Hierarchy
PDP	Packet Data Protocol
PDTCH	Packet Data Traffic Channel
PDU	Protocol Data Unit
PFC	Packet Flow Context
PGP	Pretty Good Privacy
PHB	Per Hop Behavior
PHY	Physical
PHP	Hypertext Preprocessor
PID	Program Identifier
PII	Personally Identifiable Information
PIM	Personal Information Management
PIM	Protocol Independent Multicast
PIN	Personal Identification Number
PJAE	PersonalJava™ Application Environment
pJava	PJAE, PersonalJava™ Technology
PKC	Public Key Cryptography
PKI	Public Key Infrastructure
PLCP	Physical Layer Convergence Protocol
PLMN	Public Land Mobile Network
PLT	PowerLine Telecommunications
PMD	Physical Medium Dependent
PMO	Project Management Office

PNG	Portable Network Graphics
POI	Proof Of Identity
POP	Post Office Protocol
POP3	Post Office Protocol 3
POP	Proof Of Possession
POS	Point-Of-Sale
PPP	Point-to-Point Protocol
PRD	Program Reference Document
PS	Packet Scheduler
PS	Packet Switched
PS	Presence Server
PSCH	Physical SubChannel
PSK	Phase Shift Keying
PSS	Packet Switched Streaming
PSTN	Public Switched Telephone Network
PTC	Platform Technology Committee
PTCC	Protocol and Testing Competence Center
PTD	Personal Trusted Device
PTP	Personal Transaction Protocol
QCIF	Quarter-CIF
QM	Quality Manager
QoS	Quality of Service
QPL	Bluetooth Qualified Products List
QPSK	Quadrature Phase Shift Keying
QR	Quarter Rate
R&D	Research and Development
RA	Registration Authority
RA	Radiocommunication Assembly
RAB	Radio Access Bearer
RADIUS	Remote Authentication Dial-In User Service
RAG	Radiocommunication Advisory Group
RAN	Radio Access Network
RANAP	RAN Application Protocol
RAST	Global Radio Standardization
RB	Radio Bearer
RC	Roadmap Coordinator
RC5	Rivest Cipher 5

RDF	Resource Description Framework
RED	Random Early Detection
REL	Rights Expression Language
RevCom	Review Committee
RF	Radio Frequency
RFC	Request For Comments
RFID	Radio Frequency ID
RFP	Request For Proposal
RI	Reference Implementation
RIP	Routing Information Protocol
RIPng	Routing Information Protocol for IPv6
RLC	Radio Link Control
RM	Resource Management
RMI	Remote Method Invocation
RMS	Record Management Store
RNC	Radio Network Controller
RNIF	RosettaNet Implementation Framework
RNSAP	Radio Network Subsystem Application Part
ROA	Recognized Operating Agencies
ROHC	Robust Header Compression
RPC	Remote Procedure Call
RR	Radio Resource
RRA	Requirement Requires Applying
RRB	Radio Regulations Board
RRC	Radio Resource Control
RRC	Regional Radiocommunication Conference
RRM	Radio Resource Management
RSA	Rivest Shamir Adleman
RSVP	Resource Reservation Protocol
RT	Railway Telecommunications
RT	Real-Time
RTCP	Real-time Transport Control Protocol
RTD	Real Time Difference
RTDC	Regional Telecommunication Development Conference
RTP	Real-time Transport Protocol
RTS	Request To Send
RTSP	Real-Time Streaming Protocol

RTT	Round Trip Time
S	Signaling
S/MIME	Secure/Multi-purpose Internet Mail Extensions
SA	Security Association
SA	Selective Availability
SACCH	Slow Associated Control Channel
SA Forum	Service Availability Forum
Safety	Telecommunications Equipment Safety
SAGE	Security Algorithms Group of Experts
SAI	Service Area Identifier
SAML	Security Assertion Markup Language
SAP	Service Access Point
SAP	Session Announcement Protocol
SAR	Segmentation And Re-assembly
SAR	Servlet Archive
SCCP	Signaling Connection Control Part
SCN	Switched Circuit Network
SCP	Smart Card Platform
S-CSCF	Serving CSCF
SCTE	Society of Cable Telecommunications Engineers
SCTP	Stream Control Transmission Protocol
SDAP	Service Discovery Application Profile
SDE	Service Discovery Engine
SDH	Synchronous Digital Hierarchy
SDK	Software Development Kit
SDO	Standards Development Organization
SDP	Session Description Protocol
SDP	Service Discovery Protocol
SDPng	SDP next generation
SDS	Service Discovery Service
SEC	Security
SEC	Sponsor Executive Committee
SES	Satellite Earth Stations and Systems
SFN	Single Frequency Network
SG	Signaling Gateway
SG	Study Group
SGML	Standard Generalized Markup Language

SGSN	Serving GPRS Support Node
SHA-1	Secure Hash Algorithm 1
S-HTTP	Secure HyperText Transfer Protocol
SI	Service Indication
SIFS	Short InterFrame Space
SIG	Special Interest Group
SIGCOMP	Signaling compression
SIIT	Stateless IP/ICMP Translation Algorithm
SILS	Standard for Interoperable LAN Security
SIM	Subscriber Identity Module
SIMPLE	SIP for Instant Messaging and Presence Leveraging Extensions
SIO	Scientific or Industrial Organization
SIP	Session Initiation Protocol
SIP-CGI	Common Gateway Interface for SIP
SIR	Signal-to-Interference Ratio
SLF	Subscriber Locator Function
SLP	Service Location Protocol
SM	Session Management
SMATV	Satellite Master Antenna Television
SMIL	Synchronized Multimedia Integration Language
SMP	Symmetric Multi-Processing
SMS	Short Message Service
SMSC	Short Message Service Center
SMSGW	SMS Gateway
SMTP	Simple Mail Transfer Protocol
SNAP	Subnetwork Access Protocol
SNMP	Simple Network Management Protocol
SOAP	Simple Object Access Protocol
SOAP-DSIG	SOAP Digital Signature
SP	Service Provider
SP	Synchronization Profile
SPA	Self Provided Application
SPAN	Services and Protocols for Advanced Networks
SPD	Security Policy Database
SPI	Service Provisioning Infrastructure
SPP	Serial Port Profile
SPSCH	Shared Physical SubChannel

SRES	Signed RESponse
SS	Station Services
SS	Supplementary Services
SS7	Signaling System No. 7
SSA	Subsystem Architecture
SSCF	Service Specific Co-operation Function
SSCOP	Service Specific Connection Oriented Protocol
SSG	Special Study Group
SSI	System Software Interfaces
SSL	Secure Sockets Layer
SSO	Single Sign-On
SSP	Server-to-Server Protocol
SSPI	Security Service Application Programming Interface
STA	Station
STF	Specialist Task Force
STP	Scalable Test Platform
STQ	Speech processing, Transmission and Quality aspects
SwA	SOAP with Attachments
SWA	Systems Software Architecture
SVG	Scalable Vector Graphics
SVR4	System V Release 4.x
SWT	Standardized Web Services Technologies
SyncML	Synchronization Markup Language
T1	Standards Committee T1 - Telecommunications
TA	Timing Advance
TAP	Traditional Approval Process
TC	Technical Committee
TC	Tunnel Client
TCH	Traffic Channel
TCK	Technology Compatibility Kit
TCP	Transmission Control Protocol
TCP/IP	Transmission Control Protocol/Internet Protocol
TCS	Telephony Control System
TDAG	Telecommunication Development Advisory Group
TDD	Time Division Duplex
TDMA	Time Division Multiple Access
Tdoc	Temporary Document

TE	Terminal Equipment
TechCom	Technical Committee
TELNET	Terminal Emulation Protocol
TETRA	Terrestrial Trunked Radio
TF	Transport Format
TGW	Terminal Gateway
TIA	Telecommunications Industry Association
TIPHON	Telecommunications and Internet Protocol Harmonization Over Networks
TLS	Transport Layer Security
TM	Transmission and Multiplexing
TM Forum	TeleManagement Forum
TMN	Telecommunication Management Network
TOA	Time Of Arrival
TR	Technical Reports
TRAU	Transcoder and Rate Adaptation Unit
TRX	Transceiver
TS	TimeSlot
TS	Technical Specification
TSACC	Telecommunications Standards Advisory Council of Canada
TSAG	Telecommunication Standardization Advisory Group
TSB	Telecommunication Standardization Bureau
TSG	Technical Specification Group
TSG CN	Technical Specification Group Core Network
TSG GERAN	Technical Specification Group GSM/EDGE Radio Access Network
TSG RAN	Technical Specification Group Radio Access Network
TSG SA	Technical Specification Group System Aspects
TSG T	Technical Specification Group Terminals
TTA	Telecommunications Technology Association
TTC	Telecommunication Technology Committee
TTCN	Tree and Tabular Combined Notation
TTI	Transmission Time Interval
TTP	Trusted Third Party
TU	Transaction User
TU3	Typical Urban 3 km/h
UA	User Agent
UAC	User Agent Client
UAProf	User Agent Profile

UAS	User Agent Server
UDDI	Universal Description, Discovery and Integration
UDP	User Datagram Protocol
UDP	Unacknowledged Data Protocol
UDVM	Universal Decompressor Virtual Machine
UE	User Equipment
UHF	Ultrahigh Frequency
UI	User Interface
UID	Unique Identification code
UML	Unified Modeling Language
UMTS	Universal Mobile Telecommunication System
UNI	User-Network Interface
U-NII	Unlicensed National Information Infrastructure
URI	Uniform Resource Identifier
URL	Uniform Resource Locator
USB	Universal Serial Bus
USER	Special Committee User Group
USIM	UMTS Subscriber Identity Module
USSD	Unstructured Supplementary Service Data
UTC	Universal Time Co-ordinates
UTF-8	Unicode Transformation Format 8
UTRA	UMTS Terrestrial Radio Access
UTRAN	UMTS Terrestrial Radio Access Network
UWCC	Universal Wireless Communications Consortium
VAS	Value Added Service
VASP	Value Added Service Provider
VC	Virtual Cursor
VGA	Video Graphics Array
VHF	Very High Frequency
VLAN	Virtual Local Area Network
VM	Virtual Machine
VoiceXML	Voice Extensible Markup Language
VoIP	Voice over IP
VPN	Virtual Private Network
W3C	World Wide Web Consortium
WAE	Wireless Application Environment
WAI	Web Accessibility Initiative

WAP	Wireless Application Protocol
WARC	World Administrative Radio Conference
WAV	Windows Audio File
WBMP	Wireless BitMap
WCDMA	Wideband Code Division Multiple Access
WCIT	World Conference on International Telecommunication
WDCTL	WLAN Device Controller
WECA	Wireless Ethernet Compatibility Alliance
Web-Ont	W3C Web Ontology Working Group
WEP	Wired Equivalent Privacy
WG	Working Group
WGR	Working Group on ITU Reform
WI	Work Item
WIM	Wireless Identity Module
WIM	WAP Identity Module
WINS	Windows Internet Name Service
WIP	WLAN Interworking Protocol
WLAN	Wireless Local Area Network
WMF	Wireless Multimedia Forum
WML	Wireless Markup Language
WMLS	Wireless Markup Language Script
WPAN	Wireless Personal Area Network
WP8F	ITU-R Working Party 8F
WPKI	Wireless Public Key Infrastructure
WRC	World Radiocommunication Conference
WSCL	Web Services Conversation Language
WSDL	Web Services Description Language
WSFL	Web Services Flow Language
WS-I	Web Services Interoperability Organization
WSIA	Web Services Interactive Applications
WSIL	Web Services Inspection Language
WSIS	World Summit on the Information Society
WS-License	Web Service License Language
WSP	Wireless Session Protocol
WS-Security	Web Service Security Language
WTA	Wireless Telephony Applications
WTAI	Wireless Telephony Applications Interface

WTDC	World Telecommunication Development Conference
WTLS	Wireless Transport Layer Security
WTP	Wireless Transport Protocol
WTPF	World Telecommunication Policy Forum
WTSA	World Telecommunication Standardization Assembly
WV	Wireless Village
WWW	World Wide Web
XACML	eXtensible Access Control Markup Language
xDSL	any Digital Subscription Line
XHTML	eXtensible HyperText Markup Language
XHTML MP	XHTML Mobile Profile
XKMS	XML Key Management Specification
XLANG	Web Services for Business Process Design
XMI	XML Metadata Interchange
XML	eXtensible Markup Language
XML-DSIG	XML Digital Signature
XMLP	XML Protocol
XMLP-WG	XML Protocol Working Protocol
XSD	XML Schema Definition
XSL	eXtensible Stylesheet Language
XSLT	eXtensible Stylesheet Language Transformations
xSP	any Service Provider

Index

A

B

C

D

E

F

G

H

I

J

K

L

M

N

O

P

Q

R

S

T

U

V

W

X